DATE DUE FOR RETURN

17

CLASSICS OF SCIENCE SERIES

under the General Editorship of

Gerald Holton
Professor of Physics, Harvard University

SCHEDULED AMONG THE EARLY VOLUMES IN THIS SERIES ARE:

Classics of Science, Volume II

The
Discovery of Radioactivity
and Transmutation

Edited and with commentary by

ALFRED ROMER

St. Lawrence University

DOVER PUBLICATIONS, INC.

NEW YORK

Published simultaneously in Canada by McClelland and Stewart, Ltd.

Published in the United Kingdom by Constable and Company Limited, 10 Orange Street, London, W.C.2.

The Discovery of Radioactivity and Transmutation (Volume II in the Dover "Classics of Science" series), contains sixteen papers published for the first time in collected form by Dover Publications, Inc., in 1964.
This volume also contains a new Preface, Introduction and notes by Alfred Romer.
The editors and publishers are grateful to the Mathematics Library of Columbia University for making certain of these papers available for reproduction purposes.

Library of Congress Catalog Card Number: 63-20252

Manufactured in the United States of America

Dover Publications, Inc.
180 Varick Street
New York 14, N.Y.

General Editor's Preface

This volume, together with others that are being published in this new series at about the same time, inaugurates a publishing program entitled *Classics of Science*. Each volume is a collection of fundamental essays and other basic original articles in a certain field of science, presented in the sequence of its development, together with an introduction, commentary, and clarifying notes by the scholar responsible for the selection of the papers. All areas of science are to be included as the series grows. The titles of volumes commissioned for early completion range from *The Development of High-Energy Accelerators* to *The Theory of Evolution* (*1830 to Modern Genetic Theory*). Thus, in time, we shall have here a convenient network of roads to take us to the often inaccessible sources of the great rivers of science, through its widely visible mountain ranges, its renowned battlefields, and perhaps its little-known but nevertheless choice vineyards.

The articles follow the original texts verbatim, and (with rare and clearly marked exceptions) are printed in full rather than in excerpt or in edited and abbreviated versions; they may therefore be used in lieu of the original publications. Foreign-language articles are carefully translated. In short, both the interested layman and the historian or scientist should feel assured that he is reading these documents as they were intended to be read, and in the version in which they made their original contribution.

Some of these aims are similar to those of a distinguished German series of republications, begun in 1889 under the direction of the chemist and philosopher, Wilhelm Ostwald, and reaching some 400 titles before it was discontinued. There are, however, important distinctions between these two series. Ostwald's series was composed of republications of single essays, whereas here each book sets out several essays, each in the context of the others, in order to trace the development of the whole field. Hence there will be more connective commentary in this series, and, most importantly, the commentary can now benefit from advances made in the last three-quarters of a century, both in science and in historical scholarship.

Still, many of the aims cited in the original announcement of Ostwald's *Klassiker der exakten Wissenschaften* are again applicable:

> The great progress which the sciences have made in our time, as is generally acknowledged, is in good measure owing to the cultivation and wide application of teaching methods such as demonstration lectures and laboratories. These arrangements are indeed very successful in imparting knowledge of the present state of science. But some of the most eminent persons with widest vision have frequently felt compelled to point out a deficiency that mars all too often our contemporary scientific education. This is the absence of a sense of history, and the lack of knowledge concerning those great contributions on which the edifice of science rests.
>
> Although few instructors in scientific subjects would fail to make reference to those foundations when the occasion arises, such references remain, nevertheless, generally ineffective because the source materials of science are rarely accessible. They can be obtained only in the larger libraries, and then only in single copy, so that the student is all too easily discouraged from pursuing the lead.
>
> This lack is to be remedied through the publication of the *Klassiker der exakten Wissenschaften*. In convenient format and at reasonable prices, the seminal publications of all the exact sciences will be made available to instructors and students alike. The publisher hopes to create thereby both a teaching aid that gives life and depth to the study of science, as well as a significant research tool; for in those fundamental writings lie not only the seeds which have, in the meantime, developed and borne fruit, but also unnumbered other leads that await development. To those whose study and research lie in the sciences, these works offer an inexhaustible source for stimulation and for the advancement of ideas.

Today, no less than when these words were written, the proper orientation of science is toward the future. Yet, the uses of the scientific past are also becoming clearer—not the least being the continued application of Maxwell's memorable dictum on the didactic value of the study of historical accounts and of original works in science, found in the preface of the *Treatise on Electricity and Magnetism*: "It is of great advantage to the student of any subject to read the original memoirs on that subject, for science is always most completely assimilated when it is in the nascent state. . . ."

This series of connected essays on single topics of science will help us to remember that in the development of each field the overriding characteristic of scientific growth is its continuity. If science today is so good, it is to a large extent because science in the past was so good.

Gerald Holton

Cambridge, Mass.   *Jefferson Laboratory*
December, 1963   *Harvard University*

Preface

A number of criteria may be invoked in the selection of papers for a collection of this sort—for example, importance in intellectual and cultural history, literary merit, or philosophical value. For this volume and a companion volume on *Radiochemistry and the Discovery of Isotopes* (being readied for the press), it has seemed to me that *development* furnishes the most useful principle of organization. The papers reprinted and discussed here have been chosen for their contribution to the growth of ideas and to the gradual solution of key problems in science.

In radioactivity, two sets of problems emerged. One was the need to find an explanation of the ephemeral radioactivities which were being discovered in rapid succession; growing out of this was the formulation of a transformation theory which viewed radioactive substances as elements in transition, and established long, genetic chains down which atoms slowly made their way. The second set of problems started with the need to identify these elements chemically, and to place them in the periodic table; this, in turn, forced the recognition of the notion of isotopes, of varieties of atoms which are chemically identical, but distinguishable by their physical characteristics.

Neither of these general areas of investigation was independent of the other, but they are sufficiently different for the basic papers to be collected in two separate volumes, each of which traces the development of characteristic ideas in sequence.

The reprinted papers form the backbone of the narrative. In this volume they have been linked with passages of commentary and bibliographic material. In the second, companion volume (to appear in this *Classics of Science* Series) entitled *Radiochemistry and the Discovery of Isotopes*, I have provided a comprehensive essay on the growth of knowledge of radioactivity, transmutation, and isotopes during the periods covered by both volumes, together with a full bibliography of the major original contributions from 1896 to 1913.

In the choice and organization of material, I was given a free hand by Gerald Holton, the General Editor of this series, *Classics of Science*. For this large freedom I offer my thanks, and I offer it again for the painstaking work by which he has raised the level of intelligibility of the book.

I also wish to thank Mlle. Nicole Kostomaroff, who helped in correcting my translations from the French.   What faults remain must be attributed to the intractable prose with which both had to deal.

A. R.

Canton, New York
May, 1963

Contents

List of Illustrations

Introduction

Modern nuclear physics had its beginning in radioactivity. Yet radioactivity made an interesting science in its own right, and its development is worth following for more than antiquarian reasons. Above all, it was a science of surprises, and to those who followed it an eye for the unexpected was worth quite as much as any foresight in planning. It began in 1896 because Henri Becquerel hoped to produce x-rays by purely optical means, and it reached a highpoint in 1904, when Ernest Rutherford established the possibility of the spontaneous transmutation of elements. If its end was not implied in its beginning, if half its investigations veered off unexpectedly, progress in this field was nevertheless rational. However odd the phenomena and however contradictory the results, there were always intelligence and imagination to bring them into order.

By the end of the first week in January, 1896, the world knew of Röntgen's discovery of x-rays and of their power to reveal hidden things, even the bones in a living hand. There was reason to think they might be related to the curious glow known as fluorescence; and, as we shall see, in pursuit of that relation Henri Becquerel of Paris turned up a fluorescent compound of uranium which did indeed give penetrating, photographically active rays. Although this seemed precisely what he expected, the more he worked, the weaker the link became between the fluorescence and the rays, and the more likely it grew that they were emitted by the atoms of uranium. How Becquerel was driven to so curious a conclusion is the subject of the first four papers reprinted in this volume.

There seemed no way of discovering where the atoms of uranium drew the energy which their rays continually spent, but the existence of the phenomena became at least more credible when in 1898 G. C. Schmidt of Erlangen and Marie Sklodowska Curie of Paris found that another element, thorium, shared the same ray-giving power. Then Marie and Pierre Curie went on to locate two more ray-giving elements in the mineral pitchblende, quite plausible, although unknown, which they named polonium and radium.

Except for their radioactivity, uranium, thorium, polonium, and radium seemed perfectly ordinary elements with a normal, permanent existence. The discovery of transmutation depended on the discovery of more transitory substances, and that grew from the study of gaseous ionization. It was a property of both x-rays and the rays of radioactivity that they could discharge any electrified body in their

neighborhood.   The effect was investigated for x-rays in 1896 by
J. J. Thomson and Rutherford at Cambridge University.   As they
were able to show, the x-rays could split molecules of the air into pairs
of electrically charged "ions," and it was these newly created ions,
moving under ordinary electrical forces, which produced the
discharging effect.

From x-rays, Rutherford moved to the rays from uranium and
found that they ionized in precisely the same way.   The rays from
thorium proved more difficult, since their effect varied capriciously,
and when he moved to Montreal in the fall of 1898 Rutherford passed
the problem on to R. B. Owens, a new acquaintance there.   By
shielding his thorium oxide from currents of air, Owens was able to
stabilize the ionizing effect of its rays, and, that precaution taken, he
managed to duplicate everything Rutherford had done with uranium.

In the summer of 1899, Rutherford turned to the question of why
air which had moved past the thorium oxide disturbed the experiment.   He found the air to be continually ionized, as though it were
carrying some ray-giving substance with the properties of a gas,
which in perplexity Rutherford named "the emanation."   The
radioactivity of this emanation was short-lived, however, and died
away in a geometric progression in time, losing half of its intensity
with each minute which passed.   Then in the midst of these experiments another temporary radioactivity was discovered, this one
dropping to half value in eleven hours, and, although Rutherford
called it an "excited radioactivity," it really seemed to come from a
solid deposit laid down on surfaces where the emanation had been.
His account of this work will be found in Papers 5 and 6.

There was no clear meaning to these discoveries, nor was there any
particular meaning to another which Sir William Crookes made in
London in the spring of 1900.   He had started to purify uranium
nitrate, found that he had, as far as he could tell, eliminated its radioactivity in the process, and so came upon a set of chemical operations
which separated from uranium a totally different, highly radioactive
substance which he named uranium X.   This discovery, described
in Paper 7, was presently confirmed by Becquerel in an independent
set of experiments.

As a radioactive gas, the emanation from thorium was a strange
entity, and no less so because radium produced another emanation
like it.   It was odd that thorium oxide would release it, but odd that
thorium oxide could be altered simply by intense heating in such a
way as to cut off the release.   In 1901 Rutherford persuaded a young
chemist, Frederick Soddy, to join him in solving these puzzles.
What emerged from their work was a pair of unforeseen conclusions:
that the emanation behaved like a rare gas of the argon family, and

that it was not after all thorium which released it, but a thorium X having a high radioactivity and quite different chemical properties. The report of this investigation makes up Paper 8.

Meanwhile, Becquerel had begun to realize the logical difficulties which uranium X created. It was easy to remove from uranium, it appeared to carry away the radioactivity of uranium when it went, and yet the radioactivity of uranium always returned. It seemed necessary to assume that, as often as it was purified, uranium managed to regenerate its lost radioactivity; when Becquerel tested this assumption on his carefully preserved specimens, he found that it was true (Paper 9).

Acting on this hint, Rutherford and Soddy found that in time thorium regenerated both its radioactivity and its power to produce emanation; both of which had previously been lost by the sample with the removal of thorium X. Now they had little trouble in convincing themselves that these were the signs of a new formation of thorium X. The thorium X was chemically different from the thorium, yet there was nothing but the thorium to produce it, and hence it must have been formed by a transmutation. Although the Curies had severely criticized (Paper 10) a similar hypothesis proposed by Becquerel, still Rutherford and Soddy could see no alternative to it and they published their revolutionary new theory in the spring of 1902 (Paper 11).

As the summer wore on they came to feel that the atomic transformation and the emission of energy in the rays were not really separate events. In fact, by supposing that the rays came out in a single burst at the instant that each atom transmuted, they found that they could increase the explanatory power of their theory enormously (Paper 12).

Four years before, in the study of radiation from uranium, Rutherford had distinguished and named two different kinds of rays. What he called alpha rays were strongly ionizing but had little penetrating power, while his beta rays, which ionized little, penetrated as x-rays did. As it turned out now, Crookes and Becquerel, in finding that uranium lost its radioactivity upon purification, had been testing only for penetrating rays; only beta-ray activity was carried off in the removal of uranium X from uranium, whereas easily measurable alpha-ray activity was left behind with uranium. Thorium free from thorium X also gave out alpha rays alone.

In 1900 Becquerel had proved that beta rays were streams of swift-moving, negatively charged electrons. Now that he realized their importance, Rutherford investigated alpha rays and discovered before the end of 1902 that they too were streams of particles, though they carried positive charges and were enormously larger than electrons.

Because of their size, it was quite clear to Rutherford that alpha particles carried virtually all the energy released in the transformations of radioactivity. In the spring of 1903, Soddy returned to England, and, before they separated, he and Rutherford drew up one last paper together, in the course of which they estimated what this radioactive energy might amount to (Paper 13). It came to quite an amazing figure, far more than the energy of ordinary chemical reactions. Each year, as they calculated, a gram of radium must give out 15,000 calories. While that calculation was still in the press, however, Pierre Curie and Albert Laborde published in Paris the results of actual measurements on some moderately enriched specimens of radium-barium chloride. What radium released in fact would come each year to 880,000 calories for every gram (Paper 14).

As Rutherford and Soddy knew well, their ionization measurements could detect radioactive material in amounts far too small to be seen with a microscope or weighed on the most delicate balance. Nevertheless, when the transmutations went on over geological periods of time, enough of the end products might accumulate to be detected by ordinary means. They had pointed out that helium was found only in those minerals that are radioactive and so might be one of the products of their radioactivity.

In the summer of 1903, Soddy entered the laboratory of Sir William Ramsay in London. Ramsay had shared the discovery of argon with Lord Rayleigh; but the other members of its family (neon, krypton, xenon, and helium) he had isolated by himself. Now he had a rich specimen of pure radium bromide. With Soddy's help he proposed to capture the emanation from it, since it was also an argon-like gas, to take its spectrum, and so annex it to his own collection.

In a way the experiment failed, since the spectrum of the emanation never appeared. In its place, however, Ramsay and Soddy saw the familiar lines of helium. Since helium entered into no chemical combination, there was no way in which the radium bromide could have picked it up. It must have been formed within its solid crystals in the few months since they had last been withdrawn from solution, and so it must have been formed from the substance of the radium. Since both radium and helium were acknowledged elements, this was direct and vivid evidence for the truth of the transmutation theory (Paper 15).

That autumn, in Montreal, Rutherford took up the heat measurements which Curie and Laborde had begun. It was disturbing that they had measured nearly sixty times more than he had predicted.

To be sure that the alpha particles were really the chief carriers of energy, he studied side by side the heat produced by a specimen of radium bromide from which all the emanation had been driven and the heat produced by the emanation extracted. The one went up and the other went down proportionately to the intensity of their alpha radiation. His point was made; but from these experiments he was led to study the changes in the excited radioactivity.

He knew by now that radium changed steadily by transmutation to the gaseous emanation, and that the emanation changed to a solid substance which he presently named radium A. Then step by step, by watching the growth and decay of their radiation, he established a series of other changes from radium A to radium B, and on along an alphabetical line to a radium F which seemed to transmute into a stable substance (Paper 16).

In 1902 the idea of transmutation had been a revolutionary hypothesis which a handful of chemical experiments with thorium seemed to require. By 1904 it had become an intellectual tool which Rutherford could invoke to explain every growth or decay of radioactivity which appeared, and the theory may be said to have reached maturity.

Yet this of course was not the end of radioactivity as a science. In Rutherford's hands, the continued studies of the alpha particles led to the discovery of the nuclear structure of the atom, from that to the techniques for transmuting every element, and so into modern nuclear physics. In quite another direction, with the help of the transformation theory, the chemists succeeded at last in pinning down the chemical behavior of every sort of radioactive atom and in ranking them all in the Periodic Table—although this involved the destruction of some accepted chemical laws. This, however, is a sequence of events to be examined in another volume of this *Classics of Science* series.

This survey of the contents of the present collection of papers should be of help in sketching the main lines of developments in so far as predominantly physical (rather than chemical) techniques of research were involved. More details on each separate sequence will be furnished in the commentary on the individual papers that follow.

I. The Beginning: Becquerel and Uranium

[These first four papers[1] describe the discovery of radioactivity, made in the course of a dozen weeks, from the day when Becquerel first noticed his penetrating rays until he had satisfied himself that they belonged specifically to uranium. It is not often that we can follow the progress of an investigation as intimately as this, for what Becquerel wrote here is really a series of progress reports. But he was a man of assured position who could afford the risk of mistakes, and he commanded a particularly rapid means of publication.

Henri Becquerel (1852–1908) was the third in a remarkable family of physicists. Like his father and grandfather, he was professor of physics at the Museum of Natural History in the *Jardin des Plantes* in Paris. He had been born in the professor's apartment at the Museum, and there he lived in 1896 with his home and his laboratory under one roof. He was also Professor at the École Polytechnique, and in 1889 he had been elected (like his father and grandfather before him) to the *Académie des Sciences*.[2] The *Académie* met every Monday through the year, and whatever he chose to present at one of its sessions would be in print ten days later for distribution to the world of science.

The news of the discovery of x-rays made a tremendous sensation in the early weeks of January, 1896. Röntgen had announced them soberly enough by sending offprints of his paper together with packets of his first x-ray photographs to the leading physicists of Europe. Then the daily newspapers learned that they showed (among other things) the bones in a living human hand and the story went at once around the world. Since the pictures were easy to make, bones of hands were soon appearing on photographic plates everywhere.[3]

On 20 January, two physicians named Oudin and Barthélemy submitted a pioneer x-ray photograph of hand bones for the inspection of the *Académie*, and the mathematical physicist Henri Poincaré brought to the session his copy of Röntgen's paper. Becquerel, who was present, asked how these penetrating rays were formed, and Poincaré replied that they were produced where a beam of cathode rays played on the wall of a discharge tube, a spot marked by a lively fluorescence of the glass. It occurred to Becquerel that

---

[1] Material in square brackets is supplied by the editor of this volume.

[2] G. Darboux, E. Perrier, M. Vieille, "Discours prononcés aux funérailles de M. Henri Becquerel," *Comptes rendus de l'Académie des Sciences, Paris*, 1908, *147*: 443–449.

[3] O. Glasser, *Wilhelm Conrad Röntgen and the Early History of the Roentgen Rays* (Springfield, Illinois: Thomas, 1934).

the same mechanism which produced the visible light might also produce the invisible x-rays. This hypothesis seems to have had rather wide currency, since Poincaré published it without acknowledgement ten days later, but it was enough to set Becquerel to work on the experiments that led him to the discovery of radioactivity.[4]

Fluorescence and phosphorescence are processes in which certain substances absorb energy, for example from visible or ultraviolet light, or from cathode rays or x-rays. This energy is again emitted as light of a characteristic color. The distinction between the two processes lies only in the delay or lack of delay between the absorption and reradiation of the energy. Now we know that fluorescence and phosphorescence are not the processes which *produce* x-rays, and that they are also not at all related to the kind of rays Becquerel discovered. To think that they were should have led him astray. Yet without quite abandoning his hypothesis, Becquerel succeeded in showing that neither the ability to phosphoresce nor exposure to light was needed for obtaining his rays, but only the presence of uranium. It was a curious triumph of observation over reason, and it is the more impressive because there were others (two of whom he mentions) who succeeded where he appeared to fail, and who with a little carelessness managed to obtain x-ray effects from phosphorescence.[5]—A. R.]

1

Henri Becquerel

On the Radiation Emitted in Phosphorescence

[Translation [6] of "Sur les radiations émises par phosphorescence," *Comptes rendus de l'Académie des Sciences, Paris,* 1896, *122*: 420–421 (24 February).]

At a preceding session Ch. Henry announced that phosphorescent zinc sulfide placed in the path of the rays proceeding from a Crookes tube increased the intensity of the radiations which penetrate aluminum.

---

[4] *C. R. Acad. Sci., Paris,* 1896, *122*: 150.

H. Becquerel, "Recherches sur une propriété nouvelle de la matière," *Mémoires de l'Académie des Sciences, Paris,* 1903, *46.* See pp. 3–4. (To be abbreviated Becquerel, *Mémoire.*)

[5] See Becquerel, *Mémoire,* pp. 4–7 for a discussion of these and other misleading experiments.

[6] [This and all other papers originally in French were translated by the editor of this volume. The assistance of Mlle. Nicole Kostomaroff is gratefully acknowledged. —A.R.]

In addition, Niewenglowski has found that commercial, phosphorescent calcium sulfide emits radiations which penetrate opaque substances.

This behavior extends to several phosphorescent substances, and, in particular, to the salts of uranium whose phosphorescence has a very short duration.

With the double sulfate of uranium and potassium, of which I possess some crystals in the form of a thin transparent crust, I was able to perform the following experiment:

One of Lumière's gelatine-bromide photographic plates is wrapped in two sheets of very heavy black paper, so that the plate does not fog on a day's exposure to sunlight.

A plate of the phosphorescent substance is laid above the paper on the outside and the whole exposed to the sun for several hours. When later the photographic plate is developed, the silhouette of the phosphorescent substance is discovered, appearing in black on the negative. If between the phosphorescent substance and the paper there is placed a coin or a sheet of metal pierced with an openwork design, the image of these objects can be seen appearing on the negative.

These same experiments can be repeated by placing a thin slip of glass between the phosphorescent substance and the paper, which excludes the possibility of any chemical action by vapors which might be evolved from the substance when heated by the sun's rays.

We may then conclude from these experiments that the phosphorescent substance in question emits radiations which penetrate paper opaque to light and reduce the salts of silver.

[Perhaps the most interesting thing about Becquerel's second paper is the quirk of personality which led him, on Sunday, 1 March, to develop the wasted plates from his experiments on the previous Wednesday and Thursday. Whether this represents simple thrift, an innate thoroughness, or an overriding curiosity, it was the lucky action that sent him forward. Paper 2 is a report he made at the session of the *Académie* the next day.—A. R.]

2

Henri Becquerel

On the Invisible Radiations Emitted by Phosphorescent Substances

[Translation of "Sur les radiations invisibles émises par les corps phosphorescents," *Comptes rendus de l'Académie des Sciences*, Paris, 1896, *122*: 501–503 (2 March).]

At the last session I sketched briefly the experiments I had been led to perform in order to demonstrate the invisible radiations emitted by certain phosphorescent substances, radiations which penetrate various substances which are opaque to light.

I have been able to extend these observations, and, although I propose to continue and develop the study of these phenomena, their present interest [actualité] leads me to set forth as early as today the first results I have obtained.

The experiments I shall report were made with the radiations emitted by crystalline lamellas of the double sulfate of potassium and uranium

$$[K(UO)SO_4 + H_2O],$$

a substance whose phosphorescence is very lively and whose persistence of luminosity is less than 1/100 of a second. The characteristics of the luminous radiations emitted by this substance have formerly been studied by my father, and I have since had occasion to point out a few interesting peculiarities which these luminous radiations show.

It is very simple to verify that the radiations emitted by this substance when exposed to the sun or to diffuse daylight will penetrate not only sheets of black paper but even some metals, for example, an aluminum plate and a thin copper foil. In particular, I have performed the following experiment:

A Lumière plate of silver bromide in gelatine was enclosed in an opaque plate-holder of black fabric, closed on one side by a plate of aluminum; if the plate-holder was exposed to full sunlight, even for an entire day, the plate would not be fogged; but if a lamella of the uranium salt is fastened to the outside of the aluminum plate, held down, for example, by strips of paper, and if the whole is exposed to the sun for several hours, it can be seen, after the plate has been developed in the ordinary fashion, that the silhouette of the crystalline lamella appears in black on the sensitive plate and that the silver salt has been reduced opposite the phosphorescent lamella. If the sheet of aluminum is rather thick, the intensity of the action is less than that through two sheets of black paper.

If between the lamella of the uranium salt and the aluminum sheet or the black paper we place a screen formed by a sheet of copper about 0.10 mm thick, in the shape of a cross, for example, the silhouette of this cross can be seen in the image, more transparently, but with a shading which nevertheless shows that the radiation has penetrated the sheet of copper. In another experiment, a thinner sheet of copper (0.04 mm) weakened the active radiations much less.

The phosphorescence excited no longer by the direct rays of the sun but by the solar radiations reflected on the metallic mirror of a heliostat, then refracted by a prism and lens of quartz, gave rise to the same phenomena.

I shall particularly insist on the following fact, which appears to me very important and quite outside the range of the phenomena one might expect to observe. The same crystalline lamellas, placed opposite photographic plates, under the same conditions, separated by the same screens, but shielded from excitation by incident radiation and kept in darkness, still produce the same photographic impressions. Here is the way I was led to make this observation. Among the preceding experiments, some were prepared on Wednesday the 26 and Thursday the 27 of February, and, as on those days the sun appeared only intermittently, I held back the experiments that had been prepared, and returned the plate-holders to darkness in a drawer, leaving the lamellas of the uranium salt in place. As the sun still did not appear during the following days, I developed the photographic plates on the first of March, expecting to find very weak images. To the contrary, the silhouettes appeared with great intensity. I thought at once that the action must have been going on in darkness, and I arranged the following experiment.

At the bottom of a box of opaque cardboard I placed a photographic plate; then, on the sensitive side, I placed a lamella of the uranium salt, a convex lamella, which touched the gelatine-bromide at only a few points; then nearby I arranged on the same plate another lamella of the same salt, separated from the gelatine-bromide surface by a thin slip of glass; this operation having been carried out in the dark-room, the box was closed, then shut inside another cardboard box, and then inside a drawer.

I did the same with a plate-holder closed by a sheet of aluminum, into which I put a photographic plate, and, on the outside, a lamella of the uranium salt. The whole was shut inside a cardboard box, then in a drawer. At the end of five hours I developed the plates, and the silhouettes of the crystalline lamellas appeared in black, as in the preceding experiments, and as though they had been rendered phosphorescent by light. As for the lamella laid directly on the gelatine, there was hardly any difference in action between the points of contact and the parts of the lamella which were separated by about a millimeter from the gelatine; the difference can be attributed to the differing distance of the sources of the active radiations. The action of the lamella placed on a slip of glass was very slightly weakened, but the shape of the lamella was very well reproduced. Finally, through the aluminum sheet, the action was considerably weaker but nevertheless very distinct.

It is important to notice that this phenomenon does not seem to have to be attributed to luminous radiations emitted in phosphorescence, since at the end of $1/100$ of a second these radiations have become so weak that they are hardly perceptible.

A hypothesis which presents itself rather naturally to the mind would be to suppose that these radiations, whose effects possess a strong analogy with the effects produced by the radiations studied by Lenard and Röntgen, might be invisible radiations emitted by phosphorescence, whose duration of persistence might be infinitely greater than that of the luminous radiations emitted by these substances. Nevertheless, the present experiments, without being contrary to this hypothesis, do not warrant our formulating it. The experiments I am prosecuting at the moment may, I hope, contribute some clarification to this new order of phenomena.

[Becquerel's next paper[7], published one week later, is omitted here although it contains the interesting discovery that, like x-rays, his penetrating rays could discharge electrified bodies. In it he also reports tests which convinced him that those rays could be reflected and refracted like ordinary light. It was a plausible inference from the photographic images he saw, although as he later discovered they were quite certainly produced by secondary rays ejected from his mirrors and bits of glass by the penetrating rays from the uranium.[8] By this time he had kept some of his crystals continuously in the dark for 160 hours without any weakening of their rays. He had also narrowed down his list of ray-giving substances to compounds of uranium only, with two puzzling exceptions. A pair of calcium sulfide

---

[7] H. Becquerel, "Sur quelques propriétés nouvelles des radiations invisibles émises par divers corps phosphorescents," *C. R. Acad. Sci.*, Paris, 1896, *122*: 559–564 (9 March).

[8] H. Becquerel, *Mémoire*, pp. 24–27.

specimens, for no reason that any modern reader can guess, produced convincing images through 2 mm of aluminum.[9]   It is to be noticed, however, that this extraordinary power faded within two weeks and had vanished, equally mysteriously, by the time the succeeding paper was written.

The next paper, reprinted here, is remarkable for being wrong about as often as it is right.   Becquerel concluded on the basis of experimental observation that exposure to light of the samples intensifies the emission of rays, and that the absence of light weakens it.   These were the effects he expected,[10] and it is less remarkable that he saw them than that, having so deceived himself, he could still push through to a correct conclusion.   His study of absorption shows that he still considered his rays as akin to light. The substances he used are characterized for the most part by strong absorption in or near the visible portion of the spectrum.   On the other hand, his perplexity over the vanishing of the electric charges will be easy to understand.   The theory of the ionization of gases which would have explained it was still six months in the future.

In this paper there is also the elegant experiment with uranium nitrate. It is to be remembered that the power of phosphorescence belongs specifically to certain crystals.   To destroy a crystal by dissolving it should have destroyed its power to retain energy.   To reconstitute the crystal in the dark should have created a new, energy-free structure.   Yet, as Becquerel now showed, the newly-made crystal continued to give out penetrating rays.—A. R.]

3

Henri Becquerel

On the Invisible Radiations Emitted by the Salts of Uranium

[Translation of "Sur les radiations invisibles émises par les sels d'uranium," *Comptes rendus de l'Académie des Sciences, Paris*, 1896, *122*: 689–694 (23 March).]

1. *Action on Electrified Bodies*

At one of the last sessions of the Academy, I announced that the invisible radiations emitted by the salts of uranium possessed the property of discharging electrified bodies.   I have continued the

---

[9] H. Becquerel, *C. R. Acad. Sci.*, Paris, 1896, *122*: 559–564.
[10] See Becquerel, *Mémoire*, p. 21, for his own refutation of these observations.

study of this phenomenon by the use of Hurmuzescu's electroscope, and I have been able to establish, in another way than [the work] I have done by photography, that the radiations in question penetrate various opaque substances, in particular, aluminum and copper. Platinum exhibits an absorption considerably greater than that of the two preceding metals.

If we follow the progressive approach of the gold leaves of the electroscope during the discharge, we discover that for deflections which do not exceed 30° the angular variations are very clearly proportional to the time, so that the speed of approach, or the fraction of a degree through which the gold leaves approach each other in one second, can give an idea of the relative intensity of the active radiations. I shall report here only the numbers relating to the absorption through a plate of quartz, perpendicular to the axis, 5 mm thick. The speeds are expressed in seconds of arc and in seconds of time.

A lamella of the double sulfate of uranium and potassium placed below the gold leaves dissipated the charge of the electroscope with a speed represented by 22.50. The interpositions of the plate of quartz reduced the speed to 5.43. The ratio of the two numbers is 4.15.

I have investigated whether the radiations emanating from the phosphorescent wall of a Crookes tube were weakened by the same quartz plate in a ratio of the same order of magnitude. A Crookes tube was arranged alongside the electroscope, opposite one of the faces of the lantern in which the glass had been replaced by a sheet of aluminum 0.12 mm thick. In front of this sheet was placed a screen of copper pierced with a circular hole 15 mm in diameter. The radiations which passed through the copper were sufficiently weakened to give a negligible effect in the present experiment. When the Crookes tube was excited by an induction coil, the gold leaves of the electroscope rapidly approached each other, about 1° in 1.4 sec., corresponding to a speed of 2571.4 if expressed in the units adopted above.

When the quartz plate closed the circular opening, the speed of the fall of the gold leaves became 163.63, or 15.7 times smaller.

The weakening is nearly four times greater in the second case than in the first, but it is of the same order of magnitude. That is the only point which this experiment demonstrates. The observation is not contrary to the probable hypothesis which would attribute the difference to this: that the rays emitted by the uranium salt and the rays emitted by the tube or by the phosphorescent glass do not have the same wave lengths; but the different conditions of the two experiments permit no assurance of this heterogeneity.

The electroscope has also made it possible to demonstrate the small difference between the emission from a lamella of uranium salt kept eleven days in the dark and the emission from the same lamella brilliantly illuminated by magnesium. In the first case, the speed of the fall of the leaves was 20.69, and after the excitation by light it became 23.08.

It is not known what becomes of the electric charges dissipated in this way, as though dielectrics became conductors while being traversed by these radiations. Experience has shown that a crystalline lamella, suitably insulated, did not become charged as it discharged the electrometer. In addition, a lamella standing for a long time in the presence of the apparatus communicated no charge to it.

2. *Emission by Various Salts of Uranium. Persistence. Excitation*

If the phenomenon of the emission of invisible radiations which we are studying is a phenomenon of phosphorescence, it should be possible to demonstrate its excitation by definite radiations. This study is made very difficult by the prodigious persistence of the emission when the substances are kept in darkness, shielded from luminous radiations or from the invisible radiations whose nature we know. At the end of more than fifteen days, the salts of uranium still emit radiations which are nearly as intense as on the first day. When on the same photographic plate, above black paper, we arrange a lamella held for a long time in darkness and another which has just been exposed to daylight, the impression of the silhouette of the second is a little stronger than that of the first. The light of magnesium under the same conditions produced only an imperceptible effect. If lamellas of the double sulfate of uranium and potassium are vigorously illuminated by the electric arc or by brilliant sparks from the discharge of a Leyden jar, the impressions are considerably blacker. The phenomenon then appears really to be a phenomenon of invisible phosphorescence but does not seem to be intimately linked with visible phosphorescence or fluorescence. Indeed, although the salts of the sesquioxide of uranium are very fluorescent, we know that the green uranous salts, whose curious properties of absorption I have had occasion to study, are neither phosphorescent nor fluorescent. Now, uranous sulfate behaves like uranic sulfate, and emits invisible radiations which are equally intense.

I shall report still another interesting experiment. It is known that uranium nitrate ceases to be either phosphorescent or fluorescent when in solution or melted in its water of crystallization. I then took a crystal of this salt and, after having placed it in a little tube closed by a thin plate of glass, I warmed it in darkness, managing to avoid even the radiations from the alcohol lamp that heated it. The salt melted, I let it crystallize in darkness and I then placed it on a photographic plate wrapped in black paper, protecting the salt always from the action of light. One might have expected to observe no effect, since all luminous excitation had been avoided from the moment when the substance ceased to be phosphorescent. Nevertheless the impression was as strong as for salts exposed to the light, and, at the points where the salt adhered to the glass plate, the impression was stronger than that of a fragment of uranic sulfate placed for comparison on the same plate.

On this same photographic plate there were other crystals of uranium nitrate resting with different faces on glass slips, for which the effects were substantially the same.

I also arranged some continuous surfaces, formed of uranic sulfate and also of the double uranium-potassium sulfate, and on these surfaces I projected the spectrum of the electric arc through an apparatus of quartz. The ultraviolet excitation bands were very sharply traced by fluorescence, but, when I reproduced the silhouette of these surfaces on a photographic plate, the silhouette had become almost uniformly black, indicating either that the characteristic emission of the substance masked the weak differences which might have been observed for the different regions of excitation, or that the excitation did not take place in the region of the spectrum projected on the surface studied.

3. *Absorption by Various Substances*

It is very easy to make a qualitative study of the absorption by various substances of the radiations with which we are concerned by arranging on the same photographic plate, sheets of these substances or little flat tubes full of liquids and by covering these with a lamella of the double uranium-potassium sulfate or by any other salt of uranium.

Using various substances at thicknesses differing little from 2 mm, I discovered that water was very transparent; most of the solutions, even solutions of metallic salts, copper nitrate, gold chloride, uranium nitrate, an alcoholic solution of chlorophyll, behaved as sufficiently transparent; it was the same with paraffin and modeling wax; uranium glass was more opaque, as was a red-colored glass; aluminum at this thickness is hardly transparent, tin is more opaque, and a blue, cobalt glass was more opaque than the preceding metals.

In another series of experiments I arranged various crystals, and various optical combinations, intended to exhibit the phenomena of double refraction and polarization.   The images obtained were too weak for me to give any results today; nevertheless, it was discovered that quartz absorbs more of these invisible radiations than does Iceland spar; native sulfur behaved as if transparent.

Finally, the experiments in air and in the rarefied air I mentioned at the end of my last Note, without giving very notable differences, show plainly that the negatives in the rarefied air are a little stronger, which would demonstrate an absorption by the air.

4. *Refraction*

The facts I mentioned in my last Note provide evidence for refraction by glass.   To these experiments the following may be added: on one of the faces of a crown glass prism, a few millimeters from the edge and parallel to it, a little tube of very thin glass was fastened, about 1 mm in diameter and filled with crystalline uranium nitrate, forming a line source for the emission of invisible radiation.

The other face of the prism was set on a photographic plate. When the plate was developed three days later, a diffuse impression was seen below the base of the prism, an impression separated from the trace of the edge by a white line, whose displacement is of the order of magnitude of that obtained under the same conditions with light.   The tremendous decrease in luminous intensity when the sources were removed a little from the photographic plate has so far not permitted any measurements of the index of refraction.

5. *Anomalies Presented by Various Substances*

Uranium salts emit invisible radiations with a remarkable constancy, but it is not the same with other phosphorescent substances.

I had obtained with calcium sulfide results of the same order as those which the salts of uranium give, and in my last note I mentioned a negative of remarkable intensity made through 2 mm of aluminum. The same phosphorescent material placed on a second photographic plate under the same conditions displayed no activity, and since then I have not succeeded in obtaining any images with calcium sulfide. I have had the same lack of success with pieces of hexagonal blende of various origins.   I then attempted to transmit a new activity to these substances by various known procedures.   I heated them in the presence of the photographic plate without heating the latter, and I obtained no impression.   In another series of experiments, the various substances were chilled to $-20°$, excited by daylight and the light of magnesium, then placed on the photographic plate; only the salts of uranium gave any images.

Finally, I excited the sulfides and the hexagonal blende by sparks from the discharge of a battery, and the substances (which became vividly phosphorescent) still displayed no activity through black paper. In the course of these experiments I learned that our eminent colleague, M. Troost, had observed a similar effect. Very old specimens of hexagonal blende, which had given him energetic results at first, had later given progressively decreasing results, then had become inactive. Here is a curious fact for which further experiments will perhaps give us the explanation.

[Becquerel's next paper[11] (omitted) continues in more detail the comparison of the penetrating power of his rays against x-rays. It continues the hopeless attempts to re-activate the calcium sulfide specimens, and also contains an interesting sequel to the experiment with the uranium nitrate crystals. Not only were there penetrating rays to be obtained from fluorescent material which had been crystallized in darkness, but the uranium nitrate solution itself gave out these rays although it was certainly not fluorescent.

Seven weeks more went by and the discovery was complete. Uranium always gave out the penetrating rays, whether it was in fluorescent or nonfluorescent crystals, whether in the light or in the dark, whether dissolved in water or isolated in Moissan's pure and uncombined metal.[12] Though this was now undeniable, it was nevertheless very strange, and Becquerel still puzzled over the source of the energy which maintained the rays. He had not abandoned the hope that it might be brought in by light. He still thought the rays slightly intensified when the crystals were illuminated. He still kept some crystals in darkness to see when they might run down, and he had just increased their protection against outside influences by walling them around with lead. Seven years later they would still sit in uninterrupted darkness, still giving out rays within their lead walls, but by then Becquerel would come to expect such behavior.[13] All that he could say at present was that energy was somehow stored in the uranium, and the best language he had to express that fact was to call it a form of phosphorescence.—A. R.]

---

[11] H. Becquerel, "Sur les propriétés différentes des radiations invisibles émises par les sels d'uranium, et du rayonnement de la paroi anticathodique d'un tube de Crookes," *C. R. Acad. Sci., Paris*, 1896, *122*: 762–767 (30 March).

[12] H. Moissan, "Préparation et propriétés de l'uranium," *C. R. Acad. Sci., Paris*, 1896, *122*: 1088–1093 (18 May).

[13] H. Becquerel, *Mémoire*, pp. 14–15.

4

Henri Becquerel

Emission of New Radiations by Metallic Uranium

[Translation of "Émission de radiations nouvelles par l'uranium métallique," *Comptes rendus de l'Académie des Sciences, Paris,* 1896, *122*: 1086–1088 (18 May).]

A few months ago, I showed that uranium salts emit radiations whose existence had not been recognized and that these radiations enjoyed some remarkable properties, some of which are comparable with the properties of the radiation studied by Röntgen. The radiations of the uranium salts are emitted not only when the substances are exposed to light, but even when they are kept in darkness, and for more than two months the same fragments of various salts, shielded from all the exciting radiation known, have continued to emit the new rays, almost without perceptible weakening. From the third of March to the third of May these substances were shut up in a box of opaque cardboard. Since May third they have been placed in a double lead box which never leaves the darkroom. A very simple arrangement allows a photographic plate to slip underneath a black paper stretched parallel with the bottom of the box on which the substances under experiment rest, without these substances being exposed to any radiation which does not penetrate the lead.

Under these conditions the substances studied continue to emit active radiations.

If a fragment of one of the salts kept in darkness is exposed to the sun, or better, to the electric arc or to the spark from the discharge of a Leyden jar, it receives a slight excitation from the emission of the radiations we are studying, but this excitation falls in a few hours, and the substance resumes its state of very slow decrease.

I have also shown that these radiations are reflected and refracted as light is; they decompose the silver salts of a photographic plate and the silver iodide deposited on a daguerrotype plate.

They discharge electrified bodies and penetrate substances opaque to light, such as cardboard, aluminum, copper, and platinum. The weakening of these radiations by screens of the substances we have just mentioned is less than the weakening of the radiation emanating from the anticathode wall of a Crookes tube by the same screens.

All the salts of uranium I have studied, whether phosphorescent or not with respect to light, crystallized, fused, or in solution, have given comparable results.   Thus I have been led to think that the effect was due to the presence in these salts of the element uranium, and that the metal would give more intense effects than its compounds would.

A few weeks ago an experiment with a commercial powder of uranium which had long been in my laboratory confirmed this prediction; the photographic effect is notably stronger than the impression produced by one of the salts of uranium, and, in particular, by uranium-potassium sulfate.

Before publishing this result, I wanted to wait until our colleague, M. Moissan, whose beautiful investigations on uranium are being published today,[14] could put some of the products he had prepared at my disposal.   The results were even more clear-cut, and the impressions obtained on a photographic plate through black paper with crystallized uranium, with cast uranium, and with the carbide, were much more intense than with the double sulfate put for comparison on the same plate.

The same difference is found again in the phenomenon of the discharge of electrified bodies.   Metallic uranium promotes the dissipation of charge with a greater speed than the salts do.   The following numbers, relating to the action of a disc of cast uranium which M. Moissan has obligingly lent me, give an idea of the order of magnitude of this increase.

In a first series of measurements, the disc of cast uranium was placed below and very near the gold leaves of one of Hurmuzescu's electroscopes.   For an initial charge corresponding to a 20° separation of the gold leaves, their speed of approach expressed in seconds of angle in a second of time was on the average 486.   Next, a disk of cardboard whose surface was very nearly equal to that of the uranium disc was covered with flat pieces of the double uranium-potassium sulfate, and this disc was substituted for the uranium disc. Under these conditions, the discharge did not occur regularly; the curve of the separation of the leaves as a function of time is no longer a straight line, and the mean speed of dissipation of charges equal to the former ones varied from 106.2 to 137.1, following the arrangement and the shape of the lamellas.   The ratio of the speeds corresponding to uranium and double sulfate then varied between 4.56 and 3.54.

A better arrangement consisted in placing the substances outside the electroscope, above the copper ball of its stem, substituting for

---

[14] [See reference 12. Moissan's paper is printed immediately after Becquerel's. —A. R.]

the bonnet of the apparatus a metallic cylinder closed by a flat plate in which there was a suitable opening.   In this way discharges were obtained which were very perceptibly proportional to the time, and the speeds of loss for charges separating the gold leaves by 10° were 78.75 for the uranium and 21.53 for the uranium-potassium double sulfate.   The ratio of these two numbers is 3.65.

Although I am continuing the study of these new phenomena, I thought it was not without interest to point out the emission produced by the uranium, which, I believe, is the first example of a metal exhibiting a phenomenon of the type of an invisible phosphorescence.

II. Temporary Radioactivities: Rutherford and Thorium

[Becquerel's rays were far less spectacular than the new x-rays and, to his contemporaries, must have seemed far less rewarding to investigate. It was hard to believe that they had no "cause," that there was no way to start or stop them, no way to add to the stored-up energy in the uranium or to drain it off. At any rate there was a break in the investigations. Becquerel gradually abandoned them, and no one else cared to pick them up.

For the moment we must go back to the beginning of 1896. It was a foregone conclusion that x-rays would have some electrical action, and within six weeks of Röntgen's original announcement their power of discharging electrified bodies had been discovered five times over across the length and breadth of Europe.[1] For one of these investigators, this minor discovery led to major progress. That was Professor J. J. Thomson (1856–1940) of Cambridge University, who worked out an explanation that withstood the test of experiment.

Thomson supposed that x-rays split apart some of the molecules in any gas through which they passed into pairs of "ions" which carried opposite electric charges. When the gas was left alone these ions would recombine, positive with negative, to form again uncharged molecules. If there was a charged body in the neighborhood, however, it would draw over the ions whose sign was opposite to its own, surrendering its own charge bit by bit as it neutralized theirs.

To obtain help with his experiments, Thomson called in the most promising of his research students, a young man named Ernest Rutherford (1871–1937) who had made a brilliant record in New Zealand, where in the British academic tradition he had taken in succession his B.A., his B.S., and his M.A., and where he had done research on the rapid magnetization of iron. Together they checked the first details of Thomson's theory, and then Rutherford went on alone, drawing from the gas now the positive and now the negative ions, measuring the rate at which they were produced, the rate

---

[1] L. Benoist and D. Hurmuzescu, "Nouvelles propriétés des rayons X," *C. R. Acad. Sci., Paris*, 1896, *122*: 235–236 (3 February).

J. J. Thomson, "Röntgen Rays," *The Electrician*, 1896, *36*: 491 (7 February).

A. Righi, "Sulla produzione di fenomeni elettrici per mezzo dei raggi di Röntgen," *Rendiconto delle Sessioni, Reale Accademia delle Scienze, Bologna*, 1895–96: 45–51 (14 February).

W. C. Röntgen, "Ueber eine neue Art von Strahlen. II. Mittheilung," *Sitzungs-Berichte der Physikalisch-medicinischen Gesellschaft zu Würzburg*, 1896: 11–19 (9 March).

at which they recombined, and the speed with which they moved in an electric field.[2]

As Becquerel had discovered, the rays from uranium could also ionize gases. In 1898 Rutherford began to study the process by which they acted to see how much that process depended on the nature of the rays and how much on the specific gas involved. This led him to measure the absorption of Becquerel's rays by a number of solids and by the gases themselves as well as the conductivity they produced in different gases. He studied the rate of recombination of the ions they set free and the speed with which the ions moved in an electric field. There was no difference that he could find in the ionization which the two kinds of rays produced.

As gauged by their penetrating power, Rutherford found the uranium rays to be a mixture of two quite different types. One, which for no particular reason he named the alpha rays, had enormous ionizing power but penetrated so little that they could be stopped by a sheet of heavy paper. The other, the beta rays, appeared to penetrate as x-rays did, but had a far smaller ionizing power than the alpha rays.[3]

In the summer of that year Rutherford was appointed as the junior of the two Macdonald Professors of Physics at McGill University in Montreal, with the special responsibility of building up a research school. There he promptly struck up an acquaintance with another newcomer named R. B. Owens (1870–1940), the professor of electrical engineering and a man of his own age.

Owens had a research fellowship from Columbia University, and Rutherford had a head full of projects to try. Something over a year before, G. C. Schmidt in Erlangen and Marie Curie in Paris had discovered independently that, like uranium, thorium could also emit the ionizing, penetrating, photographically active rays.[4] Owens now undertook to study their ionization as Rutherford had just done for the rays from uranium.

To be quite precise, Owens planned to work with thorium oxide, as Rutherford had worked with uranium oxide, since the oxides were easy to obtain and work with and Becquerel had shown that the rays came indifferently from every compound. At the start there was an odd instability in

[2] J. J. Thomson and E. Rutherford, "On the Passage of Electricity through Gases Exposed to Röntgen Rays," *The Philosophical Magazine* [5], 1896, *42*: 392–407 (*Phil. Mag.*).

E. Rutherford, "On the Electrification of Gases Exposed to Röntgen Rays, and the Absorption of Röntgen Radiation by Gases and Vapours," *Phil. Mag.* [5], 1897, *43*: 241–255; "The Velocity and Rate of Recombination of the Ions of Gases Exposed to Röntgen Radiation," *ibid.*, *44*: 422–440.

[3] E. Rutherford, "Uranium Radiation and the Electrical Conduction Produced by It," *Phil. Mag.* [5], 1899, *47*: 109–163.

[4] G. C. Schmidt, "Ueber die vom Thorium und den Thorverbindungen ausgehende Strahlung," *Verhandlungen der physikalischen Gesellschaft zu Berlin*, 1898, *17*: 13, 14–16; "Ueber die von den Thorverbindungen und einigen anderen Substanzen ausgehende Strahlung," *Annalen der Physik* [3], 1898, *65*: 141–151; "Sur les radiations émises par le thorium et ses composés," *C. R. Acad. Sci.*, Paris, 1898, *126*: 1264.

Mme. Sklodowska Curie, "Rayons émis par les composés de l'uranium et du thorium," *C. R. Acad. Sci.*, Paris, 1898, *126*: 1101–1103.

Owens's measurements as the ionization shifted unexpectedly from one level to another. He traced the effect eventually to air currents, and when he had eliminated them by shutting his thorium oxide specimen in a tight metal box, the measured ionization held steady, and he was able to carry through the whole series of his measurements. If he blew air through the box, however, the ionization inside dropped sharply and did not recover until the oxide sample had been left to remain quietly for a quarter of an hour.[5]

Nothing of this kind had occurred in the experiments with either x-rays or uranium. Owens stayed briefly after his principal work was over to establish the reality of the effect,[6] and then departed for a summer's vacation in England, leaving the puzzle for Rutherford to solve.

What Rutherford did is given in the next two papers. It is worth noticing how meticulously he worked to find whether a direct transfer of energy from thorium to the air around it could produce the "radioactivity" he was studying. (Radioactivity was a word the Curies had coined the year before as a name for the spontaneous emission of ionizing, penetrating rays.) When he had ruled out that process and had still to find a source for the rays which continually re-ionized the air, the most plausible mechanism to imagine was a substance of some kind which the air could pick up and carry along. In the first paper this idea was expressed only tentatively, and the emanation was said to consist vaguely of "particles"; but in the second, which concerned the question of the "excited radioactivity," he argued directly that these rays must come from something having a material substance. From the experiments it is clear that this substance is derived from the emanation rather than the thorium, though Rutherford was a little cautious about saying so explicitly.

It is also worth noticing with what care he explored the changes of radioactivity. He knew from the start how Owens's thorium oxide would recover in still air, and by following the progress of such a recovery from minute to minute he was able to relate it to the decay of the activity of his emanation. He found that a metal plate exposed to the emanation could pick up radioactivity, and he was again able to relate this process to the decay of the radioactivity of the plate when taken away from the emanation. By these measurements he began the discovery of the characteristic "half life" of the radioactive elements, and also established the phenomenon which was to lead him to the theory of transformations.—A. R.]

---

[5] R. B. Owens, "Thorium Radiation," *Phil. Mag.* [5], 1899, *48*: 360–387.

[6] E. Rutherford and R. B. Owens, "Thorium and Uranium Radiation," *Transactions of the Royal Society of Canada* [2], 1899, *5*: Sec. III: 9–12.

5

E. Rutherford

A Radio-active Substance Emitted from Thorium Compounds

[From *The London, Edinburgh, and Dublin Philosophical Magazine and Journal of Science* [5], 1900, *49*: 1–14.]

It has been shown by Schmidt[7] that thorium compounds give out a type of radiation similar in its photographic and electrical actions to uranium and Röntgen radiation. In addition to this ordinary radiation, I have found that thorium compounds continuously emit radio-active particles of some kind, which retain their radio-active powers for several minutes. This "emanation," as it will be termed for shortness, has the power of ionizing the gas in its neighbourhood and of passing through thin layers of metals, and, with great ease, through considerable thicknesses of paper.

In order to make clear the evidence of the existence of a radio-active emanation, an account will first be given of the anomalous behaviour of thorium compounds compared with those of uranium. Thorium oxide has been employed in most of the experiments, as it exhibits the "emanation" property to a greater degree than the other compounds; but what is true for the oxide is also true, but to a less extent, of the other thorium compounds examined, viz., the nitrate, sulphate, acetate, and oxalate.

In a previous paper[8] the author has shown that the radiation from thorium is of a more penetrating character than the radiation from uranium. Attention was also directed to the inconstancy of thorium as a source of radiation. Owens[9] has investigated in more detail the radiation from thorium compounds. He has shown that the radiations from the different compounds are of the same kind, and, with the exception of thorium oxide in thick layers, approximately homogeneous in character.

The intensity of thorium radiation, when examined by means of the electrical discharge produced, is found to be very variable; and this inconstancy is due to slow currents of air produced in an open room. When the apparatus is placed in a closed vessel, to do away

---

[7] Wied. *Ann.* May 1898.

[8] *Phil. Mag.* Jan. 1899, p. 109.

[9] *Phil. Mag.* Oct. 1899, p. 360.

with air-currents, the intensity is found to be practically constant. The sensitiveness of thorium oxide to slight currents of air is very remarkable. The movement of the air caused by the opening or closing of a door at the end of the room opposite to where the apparatus is placed, is often sufficient to considerably diminish the rate of discharge. In this respect thorium compounds differ from those of uranium, which are not appreciably affected by slight currents of air. Another anomaly that thorium compounds exhibit is the ease with which the radiation apparently passes through paper. The following table is an example of the way the rate of leak between two parallel plates, one of which is covered with a *thick* layer of thorium oxide, varies with the number of layers of ordinary foolscap-paper placed over the radio-active substance.

TABLE I

Thickness of each Layer of Paper = .008 cm.   50 volts
between plates

Number of Layers of Paper	Rate of Discharge
0	1
1	.74
2	.74
5	.72
10	.67
20	.55

In the above table the rate of leak with the thorium oxide uncovered is taken as unity. It will be observed that the first layer reduced the rate of leak to .74, and the five succeeding layers produce very little effect.

The action, however, is quite different if we use a *thin*[10] layer of thorium oxide. With one layer of paper, the rate of discharge is then reduced to less than $\frac{1}{16}$ of its value. At first sight it appears as if the thorium oxide gave out two types of radiation, one of which is readily absorbed by paper, and the other to only a slight extent. If we examine the radiation given out by a thin layer of thorium oxide, by

---

[10] To produce a thin layer on a plate, the oxide, in the form of a fine powder, was sprinkled by means of a fine gauze, so as to cover the plate to a very small depth. By a thick layer is meant a layer of oxide over a millimetre in thickness.

HENRI BECQUEREL (1852-1908)

SIR ERNEST RUTHERFORD (1871-1937)

placing successive layers of thin paper upon it, we find the radiation is approximately homogeneous, as the following table shows.

TABLE II

Thickness of Paper = .0027 cm.

Number of Layers of Thin Paper	Rate of Discharge
0	1
1	·37
2	.16
3	.08

The rate of leak of the bare salt is taken as unity. If the radiation is of one kind, we should expect the rate of discharge (which is proportional to the intensity of the radiation) to diminish in geometrical progression with the addition of equal thicknesses of paper. The above figures show that this is approximately the case. With a thick layer of thorium oxide, by adding successive layers of thin paper, we find the rate of discharge gradually diminish, till after a few layers it reaches a constant value. The amount that is cut off by the first layer of foolscap-paper (see Table I) is of the same kind of radiation as that which is emitted by a thin layer of oxide.

On directing a slight current of air between the test-plates, the rate of discharge due to a thick layer of thorium oxide is greatly diminished. The amount of diminution is to a great extent independent of the electromotive force acting between the plates. Under similar conditions with uranium, the rate of leak is not appreciably affected. With a thin layer of oxide, the diminution of the rate of leak is small; but with a thick layer of oxide, the rate of leak may be reduced to less than one-third of its previous value. If two thicknesses of foolscap-paper are placed over the thorium oxide, the resulting rate of leak between the plates may be diminished to less than $\frac{1}{20}$ of its value by a slight continuous blast of air from a gasometer or bellows.

The phenomena exhibited by thorium compounds receive a complete explanation if we suppose that, in addition to the ordinary radiation, a large number of radio-active particles are given out from the mass of the active substance. This "emanation" can pass through considerable thicknesses of paper. The radio-active particles emitted by the thorium compounds gradually diffuse

through the gas in its neighbourhood and become centres of ionization throughout the gas.   The fact that the effect of air-currents is
only observed to a slight extent with thin layers of thorium oxide is
due to the preponderance, in that case, of the rate of leak due to the
ordinary radiation over that due to the emanation.   With a thick
layer of thorium oxide, the rate of leak due to the ordinary radiation
is practically that due to a thin surface-layer, as the radiation can only
penetrate a short distance through the salt.   On the other hand, the
"emanation" is able to diffuse from a distance of several millimetres
below the surface of the compound, and the rate of leak due to it
becomes much greater than that due to the radiation alone.

The explanation of the action of slight currents of air is clear on
the "emanation" theory.   Since the radio-active particles are not

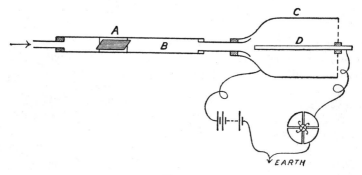

FIG. 1

affected by an electrical field, extremely minute motions of air, if
continuous, remove many of the radio-active centres from between
the plates.   It will be shown shortly that the emanation continues to
ionize the gas in its neighbourhood for several minutes, so that the
removal of the particles from between the plates diminishes the rate
of discharge between the plates.

Duration of the Radio-activity of the Emanation

The emanation gradually loses its radio-active power.   The
following method was adopted to determine the rate of decay of the
intensity of the radiation of the radio-active particles emitted by
thorium oxide.

A thick layer of thorium oxide was enclosed in a narrow rectangular paper vessel A (fig. 1), made up of two thicknesses of foolscap-
paper.   The paper cut off the regular radiation almost entirely, but
allowed the emanation to pass through.   The thorium thus enclosed

was placed inside a long metal tube B. One end of the tube was connected to a large insulated cylindrical vessel C, which had a number of small holes in the end for the passage of air. Inside C was fixed an insulated electrode, D, connected with one pair of quadrants of a Thomson electrometer. The cylinder, C, was connected to one terminal of a battery of 100 volts, the other terminal of which was connected to earth.

A slow current of air from an aspirator or gasometer, which had been freed from dust by its passage through a plug of cotton-wool, was passed through the apparatus. The current of air, in its passage by the thorium oxide, carried away the radio-active particles with it, and these were gradually conveyed into the large cylinder C. The electrometer-needle showed no sign of movement until the radio-active particles were carried into C. In consequence of the ionization of the gas in the cylinder by the radio-active particles, a current passed between the electrodes C and D. The value of the current was the same whether C was connected with the positive or negative pole of the battery. When the current of air had been flowing for some minutes, the current between C and D reached a constant value. The flow of air was then stopped, and the rate of leak between C and D observed at regular intervals. It was found that the current between C and D persisted for over ten minutes.

The following is a series of observations.

TABLE III

Potential-difference 100 volts

Time in Seconds	Current
0	1
28	.69
62	.51
118	.23
155	.14
210	.067
272	.041
360	.018

Fig. 2, curve A, shows the relation existing between the current through the gas and the time. The current, just before the flow of air is stopped, is taken as unity. It will be observed that the current through the gas diminishes in a geometrical progression with the time.   It can easily be shown, by the theory of ionization, that the current through the gas is proportional to the intensity of the radiation emitted by the radio-active particles.   We therefore see that the intensity of the radiation given out by the radio-active particles falls off in a geometrical progression with the time.   The result shows that the intensity of the radiation has fallen to one-half its value after an interval of about *one minute*. The rate of leak due to the emanation was too small for measurement after an interval of ten minutes.

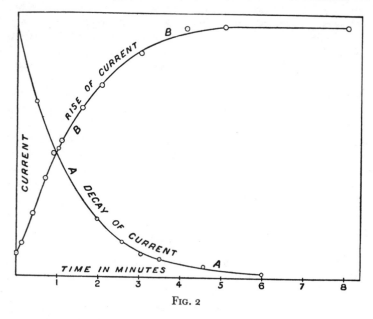

FIG. 2

If the ionized gas had been produced from a uranium compound, the duration of the conductivity, for voltages such as were used, would only have been a fraction of a second.

The rate of decay of intensity is independent of the electromotive force acting on the gas.   This shows that the radio-active particles are not destroyed by the electric field.   The current through the gas at any particular instant, after stoppage of the flow of air, was found to be the same whether the electromotive force had been acting the whole time or just applied for the time of the test.

The current through the gas in the cylinder depends on the electromotive force in the same way as the current through a gas made conducting by Röntgen rays.   The current at first increases nearly in proportion to the electromotive force, but soon reaches an approximate "saturation" value.

The duration of the radio-activity was also tested by another method. The paper vessel containing the thorium oxide was placed inside a long brass cylinder over 200 cms. in length. A slow current of air (with a velocity of about 2 cms. per second along the tube) was passed over the thorium oxide along the tube, and then between two insulated concentric cylinders. The rate of leak between the two concentric cylinders (potential-difference 270 volts) was observed when the air had been passing sufficiently long to produce a steady state. The rates of leak were observed for varying positions of the thorium oxide along the tube. Knowing the velocity of the current of air along the tube, the time taken to carry the radio-active particles to the testing-apparatus could be determined. In this way it was found that the rate of decay was about the same as determined by the first method, *i.e.*, the intensity fell to half its value in about one minute.

In this apparatus experiments were also tried to see whether the radio-active particles moved in an electric field. The experiments on the effect of a current of air on the rate of discharge naturally suggest that possibly one of the ions was so large that it moved extremely slowly even in strong electric fields. The results obtained showed that the particles did not move with a greater velocity than $\frac{1}{100,000}$ cm. per second for a potential-gradient of one volt per cm.; and it is probable that the particles do not move at all in an electric field. By blowing the emanation into an inductor, no evidence of any charge in the emanation could be detected. We may therefore conclude that the emanation is uncharged, and is not appreciably affected by an electric field.

Properties of the Emanation

The emanation passes through a plug of cotton-wool without any loss of its radio-active powers. It is also unaffected by bubbling through hot or cold water, weak or strong sulphuric acid. In this respect it acts like an ordinary gas. An ion, on the other hand, is not able to pass through a plug of cotton-wool, or to bubble through water, without losing its charge.

The emanation is similar to uranium in its photographic and electrical actions. It can ionize the gas in its neighbourhood, and can affect a photographic plate in the dark after several days' exposure. Russell[11] has shown that the active agent in producing photographic action in the case of metals, paper, &c., is due to hydrogen peroxide. Hydrogen peroxide apparently has the power

---

[11] *Proc. Roy. Soc.* 1897.

of passing in some way through considerable thicknesses of special substances, and in this respect the emanation resembles it.   Hydrogen peroxide, however, does not ionize the gas in its neighbourhood. The action of hydrogen peroxide on the photographic plate is purely a chemical one; but it is the radiation from the emanation, and not the emanation itself, that produces ionizing and photographic actions.

The radio-active emanation passes through all metals if sufficiently thin.   In order to make certain that the emanation passed through the material to be examined and did not diffuse round the edges, the radio-active substance was placed in a square groove of a thick lead plate.   Two layers of paper were pasted tightly over the opening to cut off the regular radiation.   The material to be tested was then firmly waxed down on the lead plate.

The following numbers illustrate the effect of different metals. The rate of discharge, due to the emanation between two parallel plates 4 cms. apart, was observed.

Aluminium Foil, thickness = .0008 cm.

Number of Layers	Rate of Discharge
0	1
1	.66
3	.42
6	.16

Cardboard, thickness .08 cm.

Layers	Rate of Discharge
0	1
1	.40
2	.21

The emanation passed readily through several thicknesses of gold- and silver-leaf.   A plate of mica, thickness .006 cm., was completely impervious to the emanation.

When a thick layer of thorium oxide, covered over with several thicknesses of paper, is placed inside a closed vessel, the rate of discharge due to the emanation is small at first, but gradually increases, until after a few minutes a steady state is reached.

These results are to be expected, for the emanation can only slowly diffuse through the paper and the surrounding air.   A steady state is reached when the rate of loss of intensity due to the gradual decay of the radio-activity of the emanation is recompensed by the number of new radio-active centres supplied from the thorium compound.

Let n = number of ions produced per second by the radio-active particles between the plates.

Let q = number of ions supplied per second by the emanation diffusing from the thorium.

The rate of variation of the number of ions at any time t is given by

$$\frac{dn}{dt} = q - \lambda n,$$

where λ is a constant.

The results given in Table III show that the rate of diminution of the number of ions is proportional to the number present.

Solving the equation, it is seen that

$$\log_e (q - \lambda n) = -\lambda t + A,$$

where A is a constant.

When $t = 0, \quad n = 0;$

therefore $A = \log_e q.$

Thus $n = \frac{q}{\lambda}(1 - e^{-\lambda t}).$

With a large potential-difference between the test-plates the current i through the gas at any time is given by

$$i = ne,$$

where e is the charge on an ion.

When a steady state is reached, $\frac{dn}{dt} = 0;$ and the maximum number N of ions produced per second by the radio-active particles between the plates is given by

$$N = \frac{q}{\lambda},$$

and the maximum current I is given by

$$I = Ne.$$

Therefore $\dfrac{i}{I} = 1 - e^{-\lambda t}.$

The current thus increases according to the same law as a current of electricity rises in a circuit of constant inductance.

This result is confirmed by an experiment on the rise of the current between two concentric cylinders. The thorium oxide enclosed in paper was placed inside the cylinder. A current of air was sent between the cylinders in order to remove the emanation as rapidly as it was formed. The current of air was then stopped and the current between the two cylinders observed, by means of an electrometer, for successive intervals after the current of air ceased. Table IV gives the results obtained.

TABLE IV

Length of cylinder = 30 cms.

Internal diameter outer cylinder = 5.5 cms.
External   ,,   inner   ,,   = .8 cm.
100 volts between cylinders

Time in Seconds	Current in Scale-divisions per second
0	2.4
7.5	3.3
2.3	6.5
4.0	10.0
5.3	12.5
6.7	13.8
9.6	17.1
12.5	19.4
18.4	22.7
24.4	25.3
30.4	25.6
48.4	25.6

The results are expressed in fig. 2, curve B, where the ordinate represents current and the abscissa time. It will be observed that the curve of rise of the current is similar in form to the rise of an electric current in a circuit of constant inductance. The current reaches half its value about one minute after the current of air has stopped—a result which agrees with the equation given, for $e^{-\lambda t} = \frac{1}{2}$ when $t = 60$ seconds (see Table IV). At the instant of stopping the current of air the current has a definite value, since most of the ions given off by the emanation, before it is blown out of the cylinders, reach the electrodes.

When the source of the emanation is removed, $q = 0$, and the decay of the number of ions produced by the emanation is given by the equation

$$\frac{dn}{dt} = -\lambda n.$$

If $n = N$ when $t = 0$, it is easily seen that

$$\frac{n}{N} = e^{-\lambda t},$$

or

$$\frac{i}{I} = e^{-\lambda t};$$

i.e., the current through the gas diminishes in a geometrical progression. After 20 minutes the current through the gas is only about one millionth part of its initial value.

It has been shown that $e^{-\lambda t} = \frac{1}{2}$ when $t = 60$ seconds.

Therefore $$\lambda = \tfrac{1}{86},$$

and $$N = \frac{q}{\lambda} = 86q;$$

or the total number of ions produced per second when a steady state is reached is 86 times the number of ions supplied per second by the emanation.

The amount of emanation from thorium oxide increases with the thickness of the layer. When 1 gramme of thorium oxide was spread over a surface of 25 cms., the amount of discharge due to the ordinary radiation had practically reached a maximum. The rate of leak due to the emanation for the same thickness was small. With 9 grammes of oxide spread over the same area, the rate of leak due to the emanation had reached about half its maximum value, which for that case corresponded to four times the rate of leak caused by the ordinary radiation. The emanation thus still preserves its radio-active properties after diffusing through several millimetres of thorium compound.

The emanation is given out whatever the gas by which the thorium is surrounded. The action is very similar whether air, oxygen, hydrogen, or carbonic acid is used.

The rate of discharge due to the emanation diminishes with lowering of the pressure of the air surrounding it. Only a few observations have been made, but the results seem to point to a uniform rate of emission of the emanation at all pressures; but since the intensity of the ionization of the gas varies directly as the pressure, the rate of leak decreases with lowering of the pressure.

The amount of the emanation, so far as the experiments have gone, is also independent of the quantity of water-vapour present.

The power of emitting radio-active particles is not possessed to any appreciable extent by other radio-active substances besides thorium.   All the compounds of thorium examined possess it to a marked degree, and it is especially large in the oxide.   Two different specimens of the oxide have been used, one obtained from Schuchart of Germany, and the other from Eimer & Amend of New York.   The oxide is prepared by the latter by igniting thorium nitrate obtained from monazite sand.

The amount of discharge caused by the emanation is increased several times by the conversion of the nitrate into the oxide; but at the same time, the rate of discharge due to the ordinary radiation emitted by the thorium is increased in about an equal ratio.   The conversion of the nitrate into the oxide took place below a red heat. On heating in a muffle for some time at white heat, the amount of emanation continually diminished, till after four hours' exposure to the heat, the rate of discharge due to the emanation was only $\frac{1}{20}$ of the value immediately after its conversion into oxide.

Both thorium oxalate and sulphate act in a similar manner to the nitrate; but the emanation is still given off to a considerable extent after continued heating.

In considering the question of the origin and nature of the emanation, two possible explanations naturally suggest themselves, viz.:—

(1) That the emanation may be due to fine dust particles of the radio-active substance emitted by the thorium compounds.

(2) That the emanation may be a vapour given off from thorium compounds.

The fact that the emanation can pass through metals and large thicknesses of paper and through plugs of cotton-wool, is strong evidence against the dust hypothesis.   Special experiments, however, were tried to settle the question.   The experiments of Aitken and Wilson [12] have shown that ordinary air can be completely freed from dust particles by repeated small expansions of the air over a water-surface.   The dust particles act as nuclei for the formation of small drops, and are removed from the gas by the action of gravity.

The experiment was repeated with thorium oxide present in the vessel.   The oxide was enclosed in a paper cylinder, which allowed the emanation to pass through it.   After repeated expansions no

---

[12] *Trans. Roy. Soc.* 1897.

cloud was formed, showing that for the expansions used the particles of the emanation were too small to become centres of condensation of the water-vapour. We may therefore conclude, from this experiment, that the emanation does not consist of dust particles of thorium oxide.

It would be of interest to examine the behaviour of the emanation for greater and more sudden expansions, after the manner employed by C. T. R. Wilson [13] in his experiments on the action of ions as centres of condensation.

The emanation may possibly be a vapour of thorium. There is reason to believe that all metals and substances give off vapour to some degree. If the radio-active power of thorium is possessed by the molecules of the substance, it would be expected that the vapour of the substance would be itself radio-active for a short time, but the radio-active power would diminish in consequence of the rapid radiation of energy. Some information on this point could probably be obtained by observation of the rate of diffusion of the emanation into gases. It is hoped that experimental data of this kind will lead to an approximate determination of the molecular weight of the emanation.

Experiments have been tried to see if the amount of the emanation from thorium oxide is sufficient to appreciably alter the pressure of the gas in an exhausted tube. The oxide was placed in a bulb connected with a Plücker spectroscopic tube. The whole was exhausted, and the pressure noted by a McLeod gauge. The bulb of thorium oxide was disconnected from the main tube by means of a stopcock. The Plücker tube was refilled and exhausted again to the same pressure. On connecting the two tubes together again, no appreciable difference in the pressure or in the appearance of the discharge from an induction-coil was observed. The spectrum of the gas was unchanged.

Experiments, which are still in progress, show that the emanation possesses a very remarkable property. I have found that the positive ion produced in a gas by the emanation possesses the power of producing radio-activity in all substances on which it falls. This power of giving forth a radiation lasts for several days. The radiation is of a more penetrating character than that given out by thorium or uranium. The emanation from thorium compounds thus has properties which the thorium itself does not possess. A more complete account of the results obtained is reserved for a later communication.

McGill University, Montreal,
    September 13th, 1899.

---

[13] *Phil. Trans. Roy. Soc.* vol. clxxxix. (1897).

6

E. Rutherford

Radioactivity Produced in Substances by the Action of Thorium Compounds

[From *The London, Edinburgh, and Dublin Philosophical Magazine and Journal of Science* [5], 1900, *49*: 161–192.]

Thorium compounds under certain conditions possess the property of producing temporary radioactivity in all solid substances in their neighbourhood. The substance made radio-active behaves, with regard to its photographic and electrical actions, as if it were covered with a layer of radio-active substance like uranium or thorium. Unlike the radiations from thorium and uranium, which are given out uniformly for long periods of time, the intensity of the excited radiation is not constant, but gradually diminishes. The intensity falls to half its value about eleven hours after the removal of the substance from the neighbourhood of the thorium. The radiation given out is more penetrating in character than the similar radiations emitted by uranium and thorium and the radio-active derivatives from pitchblende, radium[14], and polonium[15].

Attention was first drawn to this phenomenon of what may be termed "excited radioactivity" by the apparent failure of good insulators, like ebonite and paraffin, to continue to insulate in the presence of thorium compounds.

The apparatus first used is shown in fig. 1.

Two insulated plates, B and C, were placed parallel to one another. In a shallow square depression LM in the plate C, a layer of thorium oxide was placed and covered with several layers of foolscap-paper. The whole was enclosed in a lead vessel A, with a door in the side to allow the plate C to be readily moved. The crossed lines show the position of insulators. The plate C was connected to the + pole of a battery of 50 volts, the other terminal of which was to earth. The plate B was connected to one pair of quadrants of a delicate Thomson electrometer with a replenisher and gauge, the other pair of quadrants of which was connected to earth.

With the arrangement in the figure, when B is insulated, there can be no conduction-current from C along or through the insulators,

---

[14] Curie, *C. R.* 1898, p. 175.
[15] Curie, *ibid.* 26 Dec. 1898.

since the earth-connected vessel intervenes. If the thorium-covered plate C was removed, and a brass one of the same dimensions substituted, there was no appreciable movement of the electrometer-needle. If, however, the plate C, covered with thorium oxide, were left in the vessel for several hours with the plate B charged −, on removal of C and the substitution of a non-active metal plate, the movement of the electrometer-needle showed that B was receiving a + charge. On reversing the battery, the current was reversed in direction but equal in amount. The current between the plates gradually decreased with the time, and became inappreciable after a few days. By replacing the thorium oxide, the experiment could be repeated.

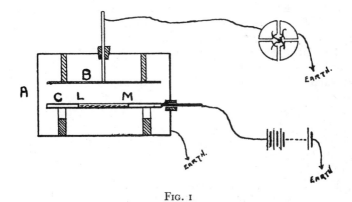

Fig. 1

It was at first thought that possibly dust particles from the thorium oxide might have escaped from under the paper and in some way adhered to the upper plate. An examination of the plate B, however, revealed no trace of thorium oxide on its surface. The plate made the air a conductor in its neighbourhood, as if it were covered with a thick layer of radio-active substance. If the surface of the plate was carefully scrubbed with sand- or emery-paper, the radio-active power was to a great extent destroyed. It was found possible to make the plate B active, even if the thorium oxide were covered with 30 layers of foolscap paper tightly waxed down so as to prevent the escape of dust particles.

If the plate C was charged − and B +, the plate B no longer became radio-active, but the top layer of paper over the thorium was found to be active on its upper side to about the same extent as the plate B in the previous case; *i.e.*, the negatively charged surface was made active in both cases.

All the compounds of thorium examined have the power of causing radioactivity in substances. The oxide, however, gives far the largest effects, and has consequently been used in most of the experiments.

The thorium compounds used were supplied by Messrs. Eimer & Amend, New York. The oxide was obtained by igniting the nitrate which had been manufactured from monazite sand. If the oxide is heated for some hours to a white heat in a platinum crucible, it loses its power of exciting radioactivity in substances to a very large extent.

Comparison of Intensities of Radiation

The intensity of the radiation, excited in substances in the manner described, was in all cases compared by the electrical method. In general, for the purposes of measurement, the radioactivity was excited in flat plates or circular cylinders.

For flat plates the testing apparatus was similar to fig. 1. The brass plates corresponding to B and C were 5 cms. apart, with a potential-difference of 50 volts between them. The current between the plates, measured by the rate of movement of the electrometer-needle, was taken as proportional to the intensity of the radiation at the surface. With radio-active cylinders, the active cylinder was placed in a larger cylinder and concentric with it. The current for 50 volts between the cylinders was taken as a measure of the intensity of the radiation at the surface.

For experiments, extending in some cases over several days or weeks, it was necessary that for each observation the electrometer should be of the same degree of sensitiveness. This was roughly ensured by the Thomson Replenisher and Gauge, attached to the electrometer. For small variations from the standard sensitiveness, the values of the current were corrected by observing the number of divisions on the electrometer-scale corresponding to the E.M.F. of a Clark cell.

As in the course of this paper it will be necessary to compare the intensity of the radiation from radio-active plates and cylinders, a brief theoretical discussion will be given of the relation that exists between the intensity of the radiation, the area of the active surface, and the maximum current through the gas.

Two cases will be considered—

    (I) When the radiation is given out uniformly from a plane surface and the current through the gas is measured between two parallel planes.

    (II) When the radiation is given out from a cylinder and the current measured between concentric cylinders.

Case I.—We will first consider the case of a uniformly radio-active plate C, of area S, which is placed between two large parallel plates A and B (fig. 2*a*).

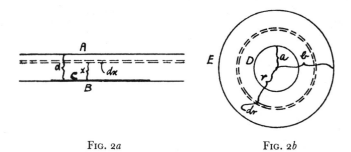

FIG. 2*a*   FIG. 2*b*

We will suppose the plate C to be of large dimensions compared with the distance d of the plate C from A, and to give out radiation equally from all points of its surface. The gas is ionized by the passage of the radiation through it, and the ions produced travel to the plates A and C under the influence of the electric field.

In consequence of the energy required to ionize the gas, the intensity of the radiation diminishes in its passage through it.

Suppose the radiation is homogeneous in character, and that λ is the coefficient of absorption of the radiation by the gas. Let I_0 be the intensity of the radiation at the surface of the plate. Since the plate is large compared with the distance d, the value of the intensity may be considered approximately equal at equal distances from the surface C. In consequence of the absorption of the radiation by the gas, the intensity I at a distance x from the active plate is given by

$$I = I_0 e^{-\lambda x}.$$

Let dn be the number of ions produced per second between two planes parallel to C and distant x and $x + dx$ from it.

Since the rate of production of ions is proportional to the intensity of the radiation, the total number of ions n produced per second between A and C, distant d apart, is given by

$$n = \int_0^d KSI_0 e^{-\lambda x} \, dx, \text{ where K is a constant,}$$

$$= \frac{KSI_0}{\lambda} \left(1 - e^{-\lambda d} \right).$$

If ϵ is the charge on an ion, the current i through the gas, when an E.M.F. is applied sufficient to remove all the ions before recombination takes place, is given by

$$i = n\epsilon.$$

Therefore

$$SI_0 = \frac{i\lambda}{K\epsilon(1 - e^{-\lambda d})};$$

or the product of the intensity of the radiation and the area of the active surface is proportional to the current through the gas.

It is of interest to develop the above equation from considerations of the energy required to produce an ion.

Let W be the average amount of energy used up in producing an ion in the gas. We will assume that the absorption of the energy of the radiation in its passage through the gas is due solely to the production of ions. On account of the absorption, the intensity of the radiation varies from I_0 at the surface of the active plate to $I_0 e^{-\lambda d}$ at the surface of the top plate. If n be the total number of ions produced, we thus obtain

$$n \cdot W = SI_0(1 - e^{-\lambda d});$$

where the energy absorbed over an area S is given by the right-hand side of the equation; or

$$SI_0 = \frac{Wi}{\epsilon(1 - e^{-\lambda d})},$$

where current $i = n\epsilon$, as before.

Some experiments given in previous papers[16] point to the conclusion that the energy required to produce an ion may possibly be the same for all gases at all pressures, and it has been shown by Prof. J. J. Thomson and Mr. Townsend that the charge of the ions[17] in different gases is the same. If such is the case, W/ϵ is a constant for all gases and the current through the gas will depend only on λ, d, and SI_0.

Case II.—We will now consider the case of a radio-active cylinder, where the current is measured between two concentric cylinders. Let fig. 2b represent a cross-section of the cylinders. Let $a =$ radius of radio-active cylinder D, $b =$ radius of concentric cylinder E. Suppose length of cylinder D to be large compared with the distance

---

[16] Rutherford, *Phil. Mag.* Jan. 1899.
[17] J. J. Thomson, *Phil. Mag.* Dec. 1898; J. S. Townsend, *Trans. Roy. Soc.* 1899.

between the cylinders. If λ is the coefficient of absorption of the radiation, the intensity I at a distance r (outside D) from the centre is easily seen to be

$$\frac{I}{I_0} = \frac{a}{r} e^{-\lambda(r-a)},$$

where I_0 = intensity of radiation at the surface, since without any absorption the value of I would fall off inversely as the distance. The total energy of the radiation near the surface of the external cylinder is given per unit length by

$$I_0 \frac{a}{b} e^{-\lambda(b-a)} . 2\pi b,$$

the energy per unit length close to the surface of the active cylinder by $I_0 . 2\pi a$.

The total energy absorbed in the gas is thus equal to

$$I_0 . 2\pi a \{1 - e^{-\lambda(b-a)}\}.$$

If n = the number of ions produced per second due to the length l of the active rod,

$$W . n = I_0 . 2\pi a l \{1 - e^{-\lambda(b-a)}\}$$
$$= I_0 . S \{1 - e^{-\lambda(b-a)}\},$$

where S is surface-area of active cylinder;

$$SI_0 = \frac{W . i}{\epsilon \{1 - e^{-\lambda(b-a)}\}}, \text{ where } i = n\epsilon,$$

$$= \frac{Ai}{1 - e^{-\lambda(b-a)}}, \text{ where } A = \frac{W}{\epsilon} = \text{constant.}$$

In both of the cases considered, half the radiation has been absorbed in the substance which is made radio-active, and the other half passes through the gas, since the radiation is given out from the surface in all directions. In the case of complete absorption of the radiation in the passage through the gas, the maximum current i is given by

$$SI_0 = Ai.$$

An investigation is now in progress to determine the value of A, that is, W/ϵ. If A is determined, the intensity of the radiation can at once be expressed in absolute measure.

Conditions for the Production of Radioactivity in Substances

In order to *confine* the induced radioactivity produced by thorium compounds to any particular conductor, it is necessary that it should be charged — and all other bodies in the field +. In order to produce radioactivity in all bodies in the neighbourhood, no electric field is required.   If thorium oxide is placed in a closed vessel connected to earth, the sides of the vessel and any solid bodies near, whether conductors or insulators, become radio-active.   If, in addition, the surface of the thorium oxide is covered with paper or thin aluminium-foil, the side of the paper away from the oxide becomes radio-active.   When no electromotive forces are acting, the amount of radioactivity in a given time per unit area is greater the nearer the body to the thorium oxide.

With electromotive forces acting, the substance to which the radioactivity is due appears to travel along the lines of force from the + to the — charged body.   It is thus possible to *concentrate* the radio-

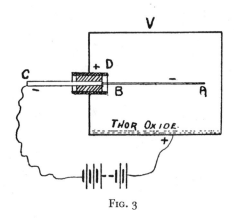

FIG. 3

activity on small plates or fine wires by placing them in a closed metal vessel connected to earth and charging them —.

If the bodies are all uncharged, the particles producing radioactivity, by the process of diffusion through the gas, are carried to the sides of the bodies and adhere to them.   A fine wire fixed in the centre of a vessel on the bottom of which the active salt is placed becomes only slightly radio-active, since only a few of the active particles reach its surface.   The closer a body is to the thorium, other conditions remaining unaltered, the more active it becomes.

Fig. 3 shows the general arrangement for concentrating the activity on a small area of a conductor.   A metal vessel V was connected to the + pole of a battery of small lead accumulators of 300 volts, the other pole of which was to earth.

A thick layer of thorium oxide was placed in the bottom of the vessel and covered with several thicknesses of paper.   A brass tube D was fixed in the side of the vessel and metallically connected with it. A fine platinum wire AB was fixed on the end of a stouter brass rod BC. The brass rod was fixed centrally in the cylinder D and insulated from it. The end of the brass rod B was placed well inside the cylinder D. The conductor AC was connected to earth.

The fine wire is thus the only body exposed in the field with a charge, and, under the influence of electric forces, the active particles are carried to the wire AB and adhere to its surface.

The same general results are obtained whether the surface of the thorium oxide is bare or covered with paper or thin layers of metal-foil.

Two or three layers of paper almost completely cut off the ordinary radiation [18] from thorium; so the effect cannot be due to the direct radiation from its surface.

In this way I have been able to cause a piece of platinum wire of length 1 cm. and diameter .018 cm., *i.e.* with a surface area of .056 cm., to give more than 20 times the rate of discharge given by a thick layer of uranium oxide of 25 sq. cms. area. A rate of movement of an electrometer-needle of 200 divisions in 5 seconds is quite easily obtained from the action of such a small active surface. (1 volt gave a deflexion of 40 divisions on the electrometer-scale, and the capacity of the whole circuit was about 50 electrostatic units.)

I have spoken of using a platinum wire, but any other metal wire will serve equally well. Using large electromotive forces and a large surface of thorium oxide, it would be quite possible to increase the radioactivity of unit area of the conductor to more than 20 times the value cited in the above case. So far as the results obtained indicate, there is no limit to the amount of increase, since we can suppose the area of the − charged conductor diminished and the amount of thorium increased. In practice, however, a limit would soon be reached, as it would be difficult to cause all the radio-active particles to move to the small conductor without very large electric forces.

Connexion between the " Emanation" from Thorium and " Excited"
Radio-activity

In a previous paper [19] I have shown that compounds of thorium emit some kind of radio-active material or "emanation," which is able to pass through considerable thicknesses of paper and thin layers of metal, and preserves its radiating power for several minutes. These particles diffuse through the gas and become centres of

---

[18] E. Rutherford, *Phil. Mag.* Jan. 1900.
[19] *Phil. Mag.* January 1900.

ionization throughout the volume of the gas. The current passing between two charged plates, on one of which is spread thorium oxide, is greatly diminished by directing a slow continuous blast of air between the plates. As the particles have no charge, they may be readily removed from between the plates by a current of air even in a strong electric field.

There is a very close connexion between this "emanation" and excited radioactivity—in fact, the emanation is in some way the direct cause of the latter. The following facts will serve to show the close connexion that exists:—

(1) All thorium compounds examined are able to make substances radio-active, but to different degrees. The greater the amount of emanation, the greater the amount of induced radioactivity. As an example, thorium oxide is the most active of all thorium compounds in producing radioactivity and giving out the emanation. A thin layer of thorium oxide gives out very little emanation, and is only slightly effective in producing radioactivity.

(2) Substances are made radio-active when the active compound is covered with several layers of paper or thin metal foil. The emanation also readily passes through paper and thin metal foil. Two or three layers of ordinary foolscap-paper completely cut off the ordinary radiation given out by thorium compounds, but do not much diminish the amount of induced radioactivity.

(3) A slow current of air, which quickly removes the emanation as it appears, also diminishes the power of producing radioactivity. The amount of induced radiation is greater in closed than in open vessels, on account of the disturbance of air-currents in the latter case.

(4) Thorium oxide which had been heated to a sufficiently high temperature gave out very little emanation and produced little radioactivity.

Speaking generally, it may be said that the presence of the emanation is necessary for the production of radioactivity in substances, and that the amount of radioactivity depends upon the amount of the "emanation." A radio-active substance like uranium, which gives out no emanation, produces no trace of excited radioactivity.

An experiment now to be described throws a further light on the question. The general arrangement of the experiment is shown in fig. 4.

A slow current of air from a gas-bag, after bubbling through sulphuric acid, passed down through a rectangular wooden vessel, 60 cms. in length. In order to remove spray and dust and to equalize the current of air over the cross-section, the air was passed through cotton-wool at W. A metal plate covered the bottom of the vessel and was charged +. Four insulated metal plates, A, B, C, D, placed at equal distances, were attached to a top metal plate connected to earth.   Thorium oxide covered with paper was placed under the electrode A.

The current of air was passed through the vessel at the steady rate of about .2 cm. per second for a period of 7 hours, with 300 volts

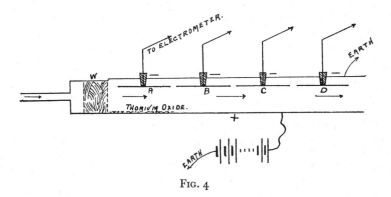

Fig. 4

between the lower and upper plates.   The following results were obtained for the current due to the emanation which reached A, B, C, D and the corresponding radioactivity produced:—

	Relative current due to emanation	Relative excited radioactivity
Plate A	I	I
„ B	.55	.43
„ C	.18	.16
„ D	.072	.061

The current due to the emanation which reaches A, and the radioactivity produced in A, is in each case taken as unity for the purpose of comparison.   It will be observed that radioactivity is produced on the plates some distance away from the thorium oxide, and is roughly proportional to the emanation-current at the plate.   We may conclude from this experiment that the radioactivity is, in some way, due to the "emanation," or to something that accompanies it, but is not caused by the direct action of a radiation from thorium oxide.

Absorption of the Radiation by Substances

All radio-active substances, as well as bodies made radio-active in the manner described, ionize the gas in their neighbourhood and act upon a photographic plate in the dark. A simple method of testing whether two types of radiation are the same, is to determine the absorption of the radiation by layers of thin metal foil. If the absorption is different for the two types of radiation, we may consider them distinct kinds of radiation.

The current between two parallel plates, one surface of which was radio-active, was determined when successive layers of a substance of equal thickness were placed over the radio-active plate. The following table is an example of the way the current (which is proportional to the intensity of the radiation) diminishes with successive layers of aluminium-foil over a plate of zinc, which had been made radio-active:—

Zinc plate = 12 × 18 cms.
Thickness of foil = .0004 cm.
95 volts between plates.

No. of layers alum. foil	Current for radiation from zinc	Current for thin layer of thorium oxide
0	1	1
1	·71	·57
2	·55	·36
3	·43	·23
4	·32	·13
5	—	.084
6	·155	.056

The third column of the table gives the variation of the current with thickness of foil for a *thin* layer of thorium oxide, and serves as a basis of comparison with the excited radiation. The current for the bare radio-active surface is in each case taken as unity for the purpose of comparison.

Fig. 5, curves A, B, show these results graphically when the ordinates denote current and the abscissæ thicknesses of aluminium.

It will be observed that the radiations from zinc and thorium oxide are quite different in character, the radiation from the former being far more penetrating as regards aluminium. Both types of radiation are approximately homogeneous. The current, which is proportional to the intensity of the radiation, diminishes approximately in a geometrical progression as the thickness of the metal increases in arithmetical progression.

The same general difference is shown for the two types of radiation by testing their comparative absorption by thin layers of paper, gold-leaf, silver-foil, and Dutch metal.

The following table is an example of the absorption of the radiation from a zinc plate and a thin layer of thorium oxide for thin tissue-paper:—

Thickness of layer of paper = .0030 cm.
Potential-difference between plates = 50 volts.

| | Current | |
No. of layers of paper	Radiation from zinc	Radiation from thorium oxide
0	I	I
I	·57	·37
2	·35	.16
3	.20	.080
4	.12	.055

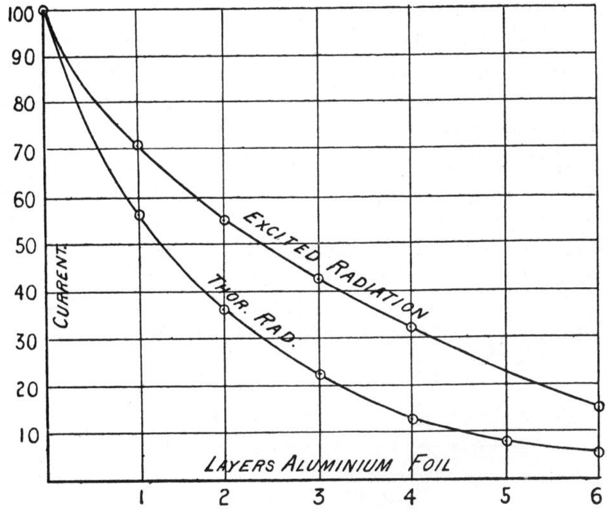

Fig. 5

This method can also be used to compare the radiations from the various metals when made radio-active. In this way it was found that all the substances tried, viz., Cu, Pb, Pt, Al, Zn, brass, cardboard, paper, which had been made radio-active, gave out radiations of the same penetrating power. It was also found that the same type of radiation was given out from polished and dull surfaces, and that it was unaffected by the concentration of the radioactivity.

Since the same radiation is given out by all the metals and non-metallic substances like cardboard or paper, under varying conditions, we may conclude that either the substance itself which has been made radio-active plays no direct part in determining the kind of radiation, or that all exert exactly the same action.

The "excited" radiation is also of a more penetrating character than that given out by uranium, thorium, and the pitchblende derivatives radium and polonium.

Absorption of the Radiation in Air

The absorption of the induced radiation in air was also determined. The method employed was similar to one previously used and described by the author[20] for determining the absorption of uranium radiation by different gases. A similar apparatus has been employed by Owens[21] for thorium radiation.

Two insulated parallel plates, kept a fixed distance apart, could be moved by means of a screw to different distances from the parallel radio-active surface. The radiation from the active surface passed through a circular opening in the lower plate, covered with thin aluminium-foil, and was stopped by the upper plate. The current between the two fixed plates for a large voltage was determined for different distances from the radio-active plate. If the radius of the active surface is large compared with the distance of the lower of the pair of plates from it, the current between the plates for a distance x of the lower plate from the active surface varies as $e^{-\lambda x}$, where λ is the coefficient of absorption of the radiation in the gas.

The following table gives the results obtained for the radiation from a lead surface which had been made strongly radio-active:—

Lead Radiation

Distance from surface	Current
d (= 3 mms.)	I
$d+6.25$ mms.	·79
$d+12.5$,,	·59
$d+18.7$,,	.46
$d+25$,,	·35
$d+31.2$,,	.27
$d+37.5$,,	.21

[20] *Phil. Mag.* Jan. 1899, p. 124.
[21] *Ibid.* Oct. 1899, p. 378.

The current is taken as unity when the measurements began at a distance $d = 3$ mms. from the active lead plate.

For the purposes of comparison, the numbers obtained in a similar manner for thin layers of thorium oxide and uranium oxide on a bare plate are given below.

Thorium Radiation   Uranium Radiation

Distance	Current		Distance	Current
d (= 2.25 mms.)	I		d (= 2.25 mms.)	I
$d+$ 5 mms.	.73		$d+$ 2.5 mms.	.685
$d+10$,,	.50		$d+$ 5 ,,	.445
$d+15$,,	.35		$d+$ 7.5 ,,	.296
$d+20$,,	.25		$d+10$,,	.188
			$d+15$,,	.088
			$d+20$,,	.059

The curves in fig. 6 show the results graphically.   It will be seen that the intensity of the radiation falls off approximately in a geometrical progression as the distance increases in arithmetical progression.   Curves of absorption of thorium radiation in air at different pressures have been obtained by Owens. [22]

The distances through which the three types of radiation from uranium, thorium, and active lead pass through air at ordinary pressures and temperatures before the intensity is reduced to one-half its value, are about 4, 10, and 16.5 mms. respectively.

Assuming that the intensity falls off as $e^{-\lambda x}$, the values of λ for the types of radiation are given below.

Value of λ

	Value of λ
"Excited" radiation	.42
Uranium ,, ...	1.6
Thorium ,, ...	.69

The order of absorption in air of the above three types of radiation is the same as for aluminium and paper.

The "excited" radiation is of a more penetrating kind than the easily absorbed type (the α radiation) [23] given out by uranium, but much less than the β type.   The radiations from uranium and

---

[22] Owens, *Phil. Mag.* Oct. 1899.
[23] Rutherford, *Phil. Mag.* Jan. 1899, p. 116.

polonium are also more readily absorbed in air than the excited radiation is.

Duration of the Radioactivity

If a plate or wire which has been made radio-active is removed from the action of the thorium, the intensity of the radiation diminishes according to a very simple law.

A large number of experiments have been made on the duration of the induced radioactivity in various substances under varying conditions. A typical table of the results obtained is given below for a rod of brass which has been made active. In order to test the rate of decay of the intensity, the active rod was placed inside a cylinder and concentric with it. The current between the two cylinders for a potential-difference of 50 volts was measured in the usual manner, and at intervals of several hours.

Length of rod = 31.5 cms.
Diameter = .40 cms.
Testing-cylinder, inside diameter = 7.3 cms.

Time in hours	Current
0	1
7.9	.640
11.8	.474
23.4	.196
29.2	.138
32.6	.103
49.2	.0370
62.1	.0186
71.4	.0086

The value of the maximum current, which is taken as unity, was 1.6×10^{-11} amperes.

Fig. 7 shows graphically the results obtained. The results show that the current through the gas (which is proportional to the intensity of the radiation) diminishes in geometrical progression with the time. The time taken for the intensity of the radiation to fall to half its value is about eleven hours. If I_0 be the intensity at the beginning, the intensity I after a time t is given by

$$I = I_0 e^{-Lt},$$

where L is a constant.

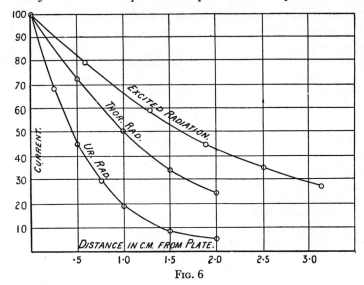

Fig. 6

The above law appears to hold accurately for all substances made radio-active. No difference in the rate of decay has been observed, whether the radiation is on a plate of large area or concentrated on a fine wire. The rate of decay is also independent of the substance made radio-active. A piece of paper, mica, or metal, all give the

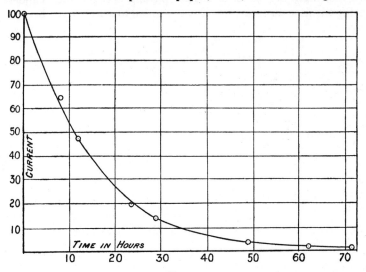

Fig. 7

same rate of loss of intensity. As far as experiments have gone, the rate of decay is unaffected by the pressure of the gas surrounding it, or whether the air is dry or full of moisture. The same rate of decay has always been obtained under all the conditions tried, provided the surface is not acted on mechanically or by chemicals.

The mean value of L deduced from the above results is

$$L = .0000189.$$

In a previous paper [24] I have shown that the radio-active "emanation" from thorium compounds quickly loses its radio-active power.

The intensity in that case falls to half its value in about one minute, while the intensity of the "excited" radiation falls to half its value in about eleven hours, or one decays 660 times faster than the other. The law of falling off of intensity is the same in the two cases.

On page 43 it has been shown that the current i (for a "saturating" E.M.F.) between two cylinders is given by

$$i = \frac{SI_0}{A}\{1 - e^{-\lambda(b-a)}\},$$

with the same notation as before.

The intensity I of the radiation after a time t is given by

$$I = I_0 e^{-Lt},$$

and the total quantity of electricity passing between the cylinders during the time taken for the intensity to fall to zero is given by

$$Q = \int_0^\infty i\,dt = \frac{SI_0}{A}\{1 - e^{-\lambda(b-a)}\} \int_0^\infty e^{-Lt}dt$$

$$= \frac{SI_0}{LA}\{1 - e^{-\lambda(b-a)}\};$$

if $i_0 =$ initial current, it is clear that

$$Q = \frac{i_0}{L}.$$

In the case given in the last table, the initial current was 1.6×10^{-11} amperes, and the value of $L = .0000189$; therefore the total quantity of electricity passing between the cylinders is equal to 8.5×10^{-7} coulombs.

---

[24] *Phil. Mag.* Jan. 1900.

The total quantity of electricity separated, if the radiation has been completely absorbed in the gas, is obviously

$$\frac{1}{1 - e^{-\lambda(b-a)}}$$

of this quantity.

In the above case, $a = .20$ cm., $b = 3.65$ cms., $\lambda = .42$.

Therefore quantity passing between cylinders $= 11.1 \times 10^{-7}$ coulombs.

Increase of Induced Radioactivity with Time

If a plate or wire is exposed to the action of thorium oxide in a closed vessel, the radioactivity at first increases nearly proportionally with the time, and then more slowly, finally tending to a maximum value after several days' exposure.

The table given below is an example of the results obtained for a square zinc plate, area 86 sq. cms., exposed in a metal vessel, with a potential-difference of 300 volts between thorium and surface to be made active.   The plate was removed from the action of the thorium at intervals for sufficient time to determine the current produced by it between two charged parallel plates, as in fig. 1.

Time of exposure in hours	Current
1.58	.063
3.25	.105
5.83	.289
9.83	.398
14.00	.586
23.41	.773
29.83	.834
47.00	.898
72.50	.951
96.00	1.00

The current after four days' exposure is taken as unity, as the rate of leak had nearly reached its maximum value.

The maximum value of the current produced by the active plate between two test-plates 4 cms. apart was 1.7×10^{-11} amperes.

Fig. 8 shows the results graphically.   From the table it will be seen that the intensity has reached half its final value in about twelve hours.

We will now consider the conditions which influence the increase of the intensity of radiation from a given surface exposed to the action of a thorium compound.   We will suppose that the surface to be made radio-active is negatively charged.

Two opposing actions are evidently at work.   Fresh radio-active particles are being continually carried to the plate, while the intensity of the radiation given out by the active surface continually diminishes, owing to the radiation of energy.   A steady state will be reached when the rate of increase of intensity due to the supply of fresh radio-active particles is equal to the rate of decrease of the intensity due to the radiation of energy from the active surface.

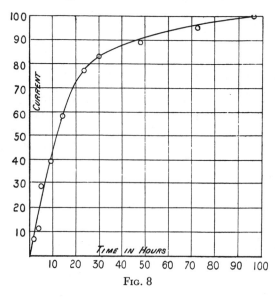

FIG. 8

Let I be the intensity of the radiation at the surface of the plate at any time.   The rate of diminution of the intensity is equal to LI, since the intensity I at any time is given by

$$I = I_0 e^{-Lt}$$

and

$$\frac{dI}{dt} = -LI.$$

Let q be the rate of increase of the intensity due to the steady supply of radio-active material.   Then

$$\frac{dI}{dt} = q - LI$$

or

$$\log_e (q - LI) = -Lt + A.$$

But I = 0 when $t = 0$.
Therefore

$$A = -\frac{1}{L}\log_e q.$$

Therefore

$$\log_e \frac{q - LI}{q} = -Lt$$

or

$$I = \frac{q}{L}(1 - e^{-Lt}).$$

When Lt is very large, the maximum value of the intensity I_0 is given by

$$I_0 = \frac{q}{L} \quad \text{and} \quad \frac{I}{I_0} = 1 - e^{-Lt};$$

or the equation representing the rise of intensity of the radiation is the same as the rise of an electric current in a circuit of constant self-induction.

The curve which is shown in fig. 8 is in rough agreement with this equation. For example, the intensity of the radiation has risen to half its value in about twelve hours. Now $e^{-Lt} = \frac{1}{2}$ when $t = 11$ hours, *i.e.*, according to theory, the current should have reached half its value in about eleven hours.

There is a divergence between the theoretical and observed results in the first part of the curve. The rate of increase of intensity is slower at first than the theory would suggest. It is probable, however, that the rate of supply of radio-active material does not reach a steady value for a considerable time after the exposure of the plate, and such a cause would account for the results observed. Other results obtained, under different conditions, all show too small a value of the intensity for the first few hours of exposure.

We have so far assumed that the radio-active particles were conveyed to the surface under the influence of an electric field. The equations which have been given will, however, apply equally well to the case of diffusion. If no electromotive forces are acting, the radio-active particles diffuse through the gas and adhere to the surface on which they impinge. A steady state will be reached when the rate of supply of fresh radio-active particles due to diffusion is balanced by the decay of the radiation from the surface. The maximum intensity of the radiation on any surface in the neighbourhood of a thorium compound is thus proportional to the number of radio-active particles that reach it by the processes of diffusion.

Effect of E.M.F. on the Amount of Radioactivity

The amount of induced radioactivity in a given time increases with the voltage for small voltages, but soon reaches a point beyond which large increases in the E.M.F. have a very small effect on it.   In order to investigate the relation in detail, the following arrangement was employed:—

Two insulated concentric brass cylinders A and B (fig. 9) were used, of diameter 5.5 and .7 centim. respectively.   The ends were

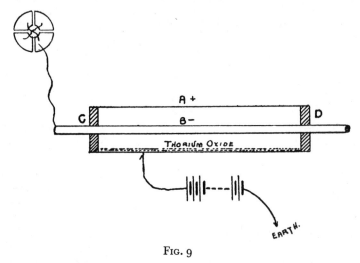

Fig. 9

closed with paraffin stoppers C and D.   The cylinder A was connected with the + pole of a battery, the other pole of which was to earth.   The cylinder B was connected to the electrometer in the usual manner.   A layer of thorium oxide in a paper envelope was placed along the bottom of the cylinder A.   The whole was exposed to the action of thorium oxide for three days.   The intensity of the radiation given out by B had, after that interval, nearly reached its maximum value.   The following measurements were made for each experiment at different voltages:—

    (1) The current between A and B was measured with the thorium oxide in the cylinder.
    (2) After the thorium oxide had been removed and the air blown out, the current between A and B was again determined.
    (3) The cylinder B was then removed and a non-active one of the same dimensions substituted and the current again observed.

The electrometer was brought to the same sensitiveness every day by means of a Thomson Replenisher.   For rapid rates of discharge, a condenser of .001 microfarad capacity was placed in the electrometer circuit.

The current (3) includes the small leak (if any) over the insulators plus the current due to the radioactivity produced in the end paraffin stoppers. The current (2) was due to the radio-active cylinder B, together with the current (3). The current (1) was due to the "emanation" from thorium oxide plus (2) and (3).

From these three observations it was therefore possible to determine:—

(a) The rate of discharge due to the thorium alone;
(b) The rate of discharge due to radio-active cylinder B alone;
(c) The rate of discharge due to radioactivity on the sides and ends of vessel.

In the following table the results are given for different voltages between cylinders.

Results are in divisions per second of electrometer-scale.

Voltage	Emanation	Radioactivity on cylinder B	Radioactivity on sides and ends	Total Radioactivity
0	—	1.32	5.58	6.90
3	5.3	4.02	3.06	7.08
5	12.2	4.53	1.97	6.50
10	25.3	6.69	1.51	8.20
20	30.0	7.40	.59	7.99
310	32.2	9.91	.75	10.66

Fig. 10 shows the results graphically. Curve A shows the variation of the current due to the "emanation" with voltage; curve B, the variation of the amount of induced radioactivity on inside cylinder; and curve C, the variation of the amount of radioactivity on the sides and ends. The ordinates of curves B and C are increased three times in order to show them on about the same scale as A. It will be observed that the shapes of the curves A and B are similar. The "knee" of both curves occurs for about the same voltage. The curve C shows that as the voltage diminishes, the amount of radioactivity on the sides and ends increases, reaching a maximum when the voltage is zero. The currents due to the radioactivity of B, given in the third column of the table, are for 50 volts between the cylinders. The value given for 310 volts is probably too large, as it was measured for 310 volts between plates, instead of 50 as in the other experiments.

In the fifth column is given the total current due to the radioactivity on ends and sides plus the action of cylinder B.   It will be observed that the resulting values are not very different, except the value for 310 volts, which, for reasons above explained, is probably too large.

It looks as if a certain number of radio-active particles were given out from the thorium and that these were carried to various parts of the vessel, the effect due to the whole number being about the same as if they were all concentrated on the negative electrode.

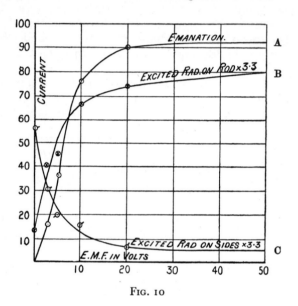

FIG. 10

Case of Diffusion of Radio-active Particles

The case where no voltage is acting is one of special interest, for there the diffusion of the radio-active particles is alone operative.   A loose layer of paper was placed over the paper envelope containing the thorium oxide.   The paper envelope bent into the arc of a circle covered about one quarter of the circumference of the cylinder.   The following numbers give the rate of leak, in divisions per second, due to the radioactivity on different portions of the vessel:—

Radioactivity on inside cylinder	1.32	divisions per sec.
,, on paper	2.26	,,
,, on outside cylinder and stoppers	3.32	,,
Total radioactivity	6.90	,,

The current due to the total radioactivity is thus about the same as the current when 20 volts acts between cylinders.   The experiments on the effect of voltage extended for more than a month, and some of the results showed that the thorium oxide was not a constant source of radiation during the whole of that time.   The variations were not, however, sufficiently large to obscure the general nature of the results.

Effect of Pressure on Radioactivity

The diminution of the pressure of the gas from 760 to 20 millim. had very little action on the amount of "excited" radioactivity on the − charged electrode.

The following apparatus was employed:—

A brass cylinder B (fig. 11a), with an ebonite stopper C, through

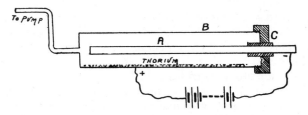

FIG. 11a.—Exciting Apparatus

which passed a brass rod A, was connected with a mercury pump. The thorium oxide inside a paper envelope was placed inside the cylinder.   B was connected to + pole of a battery of 50 volts, and C to − pole.   The apparatus was exhausted to the required pressure as rapidly as possible, and rod A exposed for several hours.   The rod

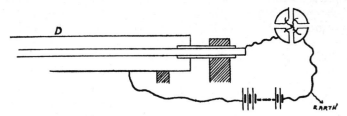

FIG. 11b.—Testing Apparatus

was then removed, and the current due to its radioactivity tested inside another cylinder D (fig. 11b).   The battery and electrometer connexions are seen in figure.   On account of the press of other work, it was not found possible to take observations at regular intervals, but the table given below suffices to show the general nature of the results.

Pressure	Time of Exposure	Divisions per second	Divisions per sec. Interpolated values
millim.	hours		
760	5.25	2.37	13.1
175	20	9.83	13.9
16	4.1	2.15	15.1
4.5	5.4	1.96	10.3
1.7	4.8	.72	4.5
.45	14.3	.38	.65
.04	25	.34	.44

The third column gives the current in divisions per second due to radio-active rod in the testing vessel.   In the fourth column are given the divisions per second corresponding to an exposure of the rod for the same time (three days) in each case, at the particular pressure. The results are interpolated from the first two columns with the help of the curve given in fig. 8.   The results must only be considered approximate, and merely serve to give a comparative estimate of the radioactivity at each pressure.   The general results are clear.   The radioactivity is about the same at 16 millim. as at 760 millim. Between the pressures of 16 and 4.5 millim. the amount begins to diminish, until at .45 millim. it is only $\frac{1}{20}$ of the value at atmospheric pressure.   Still further diminution of pressure does not have much effect.

A special experiment on the distribution of the radioactivity at low pressures throws some light on the phenomena.   If we expose a rod charged − at a low pressure to the action of thorium, it will be found that the rod is only slightly radio-active, while the top of the paper over the thorium oxide and the sides of the vessel are strongly radio-active.   At atmospheric pressure, other conditions remaining the same, it will be found that most of the radioactivity is confined to the rod, and only a slight amount is produced on the paper and sides of the vessel.   It appears as if the radio-active particles are unable to be all carried to the negative electrode at low pressures.   This may be due to the increased rate of diffusion of the active particles at low pressures, or more probably to the small number of ions produced by the "emanation" at low pressures.

It is found that the current through the gas due to the "emanation" falls off nearly proportionally to the pressure, so that the number of ions present between cylinders at low pressures is a very small fraction of those at atmospheric pressure.

The following table gives results of the variation of the current, due to the emanation, with pressure of air in the apparatus of fig. 11*a*.

Pressure of Gas millim.	Current due to Emanation
760	1
587	.819
402	.582
214	.297
145	.203
93	.133
25	.046

Fig. 12 shows the results graphically. The curve is nearly a straight line. If the conveyance of the radio-active particles to the

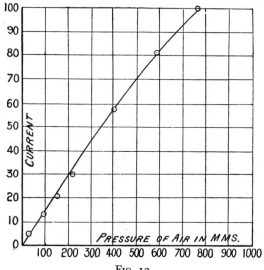

FIG. 12

electrode is due to the movements of the ions between cylinders, at low pressures the number of ions may be too small to be effective in that respect.

Effect of Gases

The apparatus shown in fig. 11 was used. The amount of radio-activity produced on the central rod was not very different whether the gas was hydrogen, air, or carbonic acid. No definite difference was observed whether the gas was free from water-vapour or not. The amount of current due to the emanation from thorium oxide was found, however, to vary greatly with the gas. Taking the current due to air as unity with 50 volts acting, the currents due to the "emanation" were

Air	1
H	·35
CO_2	1.1

These numbers are not necessarily proportional to the ionization constants of the gas, as the current produced depends on the relative absorption of the rays between the cylinders.

These results, together with those obtained for lowering of the pressure in air, show that there is no evident quantitative connexion between the current due to the emanation and the amount of induced radioactivity.

Chemical and Mechanical Actions on the Radio-active Surface

We have previously considered the conditions which govern the production and decay of the induced radioactivity. We will now describe some experiments that have been made to try and throw some light on the question as to what the induced radioactivity is really due to.

If the radioactivity is caused by some radio-active dust deposited on the substance, we should expect to find evidence of it by examining the surface with a microscope, or by noting whether there is any increase in weight. A fine piece of platinum wire, which had been carefully weighed, was made strongly radio-active by five days' exposure to thorium oxide covered over with paper. Within the limits of accuracy of the balance no certain variation of the weight could be detected. The increase of weight, if any, was certainly less than $\frac{1}{20}$ of a milligramme. On examination by a microscope no collection of dust particles on the surface could be observed. We may conclude from this experiment, that if the radioactivity is due to the deposition of radio-active particles on the surface, these particles must be extraordinarily radio-active compared with their weight. A rough estimate shows that the radioactivity of the surface-layer must be at least a million times greater than that of uranium or thorium.

The amount of radiation from an active surface is always lessened by mechanical actions, such as rubbing the surface with a cloth or fine sand-paper. In order to completely remove the radioactivity, it is necessary to remove the surface-layer by long scouring with sand- or emery-paper.

A blast of air directed against a radio-active plate has no appreciable effect on the amount of radiation given out.

A radio-active platinum wire or plate can be heated white-hot without much altering the amount of radiation given out from it.   A strongly active fine wire is more affected than a plate; but that is probably chiefly due to action of the flame-gases upon it.

Chemical Actions

The radioactivity of a platinum plate is not much affected by dipping it in water, caustic soda, or nitric acid, whether hot or cold. Sulphuric or hydrochloric acid has the power of rapidly destroying the intensity of the radiation in a few minutes.   A copper-sulphate solution, if only slightly acid, does not act on the wire rapidly.   The following example of a test shows the effect of several of the solutions on a radio-active platinum plate.   After each immersion the plate was washed in water and dried over a Bunsen-flame.   After exposure of 4 minutes to gradually heated water and 2 minutes to boiling water, the rate of discharge fell from 100 divisions in 15.5 secs. to 100 divisions in 20 secs.   After 5 minutes' boiling in caustic soda, the rate of discharge fell to 100 in 27 secs.   After 10 minutes' exposure to strong hot nitric acid, the rate of discharge was cut down to one-half its previous value.   Dilute sulphuric acid reduced the rate of discharge to one-half in 10 secs. and one-quarter in 60 secs.   Both hydrochloric and sulphuric acids are more powerful in destroying the radio-active power than the other solutions examined.   In the case of water and caustic soda, the small diminution of intensity appears to be due as much to the mechanical action of the bubbling as to the chemical action on the surface.

The question now arises, whether the loss of radioactivity of the active plate by immersion in solutions is due to the destruction of the radio-active power of the particles or their removal from the plate to the solution.   A fine platinum wire, very strongly active, was placed in a few drops of dilute sulphuric acid for several minutes.   The wire lost a large proportion of its radioactivity.   The dilute acid was then evaporated down to dryness in a sand-bath, and on examination it was found that the residue on the glass surface was strongly active. We may conclude from this experiment that the radioactivity of the particles is not destroyed, but that they pass into solution, and that on evaporating the solvent the substance still remains.

Some experiments were tried to see whether a plate preserved its radio-active power when a layer of copper was electrolytically deposited upon it. A radio-active platinum wire was made a cathode in a copper-sulphate solution, and a current of about half an ampere passed through for 1 minute. The radioactivity was diminished to about .7 of its value when tested in the usual way. After washing the wire in water, it was allowed to stand some time in air, and the rate of diminution of the radioactivity observed. The intensity diminished more rapidly at first than for an unacted-on wire; but after 10 hours the rate of diminution became normal. The more rapid decrease at first is probably due to the dilute sulphuric acid which remained in the pores of the copper deposit. When the platinum wire was made the anode in a copper-sulphate solution, the radioactivity rapidly diminished. The action in this case was probably due to the production of sulphuric acid at the surface of the anode by the passage of the current which dissolved the radio-active material on the platinum plate.

Discussion of the Results

Before entering on the question of the cause and nature of induced radioactivity, a brief review may be given of the results obtained:—

(1) All thorium compounds examined produce radioactivity in substances in their neighbourhood, if the bodies are all uncharged. With charged conductors the radioactivity is produced on the − charged body. In strong electric fields, the radioactivity can be concentrated on the surface of thin wires. Thorium oxide is the most active of the thorium compounds in causing radioactivity, but loses its power if it is heated for several hours at a high temperature.

(2) The power of producing radioactivity is closely connected with the presence of the "emanation" from thorium compounds, and is in some way dependent upon it.

(3) The radiation excited in bodies is homogeneous, and of a more penetrating character than the radiations from thorium or uranium. The radiation is confined to the surface of the substance, and is independent of whether the substance is a conductor or non-conductor and of the nature of its surface.

(4) The intensity of the radiation emitted falls off in a geometrical progression with the time, decreasing to half its value in about 11 hours. The decay of intensity is independent of the state of concentration of the radioactivity or the nature of the substance.

(5) The amount of induced radioactivity increases at first nearly proportional to the time of exposure, but soon tends to a value when the intensity of the radiation varies very little with increase of the time of exposure.

(6) The amount of induced radioactivity produced in a given time on a conductor depends on the potential-difference between the electrodes, and tends to a constant value for large E.M.F.'s.

(7) The amount of radioactivity is independent of the pressure of the gas, except at low pressures when the amount on the − charged conductor decreases with the pressure. The amount is not much affected whether the gas is hydrogen, air, or carbonic acid.

(8) No increase of weight has been observed by making a body radio-active. The radiation from a platinum wire is not much altered by placing the wire in a flame, hot or cold water, or nitric acid. Hydrochloric and sulphuric acids rapidly remove the radio-activity from its surface. The solution, when evaporated, leaves the active portion behind.

Three possible explanations of the phenomena of induced radio-activity naturally present themselves:—(a) That the radioactivity is due to a kind of phosphorescence excited in the substance by the radiation from thorium; (b) or to the deposition of the + gaseous ions produced in the gas by the "emanation"; (c) or to the deposition of particles of a radio-active material emitted by thorium compounds.

The hypothesis that the radiation is a kind of phosphorescence will not explain the results observed, since substances are made radio-active outside the incidence of the radiation, and the radioactivity can be concentrated on the − electrode. The question as to whether the induced radioactivity is due to the deposition of a foreign sub-stance on bodies, or to the action of the + ions produced in the gas, or a combination of both, is difficult to decide with certainty from the experimental evidence. The theory that the + ions produced by the emanation are responsible for the radioactivity, at first sight seems to explain many of the results. Since the radio-active particles of the emanation are very small, the intensity of the radiation must be very great near them; and in consequence of this, ions may not only be produced, but the charges on the ions set in violent vibration: these + ions would be carried to the negative electrode, and gradually dissipate the energy of their vibration by radiation into space. On this theory, however, it is difficult to explain the variation of radio-activity with pressure. At low pressures, the experiments show that the total radioactivity produced is much the same as at atmospheric pressure, but the − electrode receives only a small proportion of the radio-active particles. On the theory that the radio-active particles are + ions, we should expect them in a strong field to be all carried to the − electrode. Another experiment on the variation of the amount of radioactivity with distance also does not fall in readily with this view. The amount of radioactivity was found to be practically the same whether the distance from the radio-active surface was

3 mms. or 3 cms.   In the latter case, the number of + ions produced by the emanation is much greater than in the former; but the amount of radioactivity is unaffected.

The theory that the radioactivity is due to a deposition of radio-active particles from the thorium compounds affords a general explanation of all the results; but the difficulty is to advance a satis-factory reason for the particles obtaining the + charge which they must possess in order to be moved to the − electrode in an electric field.   If we suppose the radio-active particles from thorium com-pounds emitted at a uniform rate, independent of the nature and pressure of the gas, we should expect to obtain the same total amount of radioactivity spread over a vessel due to diffusion of the particles, as can be obtained by concentration of all the radio-active particles on the − electrode; and the amount should be independent of the pressure and nature of the gas, provided it does not act on the thorium.   Some experiments seem to point to the conclusion that the radio-active particles are not charged till they diffuse out into the gas, but that they gain a + charge in the course of time.   A possible explanation is that the + charge is obtained by the diffusion of the ions to the surface of the particles.   Since there is reason to believe that the − ions in most cases move faster than the + ions in an electric field, there is always an excess of + ions in the gas, and the particles in the gas thus tend to become positively charged.   On this supposition, the diminution of the amount of radioactivity on the − electrode at low pressures is due to the fact that there is not a sufficient number of ions in the gas to charge the particles, which thus diffuse to the sides of the vessel.

As far as experiments have gone, the power of exciting radio-activity appears to be confined to thorium compounds.   Neither uranium nor radium nor polonium has so far shown any trace of action; but the specimens[25] of radium and polonium used were not very radio-active and contained considerable amounts of impurity. A plate made radio-active is not able to excite any appreciable radio-

---

[25] As this paper was passing through the press the *Comptes Rendus* of Nov. 6th was received, which contains a paper by Curie and a note by Becquerel on the radiation excited in bodies by radium and polonium.   Curie has used specimens of these substances 10,000 to 50,000 times more radio-active than uranium and the phe-nomena observed are, in some respects, similar to those exhibited by thorium compounds; but there are not sufficient data on which to base any comparison.   No mention is made of the effect of an electric field, or whether there is an "emanation" from radium and polonium, as there is from thorium compounds.   Curie concludes that the results obtained are due to a kind of phosphorescence excited by the radia-tion; while in the case of thorium the author has shown that such a theory is in-admissible.   Further experiments on the comparison of the radioactivity produced by thorium with that produced by radium and polonium will be of interest.

activity in another plate near it.   I have tested the + and − electrodes after the passage for several hours of a strong current between them due to Röntgen rays, flames, and discharge from points, but no trace of radioactivity on them has been observed.

Macdonald Physics Building,
   McGill University, Montreal,
     Nov. 22nd, 1899.

III. An Interpolation on Uranium

[The next paper is self-explanatory. Its author, Sir William Crookes (1832–1919), was a private chemist in London who combined commercial work with personal research and journalism. He was the owner and editor of a weekly paper, *The Chemical News*, and was wealthy enough to maintain a laboratory in one room of his house, where he had done important work on cathode rays and where he had discovered the new element, thallium.[1] In the years to come, Crookes would never use any considerable quantity of radium, so apparently the plans laid down in this paper came to nothing. For all the vigor with which he attacked this puzzle of the vanishing radio-activity, at the age of sixty-eight he probably found the accumulation of radium in his solutions too slow to be endurable.—A. R.]

7

Sir William Crookes

Radio-activity of Uranium

[From *Proceedings of the Royal Society of London*, 1899–1900, *66*: 409–422.]

1. The researches of M. Henri Becquerel have shown that compounds of uranium possess the property now called "radio-activity"; that is, rays emitted by them affect a sensitive photographic plate through bodies usually considered opaque to light; they discharge an electrometer when brought near it; and they are deflected by a magnet. These rays are now called "Becquerel rays," or "uranic rays."

2. On the discovery by M. and Mdme. Curie of polonium and radium, bodies of enormous radio-active powers, it was suggested that

---

[1] E. E. Fournier d'Albe, *The Life of Sir William Crookes* (New York: Appleton, 1924).

uranium might possibly owe its power to the presence of a small quantity of one of these bodies. But in a paper published in the 'Revue Générale des Sciences' for January, 1899, Mdme. Curie says:—"This does not appear probable, for if such were the case different samples of uranium compounds would have very different radio-activities, but in the course of a number of experiments made with various samples of metallic uranium, as well as with oxides and salts from various sources, I have never found any marked difference between the relative activities of the same compound."

In another paper[2] the same author says that "the property of emitting rays . . . which act on photographic plates is a *specific property of uranium and thorium.*" "The physical condition of the metal seems to be of an altogether secondary importance." "Uranium and thorium alone are practically active."

3. When the discovery of radium was announced, and it was said to have "to all appearance the properties of almost pure barium,"[3] it occurred to me that radium might be found in detectable quantities in some barium minerals were search made among them from different localities. Accordingly specimens of the following minerals were put on sensitive plates, a sheet of black paper separating them from the sensitive surface. As it was probable that the radio-active substance would be present, if at all, in very minute quantities, the sensitive plate was exposed to their influence for forty-eight hours.

Barytes (Heavy Spar).

    ,,   from Hungary. (Three specimens.)
    ,,   ,,   Cumberland. (Eight.)
    ,,   ,,   Westmorland. (One.)
    ,,   ,,   Cumberland. (A fine crystal.)
    ,,   ,,   Derbyshire. (Three.)
    ,,   ,,   Arkendale. (One.)
    ,,   ,,   Hartz. (One.)
    ,,   ,,   Scotland. (One.)
    ,,   ,,   Ireland. (Two.)
    ,,   ,,   Northumberland. (Two.)
    ,,   ,,   Arran. (One.)
    ,,   ,,   Cherbourg. (One.)
    ,,   Several unnamed, but finely crystallised, specimens.
Witherite from Lancashire. (One.)
    ,,   ,,   Cumberland. (Four.)
    ,,   ,,   Northumberland. (One.)

---

[2] M. and Mdme Curie, *Comptes Rendus*, vol. 127, p. 175; *Chem. News*, vol. 78, p. 49, July 29, 1898.

[3] M. and Mdme. Curie and M. Bémont, *Comptes Rendus*, vol. 127, p. 1215; *Chem. News*, vol. 79, p. 1, January 3, 1899.

Not one of these minerals showed the slightest action on the sensitive plate.

4. Having obtained negative results with barium compounds, I went through every mineral in my cabinet—a somewhat extensive collection, numbering many fine specimens. Large photographic plates were covered with black paper, and the minerals were laid on them as close as they could conveniently be placed, accurate note of their names and positions being recorded. They were exposed in total darkness for forty-eight hours. By this means a list of radio-active minerals was ultimately obtained. They were then tested for order of intensity of action. The following is a list of active minerals arranged in order, the most active heading the list:—

1. Pitchblende.	9. Broggerite.
2. Uranite.	10. Monazite.
3. Autunite.	11. Xenotime.
4. Orangite.	12. Arrhenite.
5. Thorite.	13. Sipilite.
6. Euxenite.	14. Fergusonite.
7. Samarskite.	15. Chalcolite.
8. Alvite.	16. Hielmite.

It will be observed that these minerals all contain either uranium or thorium.

5. Pitchblende was the most radio-active mineral, but it varied much in different parts. A slice was cut from a piece of pitchblende from Cornwall and the surface was polished. A sensitive photographic plate was pressed against it, and after twenty-four hours the plate was developed. The impression showed the structure of the mineral in a remarkable manner, every little piece of pitchblende showing black, those portions in which the radio-active substance was not so operative showing in half tint, while the felspar, quartz, pyrites, &c., having no radio-activity, left the plate transparent (see Plate 5).

Pitchblende from different localities differed greatly in action.

6. A large crystal of orangite from Arendal was ground flat and polished at one end and side, and a piece of sensitive celluloid film, cut half through so as to allow it to bend sharply, was put on the polished surfaces, one half pressing against the end and the other half against the side. The exposure was continued for seventy-two hours. On developing, no difference could be seen in the intensity of the impression, whether made by the end or the side of the crystal. The impression also was uniform over the surface, the cracks in the surfaces not having impressed themselves.

These experiments were repeated with the interposition of a thin sheet of celluloid between the mineral and the sensitive plate. The results were practically the same as before.

7. Roughly speaking, the action of pitchblende is in proportion to the percentage of uranium in the mineral. Finely powdered pitchblende of different degrees of richness were experimented with. Cells were made of thick lead pipes half an inch internal diameter and one inch long, closed at the lower ends with card. They were filled with powdered pitchblende, one containing 43 per cent. Ur_3O_8 and the other 12 per cent. Ur_3O_8. A sensitive plate being covered with black paper, the lead cells were laid on it and kept in total darkness for 120 hours. The intensity of the spot under the 43 per cent. ore on development was found to be at least three times that of the one under the 12 per cent. ore.

Two lead cells were taken, one being a quarter of an inch long and the other two inches long. They were filled completely with the 43 per cent. ore, and a sensitive plate exposed to their action for forty-eight hours. On developing it was doubtful whether any difference existed in the intensity of the two spots, proving that the action does not pass through much thickness of active material, a quarter of an inch being equal in effect to two inches.

No difference in the action was noticed when the bottom of the cell was made of thin glass cemented on, instead of card.

Four cells were filled with pitchblende and placed side by side on a sensitive plate. After having acted twenty-four hours the first was removed, the second after forty-eight hours, the third after seventy-two hours, and the last was kept on for ninety-six hours. On developing the plate the spots had intensities varying with the lengths of exposure, and in about the right proportion, on the assumption that double the time of action gives double the intensity of blackening.

8. For convenience of comparison I had a number of glass cells made, three-quarters of an inch wide and deep, so that they could either be sealed up or closed with a cork. A piece of apparatus was made so as to take radiographs of samples with more ease and certainty. A lead plate, 2 mm. thick, $6\frac{1}{2}$ inches long, and $2\frac{1}{8}$ inches wide, has circular holes punched in it, one inch in diameter. Under the thick plate of lead is another thinner plate, made of pure assay foil, and having holes in it, concentric with the others, but barely $\frac{3}{4}$ inch in diameter, so that one of the small cells will not pass through the lower hole, but will pass easily through the upper hole, and thus be kept in place. To prevent contact between the lead plate and the sensitive surface a thin sheet of celluloid is fixed beneath, with holes punched in it concentric with those in the lead plates. In the top left corner of the lead plates is a short steel pin, which can be pressed on the sensitive plate and so register its position in respect to the cells

experimented with.   The lead and celluloid plates are then bound together and the whole is fitted into a shallow wooden tray with a light-tight cover.

A sensitive film is laid face upwards at the bottom of the wooden tray; on this are put the lead screens, and then the experimental cells of radio-active bodies in order, careful note being taken of their relative positions.

9. Wishing to prepare compounds of radium and polonium, the very curious bodies discovered by M. and Mdme. Curie, I arranged with my friend Mr. Tyrer, Stirling Chemical Works, for the systematic working up of half a ton of pitchblende.   It was necessary to examine every precipitate and filtrate in each stage of the operation, and for convenience of registration they had to be compared with a standard cell filled with a substance unvarying in action.   After many trials, I selected crystallised uranium nitrate as being strongly radio-active and easily prepared pure.   This led me to the observation which forms the subject of the present paper.

10. The following compounds of uranium were tested simultaneously, being put into glass cells and arranged on a lead screen with seven holes:—

> 1. Metallic uranium, from M. Moissan.
> 2. Uranium nitrate, $UO_2(NO_3)_2 . 6H_2O$.
> 3. Uranium acetate.
> 4. Uranium persulphate.
> 5. Uranium protosulphate.
> 6. Uranium oxide (green), $UO_2 2UO_3$.
> 7. Uranium oxide (black), $UO_2 UO_3$.

For twenty-four hours the sensitive plate was exposed to the influence of these bodies.   With the exception of metallic uranium, which showed least action, there was not much difference between the effect produced by any of the others.

11. In order to prepare uranium nitrate of great purity for a standard, I took some pounds of the commercial salt and purified it, first by solution in ether (13), and then by repeated crystallisation. After many operations a cell was filled with the crystals, and it was used as a standard.   To my surprise, after having acted on a sensitive plate for twenty-four hours, on development not a trace of image could be seen.

12. Thereupon I tried the following experiments to ascertain if the great radio-activity of some uranium compounds and the absence of it in others might be caused by some variation of physical, crystalline, or chemical condition.

Commercial uranium nitrate was taken, and—

(1) A portion was heated with excess of nitric acid to dryness on the water-bath. It was powdered and put in a cell.

(2) A similar portion of the salt was dissolved in alcohol, and the solution evaporated to dryness over the water-bath. The resulting orange-coloured pasty material was ground and put in a cell.

(3) The salt was treated in the same way as No. 1, except that the excess of water and acid were not driven off.

(4) A small quantity was heated for some time on a water-bath till it was thoroughly dry. It was then powdered and put in a cell.

(5) 50 grains were put in a glass cell and heated on a water-bath to about 75° C. till it had dissolved in its water of crystallisation.

(6) 50 grains in a glass cell were heated on a sand-bath to about 230° C. The water of crystallisation having been driven off the salt fused, and on cooling remained a hard, yellow, glassy mass.

(7) A similar quantity of the same salt was heated to a little above 230° C. till it commenced to decompose.

(8) A similar quantity was heated more strongly, till about half the nitrate had decomposed.

(9) The same quantity was heated till decomposition was complete.

(10) As a standard, some of the same lot of commercial uranium nitrate from which these lots were taken was put in a cell.

These ten cells were placed in a lead screen apparatus, and a sensitive plate was exposed to their influence for twenty-four hours. On development there was not much difference between any of the impressions, that under No. 9 being a little the strongest.

Thus it appears that no modification of physical or chemical condition materially affects the radio-active property of a uranium compound when, to begin with, the salt experimented on possesses it; other similar experiments show that, starting with an inactive uranium salt, nothing that can be done to it will cause it to acquire this property. It is therefore evident that, as I had suspected, the radioactive property ascribed to uranium and its compounds is not an inherent property of the element, but resides in some outside body which can be separated from it.

Having by repeated crystallisation succeeded in preparing a photographically inactive uranium nitrate, I started experiments with several pounds of the commercial salt to ascertain the readiest means of separating from it the active body.

13. Into a stoppered cylinder I put 1 lb. of crystallised nitrate and poured on it a pound of methylated ether, sp. gr. 0.72. The salt easily dissolved on shaking, and after a few hours the whole of the crystals had disappeared, leaving at the bottom of the cylinder 1000

fluid grains of a heavy aqueous solution.   I separated the aqueous
solution from the ethereal solution, and evaporated it to dryness to
remove traces of ether.   The ethereal solution was allowed to
evaporate spontaneously.   Equal quantities of the soluble and the
insoluble in ether I put into glass cells and added sufficient dilute
nitric acid to dissolve the salt, and then evaporated each lot to dryness
on the water-bath.   When dry the two cells, and a third containing
some of the original nitrate, were put on a sensitive plate for twenty-
four hours.

On development it was found that the action of the part undis-
solved by ether was very strong, that of the original nitrate not more
than half as strong, while no action whatever could be detected on
the part of the plate covered by the salt soluble in ether.

The portion insoluble in ether, after evaporation to dryness with
nitric acid, and then crystallisation in water, in no way differed in
appearance from ordinary uranium nitrate.   The portion soluble in
ether, when dried, heated with dilute nitric acid and crystallised, also
had the same appearance as the initial salt.

14. The crystallised nitrate from the portion insoluble in ether I
again extracted with ether.   Most of it dissolved, and a small portion
of heavy aqueous liquid settled at the bottom.   As before, the nitrate
which dissolved in ether had scarcely any radio-active power, while
the residue from this second extraction possessed it in a strong degree.
The residue after the second extraction was about double the activity
of the residue after the first extraction, showing that ether, while
dissolving uranium nitrate itself with facility, does not dissolve the
body to which it owes its radio-activity.

15. The uranium nitrate from the portion insoluble in ether was
submitted to fractional crystallisation in the following manner:—

The solution was evaporated until on cooling about three-fourths
would crystallise out.   The beaker in which this operation was performed was called No. 1.   When crystallisation had finished, the
mother-liquor was poured into a beaker called No. 2.   A little water
was added to No. 1 and it was warmed to dissolve the crystals; No. 2
was evaporated a little, and both were set aside to crystallise.   When
cold the mother-liquor from 2 was poured into a beaker No. 3, the
mother-liquor from 1 was poured into 2, a little water being added to
dissolve the crystals in 1, and the contents of the three beakers were
warmed and allowed again to crystallise separately.   This operation
was continued as long as the uranium salt would hold out, or till the
tests showed that the operations had gone far enough.

16. Tests were made to see how the operations were proceeding.
A portion of the crystals from No. 1 beaker was dried and put into a
cell.   Some mother-liquor from the last beaker was also evaporated

and crystallised, and the crystals were put in a cell. The two were placed side by side on a sensitive plate and the action was allowed to proceed for twenty-four hours. On development there was no visible spot beneath No. 1 nitrate, while that beneath the nitrate from the other end of the fractionation was strong and black.

17. The crystals were removed from their cells, ignited to the green oxide, and replaced. Tested again on a sensitive plate the results were similar to those given by the unignited nitrates. The active substance, therefore, is seen to reside in the mother-liquor.

18. In making photographic tests it is not necessary to take much of the substance. On an ordinary microscopic slide I put a small drop of liquid from each of the highest five fractionations, Nos. 10, 9, 8, 7, and 6. The drops were allowed to crystallise and the slide was laid on a sensitive plate. In twenty-four hours a good impression of No. 10, the highest fraction, was obtained; a less strong impression of the next, No. 9; a fainter one of 8; a scarcely perceptible one of 7; and no impression at all from No. 6. The slide containing the five crystalline spots was then covered with another glass, and the whole cemented together with Canada balsam and mounted in the manner usual with microscopic slides. When the balsam was dry the slide was put on a sensitive plate. In twenty-four hours a good graduated image was developed.

19. There are in commerce two kinds of uranium nitrate: one, the commercial variety, and another called "purissimum." I am informed that the "purissimum" is prepared from the former by repeated crystallisation. I purchased some of each of these nitrates and tested them on a photographic plate. The commercial variety proved to be at least twice as radio-active as the "purissimum" salt.

20. Experiments were now instituted with a view of obtaining a wholly inactive uranium nitrate. About two pounds of the salt that had been obtained from the solution in ether was repeatedly crystallised, pouring off the mother-liquor each time. This and the next succeeding two lots of crystals (Nos. 1, 2, and 3) were put into cells, and kept on a sensitive plate for seven days. On developing the plate no image could be detected where No. 1 had been; a scarcely perceptible impression could be just detected at No. 2, and a little stronger impression at No. 3.

21. Other methods were attempted for the separation of the active substance from uranium. Uranium nitrate fuses at a moderate temperature, and after some time it becomes darker, and nitrous fumes come off. Finally, the mass becomes semi-fluid, and will not run. The operation is then stopped, and the mass transferred to water; the undecomposed nitrate is dissolved out, leaving an insoluble basic nitrate. The basic nitrate is of an orange-yellow colour,

easily dissolved in nitric acid to again form the normal nitrate.   By using this method of fractionation the active body gradually accumulates towards the basic end.   But the method is neither so complete nor so easily effected as the crystallisation method, and therefore I have not pushed it very far.   I have, however, proved that the radio-activity of nitrate of uranium can be concentrated by fractionation to the basic nitrate end, the nitrate at the other end being diminished in radio-activity.

22. A highly active uranium nitrate, prepared by fractionation from the part insoluble in ether, was dissolved in water, and ammonia in excess was added.   Yellow ammonium uranate was precipitated. The filtrate was evaporated to dryness, and heated with nitric acid. The yellow precipitate and the residue of the filtrate were put into cells, and laid on a sensitive plate.   After twenty-four hours' action the plate was developed, when it was seen that the whole of the radio-activity resided in the ammonium uranate, the other substance showing nothing.   This experiment proves that the active body is precipitated by ammonia, and is insoluble in excess.

23. Another portion of active uranium nitrate was dissolved in water, with an excess of ammonium carbonate.   The first formed precipitate almost entirely re-dissolved, leaving a small quantity of insoluble light brown flocculent precipitate.   This collected on warming, like alumina.   It was filtered off, well washed and dried, and put in a glass cell.

The filtrate from the above precipitate was evaporated to drive [off] the ammonium carbonate, when a yellow precipitate came down.   This was filtered, washed, dried, and put into a cell.

These precipitates were exposed for twenty-four hours in a lead screen apparatus.   On developing, it was seen that the residue insoluble in ammonium carbonate instantly flashed out black and dense, while the salt precipitated from the ammonium carbonate solution gave a scarcely discernible image.

24. The action of the precipitate insoluble in ammonium carbonate was so strong that another experiment was tried, exposing the sensitive plate to its action for one hour.   On development, the disc of action came out strong and black, although not so black as in the twenty-four hours' experiment.   It was now laid for five minutes on a sensitive plate.   Here the action was distinct—about as strong as that given by ordinary uranium nitrate in twenty-four hours.   These experiments prove that the active body can exist apart from uranium.

If a sheet of thin glass or celluloid is laid on a sensitive plate, and the dried filter-paper with its contents laid on that, and kept down by a weight, an impression is given in as short a space of time as if a glass cell had been used.

25. The radio-active body is not entirely insoluble in ammonium carbonate. A portion of the very active precipitate left after separation from the uranium was dissolved in dilute hydrochloric acid, and an excess of ammonium carbonate added. The precipitate was very brown due to the presence of iron; it was dried and tested. The filtrate was well boiled, and as the ammonium carbonate evaporated a slight precipitate came down. This was collected on a filter and tested by the side of the first precipitate. On developing the plate the images produced by each precipitate were of about equal intensity. The brown precipitate was digested in very dilute hydrochloric acid in the cold. The iron partially dissolved before the rest of the substance, leaving the residue decidedly paler in colour. This pale body was just as radio-active as before the partial removal of the iron. Therefore the presence of iron does not interfere with the activity of the substance.

26. Having thus definitely proved that the supposed radio-activity of uranium and its salts is not an inherent property of the element, but is due to the presence of a foreign body,[4] it is necessary patiently to determine the nature of the foreign body. Several radio-active bodies claimed to be new have already been extracted from pitchblende, and experiments have been instituted to see if the newly found body UrX had similar chemical properties to those of the older active substances.

27. Polonium was first tried. A photographic plate had a thin sheet of celluloid laid on it, and over this a sheet of aluminium foil, 0.05 mm. thick. On this double layer were put two cells, one containing basic polonium nitrate, the other active UrX. Action was allowed to proceed for twenty-four hours, and the plate was then developed. A disc of blackening was seen under where the UrX stood, the action having passed through the glass, celluloid, and aluminium. Under the polonium nitrate no trace of action could be detected.

The experiment was repeated, minus the aluminium foil, and the action continued only two and a quarter hours. On development, the UrX was found to have acted well, while the polonium showed no trace of action.

28. This behaviour of polonium being excentric or contrary to published accounts,[5] I put some polonium nitrate in a very thin

---

[4] For the sake of lucidity the new body must have a name. Until it is more tractable I will call it provisionally UrX—the unknown substance in uranium.

[5] "The rays emitted by compounds of polonium render barium platinocyanide fluorescent ... To make the experiment, place on the active substance a very thin sheet of aluminium, and on this a thin layer of barium platinocyanide; in the dark

gelatine capsule, and laid it for eight hours on a sensitive plate.   No trace of an image could be seen on development.

The same polonium nitrate was put in a watch-glass, and the sensitive plate put *over it* face downwards, so that it might be exposed to the direct emanations from the polonium nitrate.   On the top of the plate was laid a sheet of lead to press it tight to the edges of the watch-glass.

The exposure was continued for twenty-eight hours.   On developing, a strong action was seen, strongest in the middle where opposed to the thickest part of the heap of polonium nitrate, and weaker towards the edge.   A well-marked action took place all over the plate exposed to the interior of the watch-glass, but it was sharply cut off at the edges.   This confirms the previous results—that the emanations from polonium are of a different character to those from radium or UrX, both of which pass through glass, aluminium, and lead.

29. Another property of polonium sharply distinguishing it from UrX is volatility.   The discoverers first obtained it by subliming pitchblende *in vacuo*.   Afterwards they used this property to separate it from bismuth, the polonium and the bismuth sulphides depositing at different parts of the hot tube.

A strongly radio-active compound of UrX was ignited in a blow-pipe flame with the addition of a drop of sulphuric acid.   Its radio-activity, on a sensitive plate, was not diminished by this treatment. This experiment was tried several times at increasingly higher temperatures, and always with the same result.

30. Polonium is precipitated by sulphuretted hydrogen, in an acid solution.   An acid or neutral solution of UrX is not precipitated by this reagent.   Therefore I am justified in saying my UrX is not polonium.

31. But it is not so easy to settle whether UrX is distinct from radium, although many arguments point to its not being radium. The discoverers of radium give several of its chemical properties, and in most of these UrX and Ra are entirely different.   Thus, radium sulphate is said to be insoluble in water and acids, while UrX dis-

---

the barium platinocyanide appears feebly luminous over the active substance" (M. and Mdme. Curie and M. Bémont, *Comptes Rendus*, vol. 127, p. 1215; *Chem. News*, vol. 79, p. 1).   "Polonic rays act on sensitive plates.   The substance we call sulphide of polonium gives a good impression after only three minutes, and there is a decided action noticed after even half a minute" (Mdme. Curie, *Revue Générale des Sci.*, January 30, 1899; *Chem. News*, vol. 79, p. 77).   In the same paper the authoress, after describing the power possessed by a polonium compound to excite phosphorescence, says: "the rays emitted by this latter body have traversed the aluminium and excited the fluorescence of the platinocyanide above it."   It is evident from the above extracts that I was justified in thinking that polonium rays were not entirely stopped by thin aluminium, glass, or celluloid.

solves easily to a clear solution in dilute sulphuric acid. Radium salts are said not to be precipitated by ammonium sulphide or by ammonia, while UrX is precipitated by both.

32. It was hoped that doubtful points might be settled conclusively by the spectrum, as both radium and polonium give well-defined and characteristic lines, especially in the ultra-violet part of the spectrum where I have chiefly worked. M. Demarçay[6] has given a list of some of the principal lines in the radium spectrum between the wave-lengths 3649.6 to 4826.3, the one at 3814.7 being very strong, and those at 4683.0, 4340.6, and 3649.6 being next in intensity. He draws special attention to the line at 3814.7 as the line showing first in a compound poor in radium. In none of my UrX compounds have I been able to detect a trace of this line; on the other hand I have failed to photograph this line in products which I know contain radium. The reason is my radium compound is too weak. M. Demarçay says the line is scarcely visible with a radium compound only sixty times as active as uranium. My substance containing radium was still weaker, judging from its action on a photographic plate.

33. The same reasoning applies to polonium. With polonium I have obtained strong lines in the ultra-violet, but I can detect none of them in the spectrum of my compound of UrX. All that I can see are lines belonging to—

> Platinum (from the poles),
> Uranium,
> Calcium,
> Aluminium,

and a few of the strongest air lines, besides a large number of faint lines difficult to identify.

34. Spectrum experiments having failed to show a difference between radium and UrX, it was thought that possibly some information might be gained by submitting them to the radiant matter test, which has proved so fruitful in its application to the yttrium earths. Some of the most active UrX was put in a tube furnished with a pair of terminals, and it was exhausted to a high point, heat being applied during exhaustion. Simultaneously a self-luminous radium compound was sealed in a vacuum tube and exhausted, heat being likewise applied. When fully exhausted a strong induction spark was passed through each tube. The UrX compound phosphoresced of a fine blue colour. In the spectroscope no discontinuity could be seen in the spectrum of the phosphorescent light.

---

[6] *Comptes Rendus*, vol. 124, p. 716; *Chem. News*, vol. 80, p. 259.

Under the influence of the induction spark, the radium compound phosphoresced of a luminous rose-colour, showing in the spectroscope a concentration of light in the red-orange, and a very faint citron band, due to a trace of yttrium, probably an impurity.

35. A powerful radium compound and one of UrX, each in a glass cell, and a paper tray full of polonium sub-nitrate, were placed side by side, and a strip of white card was put as a reflector at the back. In front a photographic camera was arranged so as to throw full-sized images of the polonium, UrX, and radium compounds on a sensitive plate, and the whole was kept in total darkness for five days. On development the image of the radium with the containing bottle was visible, but not a trace of image from the polonium could be seen. This confirms previous observations that the radiations from polonium will not pass through glass. Those from radium and UrX easily penetrate glass and other media (28).

36. Recently claims have been put forward for the existence of a third radio-active body in pitchblende. In the *Comptes Rendus* for October 16, 1899, and April 2, 1900, M. A. Debierne describes a radio-active body, to which he gives the name of "Actinium." At first he said "actinium" showed the principal analytical properties of titanium, but later he describes it as not resembling titanium in all its reactions. M. Debierne gives many reactions of the new substance, and in some instances they are like those of radium. But he qualifies them by the statement that they cannot yet be considered as belonging definitely to the new radio-active substance, because up to the present it has not been obtained sufficiently concentrated. He believes rather that these reactions should be looked upon as the result of retention, analogous to that of iron oxide by barium sulphate. He says that the chemical reactions of the most active substance which he obtained, together with its spectroscopic examination, showed that it chiefly consists of thorium. He cannot, however, be sure that it resembles thorium in all its reactions.

37. Experiments have been commenced to see if it is possible to separate thorium compounds into an active and an inactive body. A strong solution of thorium sulphate was slightly acidulated with sulphuric acid, and gradually raised to the boiling point. A copious precipitate of sulphate came down, and was filtered hot. The precipitate was dissolved in cold water, and the solution re-heated, when a precipitation of the sulphate again occurred. The mother-liquor from one crystallisation was added to the crystals from another in the systematic manner adopted in fractionation, and when the operations had proceeded some time a test was made on the "head" and "tail." A small quantity of solution from each was evaporated to dryness and strongly ignited before the blowpipe. The two lots

of earth were put in cells and a sensitive plate exposed to their action for seventy-two hours. On development not the slightest difference could be detected between the impressions produced by either of the fractions.

I next tried partial crystallisation of thorium nitrate, fractionating it in the way already described in the case of uranium (15). Great difficulties were here encountered, owing to the tendency of a strong solution of thorium nitrate to remain supersaturated for several days, when it would suddenly crystallise to a solid mass. After some weeks, however, six fractionations were effected, and tests were made on the first and last of the series.

The sensitive plate was exposed to their action for 120 hours. On development, the fraction at the first end (crystals) gave a very feeble action, while that at the other end (mother-liquors) gave an impression about three times as intense. This points to the possibility of separating from thorium its radio-active substance.

By the kindness of Dr. Knöfler, of Berlin, who makes thorium nitrate by the ton, I have at my disposal some specially prepared thorium nitrate, which is chemically pure. Thoria prepared from this, tested on a sensitive plate, gave a feeble impression in 120 hours.

38. In the present state of our knowledge of these radio-active bodies it is safest to retain an open, or even a slightly sceptical, mind. We recognise them mainly by the photographic and the electrical tests—reactions which are so sensitive that they give strong results, even when the active body is present in too small a quantity to be detected by its spectrum—one of the most delicate of tests. Knowing the tendency of ordinary chemical bodies to be carried down when a precipitate is formed in their presence, even when no question of sparse solubility is involved, it is not surprising that radium and actinium, to say nothing of UrX, appear to simulate elements which may ultimately prove to be very different from them in chemical characters. For instance, UrX dissolves easily in dilute sulphuric acid, and, I have reason to believe, forms a soluble sulphate; still, when chloride of barium is mixed with it and precipitated as a sulphate, I invariably find strong radio-activity in the precipitated sulphate as well as in the filtrate from the barium sulphate.

To adduce a simile from my previous researches, the first surmises as to the chemical characteristics of the bodies now known to be yttrium and samarium, were widely different from reality. The differences were entirely due to the perturbing cause which is active in the present case—the tendency of the bodies to be carried down and entangled in precipitates, where, according to ordinary chemical laws, they ought not to occur; and to the extreme delicacy of the radiant matter test, which in the case of samarium detects one part in

$2\frac{1}{2}$ million parts of calcium, and in the case of yttrium detects one part in the presence of a million parts of extraneous matter.

39. The radiographic test for these active bodies presents another point to be borne in mind. Other tests for the presence of an element either act quickly, or do not act at all, with a comparatively narrow margin of debateable land where the indications of the test may be doubtful. Here, however, the test is cumulative. Like an astronomer photographing stars too faint for his telescope to disclose, he has only to expose the plate for a sufficiently long time and the star reveals itself on development. So, in the case of radio-active minerals or precipitates, if no action is apparent at the end of an hour, one may be shown after twenty-four hours. If a day's exposure will show nothing, try a week's. Considering my most active UrX does not contain sufficient of the real material to show in the spectrograph, yet is powerful enough to give a good impression on a photographic plate in five minutes, what must be its dilution in compounds which require an hour, a day, or a week to give an action?

DESCRIPTION OF PLATE 5

FIG. 1. Photograph taken by daylight of a cut and polished surface of pitch-blende.

FIG. 2. Radiograph impressed in the dark by the same surface, showing the portions (white) emitting radiant energy. The luminous parts are pitch-blende, the dark parts are felspar, quartz, pyrites, &c. (see para. 5).

FIG. 1

FIG. 2

IV. Radioactivity as the Sign of a Transmutation

[Through 1900 and 1901 Rutherford continued to work with the emanation from thorium which he had found, and another emanation like it which radium released.   He gathered a small research school, to which he presently annexed a junior member of McGill's chemistry department, Frederick Soddy (1877–1956), an Oxford graduate.[1]   What he and Soddy proposed to do in a chemical attack on the thorium emanation is set forth in the next paper under *Scope of Work*: to see whether the emanation came from thorium or from something else mixed with it; to see whether the emanating power could be restored to thorium oxide which had been spoiled by overheating; to see what kind of gas the emanation might be; to detect the emanation or the matter of the excited radioactivity by weighing; and to find what chemical properties of thorium made the production of emanation possible.

For the first three of these aims, the paper gives definite answers.   The emanation is produced by thorium, since established methods of purifying thorium do not remove the emanating power.   The overheated thorium oxide might have its emanating power restored and even enhanced if it was converted to a soluble compound, dissolved in water, and recovered from solution.   (The effective change was probably an increase in the porosity of the material, although this was not evident at the time.)   The emanation had the chemical behavior of an inert gas of the argon series.   For the fourth point above, there is a discussion at the beginning of the paper concerning the sensitivity of the ionization method; this makes it rather unlikely that a balance would show up the radioactive materials they were working with.

But starting with the section *Concentration of the Radioactive Material*, the paper proceeds to contradict itself.   Before it ends, it has become highly probable that the radioactivity attributed to thorium and the production of emanation both belong to a thorium X which is different from thorium and can be separated from it by chemical operations.

This curious structure was an accident of the calendar.   Soddy's project was evidently doing well by early December 1901.   Rutherford planned to attend the meeting of the American Physical Society in New York after Christmas,[2] and it seemed a good place to wind up the work.   Then, with the bulk of the paper written, Soddy showed that one could separate thorium

---

[1] F. Soddy, *The Story of Atomic Energy* (London: Nova Atlantis, 1949), p. 43.

[2] E. Rutherford, "Transmission of Excited Radioactivity," *Bulletin of the American Physical Society*, 1901, 2: 37–43.

A. S. Eve, *Rutherford* (New York: Macmillan, 1939), pp. 80–81.

and the power of generating emanation, and there was time only to run a
few last experiments and tack them on at the end.

As it turned out, this was a dramatically appropriate place to stop.   By
the beginning of January they had the clue they needed to understand radioactivity, as we shall see later in Paper 11 of this volume.—A. R.]

.

8

E. Rutherford and Frederick Soddy

The Radioactivity of Thorium Compounds

I. An Investigation of the Radioactive Emanation

[From *Journal of the Chemical Society*, *Transactions*, 1902, *81*: 321–350.
This was to be the first in a series of papers.   The second appears as
Paper 11 in this volume.—A. R.]

The following paper contains a preliminary account of an investigation into the property possessed by the compounds of thorium of
giving a radioactive emanation, and also into the nature of the
emanation itself.

It was shown by one of us (*Phil. Mag.*, 1900, [v], *49*, 1, 161) that
the compounds of thorium, besides being radioactive in the same sense
as the uranium compounds, also continuously emit into the surrounding atmosphere, under ordinary conditions, something which, whatever its real nature may be, behaves in all respects like a radioactive
gas.   This "emanation," as it has been named, is the source of rays,
which, like the Röntgen and uranium rays, and the ordinary well-
recognised type of thorium radiation, will darken a photographic
plate, and will render a gas capable of conducting an electric current
(that is, will "ionise" it), but is sharply distinguished from them by
the following considerations.   It can be moved from the neighbourhood of the thorium compound by a current of air passing over it, or
even by the process of ordinary gaseous diffusion, and transported
long distances, so that the characteristic photographic and ionisation
effects appear in the air far away from the original source of radioactivity.   The Röntgen and uranium rays, as is well known, travel
in straight lines from their source, and any object opaque to them

interposed in their path will sharply screen the space behind.   But in the case of the thorium radiation there is no such screening effect, because here we have a case of a substance emitting, not only straight line radiation, but also particles of a gas, itself radioactive, capable of diffusing through the surrounding atmosphere around obstacles placed in its direct path, and so arriving and producing its effects at points completely screened from rays travelling from the thorium in straight lines.   It was shown in the original communication that these effects could not be ascribed to minute particles of thoria dust carried off mechanically, and all the subsequent work on the subject shows that the hypothesis that the compounds of thorium emit a radioactive gas is not merely the only one which will explain the facts, but that it does so in every observed case in a completely satisfactory manner.

Present State of the Subject from a Physical Standpoint

In the papers referred to, the general character of the phenomena in question was presented, and a short *résumé* will perhaps not be out of place here.   It was shown that the radiation from the emanation decays rapidly, but at a perfectly defined rate, that is, the effects it produces diminish with the lapse of time, falling to about one-half the original value at the end of one minute.   This "rate of decay," as will be shown later, is of great value in identifying and distinguishing between different types of emanation.

The emanation passes unchanged through cotton wool, weak and strong sulphuric acid, and aluminium and other metals in the form of foil, but not through an extremely thin sheet of mica.

The emanating power of thoria is independent of the surrounding atmosphere, but is destroyed to a large extent by intense ignition, and does not return when the substance is kept.

One of the most striking properties of the thorium emanation is its power of exciting radioactivity on all surfaces with which it comes in contact, that is, a substance after being exposed for some time in the presence of the emanation behaves as if it were covered with an invisible layer of an intensely radioactive material.   If the thoria is exposed in a strong electric field, the excited radioactivity is entirely confined to the negatively charged surface.   In this way, it is possible to concentrate the excited radioactivity on a very small area.   The excited radioactivity itself has a regular rate of decay, but different from that of the emanation, its effect falling to half value in about 11 hours.   There is a very close connection between the excited radio-activity and the emanation. It was shown that the amount of the former produced under various conditions was proportional to the amount of the latter, and if the emanating power of thoria be

SIR WILLIAM CROOKES (1832-1919)
[From *Famous Chemists, The Men and Their Work* by Sir William
A Tilden. London: George Routledge & Sons, Ltd.; New York:
E. P. Dutton & Co., 1921.]

FREDERICK SODDY (1877-1956)
[From *Svensk Kemisk Tidskrift*, Vol. 34, 1922.]

destroyed by intense ignition, its power to excite radioactivity correspondingly disappears.   Some apparent discrepancies which at first stood in the way of too close a connection being inferred have resolved themselves by recent work into strong confirmation of the view that the two are related to each other as cause and effect.

Another remarkable property of the excited radioactivity is that it is soluble in sulphuric and hydrochloric acids, that is, a platinum wire, rendered radioactive by being made the negative pole of an electric field in the neighbourhood of some thoria, will give up its radioactivity to these acids.   If the acid be then evaporated, the radioactivity remains on the dish, whilst if left to itself the radioactivity of the acid solution decays at a rate identical with that of the original excited radioactivity on the platinum wire.

Simultaneously with the discovery of excited radioactivity due to thoria, Curie showed that radioactive barium possessed a similar property.   Later, Dorn (*Abh. der Naturforsch. Ges. für Halle-a-S.*, 1900) repeated the work quoted for thoria, and extended it to include two preparations of radioactive barium compounds (radium) prepared by P. de Haen, and a preparation of radioactive bismuth (polonium). He found that radium gave out an emanation which was similar to that from thoria, but which retained its radioactive power much longer.   The excited radioactivity from radium, on the other hand, decayed more rapidly than that from thoria.   The special property of emitting an emanation is, however, confined to the compounds of radium and thorium, those of uranium and polonium do not possess it to an appreciable extent.

An approximate determination of the molecular weight of the emanation produced by radium has been carried out (Rutherford and H. T. Brooks, *Nature*, 1901, *64*, 157) by a diffusion method, taking advantage of the slow rate of decay of the radium emanation.   From comparison of the rate of diffusion of gases of known molecular weight into one another, it was found that the molecular weight probably lies between 40 and 100.

It seemed probable that an examination of the phenomena by chemical methods might throw light upon its nature, and the emanation produced by thoria was chosen as more suitable for the purpose than that produced by radium, on account of the obscurity still surrounding the chemistry of the latter, and the difficulty of producing material of even approximate uniformity of properties.   Thoria, on the other hand, is an article of commerce, and specimens from different sources show surprising uniformity in this respect.

During the progress of the work, the subject has acquired additional importance and interest through the discovery by Elster and Geitel (*Phys. Zeit.*, 1901, *2*, 590) that it is possible to produce excited radioactivity from the atmosphere, without further agency, by simply exposing a wire highly charged to a negative potential in the atmosphere for many hours, and that this also possesses the property of being dissolved off by acids, and of being left behind unchanged on the evaporation of the latter.   But here again the rate of decay is different from that of the excited radioactivity produced by thoria, which is evidence for assuming that the two are probably not identical, although so strikingly analogous.   However, the close connection between excited radioactivity and the emanation established in the case of thoria renders it probable that the excited radioactivity obtained from the atmosphere is caused by the presence there of an emanation or radioactive gas analogous to, although probably different from, the Thorium emanation.   The discovery is likely, as Elster and Geitel point out, to have important bearings on the theory of atmospheric electricity, and in our opinion renders a close study of the thorium emanation the more imperative.

The Chemical Aspect of the Question

The foregoing furnishes a short review of the physical side of the question at the present time.   With regard to the chemical aspect, this has so far not been studied.   The photographic method, almost the only one that has until now been used by chemists in the study of radioactivity, is not one which allows of the recognition and differentiation of an emanation as a component factor in producing the phenomena.   The photographic method is of a qualitative rather than a quantitative character; its effects are cumulative with time, and as a rule long exposures are necessary when the radioactivity of a feeble agent like thoria is to be demonstrated.   In addition, Russell has shown that the darkening of a photographic plate is brought about also by agents of a totally different character from those under consideration, and, moreover, under very general conditions.   Sir William Crookes (*Proc. Roy. Soc.*, 1900, *66*, 409) has sounded a timely note of warning against putting too much confidence in the indications of the photographic method of measuring radioactivity.   The uncertainty of an effect produced by cumulative action over long periods of time quite precludes its use for work of anything but a qualitative character.

Two or three chemists have studied the radioactivity of thoria, using the photographic method, without, however, distinguishing between the radioactivity due to the emanation and that due to the thoria itself.   Sir William Crookes (*loc. cit.*), who succeeded by an elegant method in separating and isolating the radioactive constituent of uranium, also describes some experiments on thorium compounds with the same object, but did not succeed in effecting a separation. A method based on the fractional precipitation of the sulphate failed completely, but another method, the fractional crystallisation of the nitrate, gave preparations showing a difference in their photographic actions in the ratio of one to three.   According to slight variations in the method employed, as, for example, whether a glass or a card bottom was used for the cell containing the substance to be tested (and both seem to have been employed), the radiation from the emanation would or would not contribute largely to the photographic action observed.

Debierne (*Compt. rend.*, 1900, *130*, 906), working on a very large scale, obtained from pitchblende, by using reactions which would lead to the separation of thorium, a material different in its chemical properties from radium (barium) and polonium (bismuth), but consisting in great part of thorium.   This preparation was 100,000 times more active than uranium, and he therefore assumed the existence of a new element, "actinium," therein.   He hazarded the suggestion that the radioactivity of thoria is due to the presence of the same substance, and derived support for this view from the recent work of one of us on the radioactivity of thoria, although on what grounds is not clear.

In the course of their work on the atomic weight of thorium, Brauner (Trans., 1898, *73*, 951) and Baskerville (*J. Amer. Chem. Soc.*, 1901, *23*, 761), have obtained evidence of the presence of a foreign substance associated with thorium.   The latter noticed that the separation, as he interpreted it, of this impurity reduced the photographic action considerably, and he concluded that the pure material would be without photographic action.   He employed a modification of Crookes' photographic method, but it cannot be decided with certainty from the description whether the radiation from the emanation would be eliminated or not.

The present work is concerned primarily with the radioactive emanation, although, of course, frequent occasion has arisen to examine correspondingly the ordinary radiation also.   The methods employed are of an electrical character, based on the property generally possessed by all radiation of the kind in question, of rendering a gas capable of discharging both positive and negative electricity. These, as will be shown, are capable of great refinement and certainty.   An ordinary quadrant electrometer is capable of detecting and measuring a difference of potential of at least 10^{-2} volts.   With special instruments, this sensitiveness may be increased a hundredfold.   An average value for the capacity of the electrometer and connections is 3×10^{-5} microfarads, and when this is charged up to 10^{-2} volts, a quantity of electricity corresponding to 3×10^{-13}

coulombs is stored up.   Now in the electrolysis of water one gram of hydrogen carries a charge of 10^5 coulombs.   Assuming, for the sake of example, that the conduction of electricity in gases is analogous to that in liquids, this amount of electricity corresponds to the transport of a mass of 3×10^{-18} grams of hydrogen, that is, a quantity of the order of 10^{-12} times that detected by the balance.   For a more delicate instrument, this amount would produce an inconveniently large effect.

The effects under investigation, from the nature of their manifestation, may well be, and probably are, produced by quantities of matter of the order of magnitude described, and therefore altogether beyond the range of the balance.   But to assume on that account that the subject is beyond the pale of profitable chemical investigation is needlessly to limit the field of chemical inquiry.   Although surpassing the spectroscope as a detective agent, as a quantitative instrument the electrometer is little inferior in accuracy to the balance.   To take as an example the case of thoria mixed with zirconia, the former could be detected and accurately measured by means of its emanation with an electrometer, even although it were only present to the extent of one part in many thousands.   A distinction must be made here between *emanation* and *emanating power*.   The quantity of the former is what is measured by the electrometer.   To express this in terms of weight, the emanating power, that is, the quantity of emanation produced by a given weight of the substance in question, must be known.   As will be shown, this value varies with the previous history and present condition of the substance.

The electrometer also affords the means of recognising and differentiating between the emanations of different chemical substances. By the rate of decay, the emanation from thorium, for example, can be instantly distinguished from that produced by radium, and although a difference in the rate of decay does not of itself argue a fundamental difference of nature, the identity of the rate of decay furnishes at least strong presumption of identity of nature.

In the sense that has just been explained, the electrometer can be said to supply the investigation of the property of emanation with methods, so to speak, of quantitative and qualitative analysis which are simple and direct, and there is therefore no reason why the property in question, and even the nature of the emanation itself, should not be the subject of chemical investigation.

Scope of Work

Of the great number of questions which immediately present themselves for answer in an investigation of this kind, the following are at present claiming our more immediate attention.

1. Is the power of producing an emanation a specific property of thorium, or is it to be ascribed to the presence of a foreign substance, possibly in minute amount, associated with it and amenable to chemical methods of separation?

2. Can the emanating power of "de-emanated" thoria be regenerated by chemical means?   It has been mentioned that thoria, when intensely ignited, loses to a very great extent its power of giving an emanation.   If such de-emanated thoria be subjected to a series of chemical changes, will it regain its emanating power or not?

3. Does the emanation or radioactive gas itself possess any property which would associate it chemically with any known kind of gravitational matter?

4. Is it possible to detect, by means of the balance, any loss in weight corresponding to the continuous emission of the emanation or any gain in weight of bodies rendered radioactive thereby?

5. Does the chemistry of thorium present any peculiarity capable of being connected with its almost unique power of producing an emanation?

To interpret rightly the results obtained, a more or less complete study of the effect of chemical and physical conditions on the emanating power is necessary.   The effect of the state of aggregation, the presence or absence of water, the influence of light, temperature, the nature of the surrounding atmosphere, the lapse of time since preparation, &c., on the emanating power, as well as the differences in this property exhibited by different compounds, have been investigated.

The present communication does not attempt a full answer to all the above questions.   The results so far obtained in answer to the first three will be presented.   The work on the fourth is in progress, whilst the results of the investigation of the fifth question will be most conveniently given later in a separate communication.

Electrometer Method of Measuring Emanating Power and Radioactivity

The term radioactive is now generally applied to a class of substances, like uranium, thorium, radium, and polonium, which have the power of spontaneously giving off radiations capable of passing through thin plates of metal.   The radiations are in some cases very complex, but in the case of the substances mentioned, a portion at least of the radiation is similar in all respects to easily absorbed Röntgen rays.   The characteristic and general property possessed by these radiations is to produce, from the gas through which they pass, positively and negatively charged carriers, which in an electric field travel to the negative and positive electrodes respectively.   In this

way, a small current is able to pass through a gas exposed to the radiations, even with a very weak electric field, and the measurement of
this current by means of the electrometer affords a means of comparing the intensities of radiation.

As has been mentioned, compounds of thorium (and radium), in
addition to radiations which travel in straight lines, emit radioactive
emanations, which behave in all respects like a temporarily radio-
active gas, and diffuse rapidly through porous substances, as, for
example, thick cardboard, which are completely opaque to straight
line radiation. Each particle of the emanation behaves as if it were
a radiating centre, producing charged carriers throughout the gas in
its neighbourhood. The emanation passes through plugs of cotton
wool and can be bubbled through liquids without appreciable loss of
radioactivity, whereas the charged carriers, produced by the emanation in common with the straight line radiation from radioactive

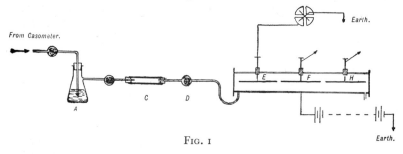

FIG. 1

substances, on the contrary, completely disappear on passing through
a plug of cotton or glass wool, or by bubbling through liquids. The
means of eliminating the effects of the straight line radiation and of
measuring the amount of the emanation alone thus suggest themselves. Air passed over uranium or other non-emanating radio-
active substance will no longer conduct a current after passage
through cotton wool. The conductivity in the case of thorium,
however, will persist, and afford a measure of the amount of emanation present.

Fig. 1 shows the experimental arrangement for comparing the
emanating power of substances. These are placed in the form of fine
powder in a shallow lead vessel inside the glass cylinder, C, 17 cm. in
length and 3.25 cm. in diameter, provided with indiarubber corks.
A current of air from a large gas-bag, after passing through a tube
containing cotton wool to remove dust particles, bubbled through
sulphuric acid in the vessel, A. It then passed through a bulb containing tightly packed cotton wool to prevent any spray being carried
over. The emanation mixed with air was carried from the vessel C

through a plug of cotton wool, D, which completely removed all the charged carriers carried with the emanation. The latter then passed into a long, brass cylinder, 75 cm. in length and 6 cm. in diameter. The cylinder insulated on paraffin blocks was connected to one pole of a battery of small lead accumulators, the other pole of which was connected to earth. Three electrodes, E, F, H, of equal length were placed along the axis of the cylinder, supported by brass rods passing through ebonite corks in the side of the cylinder. The current through the gas, due to the presence of the emanation, was measured by means of a Kelvin quadrant electrometer of the White pattern. The electrometer and the connections were suitably screened by means of wire gauze connected to earth. An insulating key was arranged so that either of the electrodes, E, F, H, or all of them together, could be rapidly connected to one pair of quadrants of the electrometer, the other two being always connected to earth.

The insulation of the electrodes was first tested by sending a current of air through the apparatus without any emanating material in C. The rate of movement of the electrometer needle was accurately observed. On placing the emanating substance in C and continuing the air current for several minutes at a constant rate, the current due to the emanation reached a steady state. On separating the quadrants of the electrometer, the deflection from zero increased uniformly with time. The time taken to pass over 100 divisions of the scale was observed with a stop-watch. The number of divisions passed over per second may be taken as a measure of the current through the gas.

With this apparatus, the emanation from 10 grams of ordinary thorium oxide produces a current of 3.3×10^{-11} amperes between the three electrodes connected together and the cylinder. With the electrometer working at average sensitiveness, this corresponded to a deflection of 100 divisions of the scale in 12 seconds, so that one-hundredth part of this current could be readily measured, that is, the emanation produced by one-tenth of a gram of thorium oxide.

An electrometer one hundred times more sensitive than this failed to detect the presence of an emanation or radioactivity in the oxides of tin, zirconium, and titanium, the other elements of the same group in the periodic table.

Variation of the Current with Voltage. The current through the gas observed with the electrometer at first increases with the voltage, but a stage is soon reached when there is a very small increase for a large additional voltage. This is one of the most characteristic properties of conducting gases. For small voltages, only a small proportion of the charged carriers reach the electrode, on account of their recombination throughout the volume of the gas. When the electric field is increased until all the carriers reach the electrode before any appreciable recombination can occur, the current is at a maximum, and remains constant for large increases of voltage, provided, of course, that the electric field is below the value necessary for a spark to pass. In the experimental case, a pressure of 50 volts was found sufficient to give the maximum current between the electrodes.

This property of conducting gases allows us at once to make sure that the insulation of the electrodes is perfect at all stages of a long experiment; 100 volts applied instead of 50 to the cylinder should give the same current if the insulation is unaffected.

Rate of Decay of the Radiation from the Emanation. The three electrodes, *E, F, H*, were used to compare the "rates of decay" of the radiations from the emanations of different substances. In the previous papers quoted, it has been shown that the radiating power of the thoria emanation falls to half its value in about a minute. In consequence of this, the current observed for the electrode *E* is greater than for electrode *H*. Knowing the velocity of the current of air along the cylinder and the respective currents to the electrodes *E, F, H*, the rate of decay of the radiation can be readily deduced. If, however, we merely require to compare the rate of decay of one emanation with another, it is only necessary to compare the ratio of the currents to the electrodes *E, F, H* in each case, keeping the current of air constant. If the ratio of the currents is the same we may conclude that the radiating power of each diminishes at the same rate. The comparison of emanation is thus rendered qualitative as well as quantitative. In most of the experiments, the current to the electrode *E*, was about twice that to the electrode *H*; the velocity of the current of air along the cylinder was thus about 0.8 cm. a second.

Comparison of Emanating Power. The experiments in all cases on the amount of emanation from different substances are comparative. The standard of comparison was usually a sample of 10 grams of thoria as obtained from the maker, which gave out a conveniently measurable quantity of emanation. Preliminary experiments were made to find the connection between the weight of thoria and the amount of emanation as tested in the cylinder. The following numbers show that the amount of emanation is directly proportional to the weight of the substance:

Weight of thoria	Divisions of scale per second
2 grams	1.41
4 ,,	2.43
10 ,,	6.33
20 ,,	13.2

This result shows that within the limit of accuracy desired we may take the amount of emanation as directly proportional to the weight of the substance. The determinations in the above table were made with the three electrodes connected together with the electrometer, and with a constant flow of air. The lead vessel in which the thoria was placed was 7.4 by 3.5 cm. in area and 3 mm. deep. In the comparison of emanating power, the maximum current between the electrodes for the standard 10 grams of thoria was first observed. This was removed and a known weight of the specimen to be tested was substituted, and the deflections again observed after the conditions had become steady.

If $d_1 =$ No. of divisions per sec. for a weight, w_1, of thoria;

$d_2 =$,,   ,, w_2, of the specimen;

then

$$\frac{\text{Emanating power of specimen}}{\text{Emanating power of thoria}} = \frac{d_2 \, w_1}{d_1 \, w_2}.$$

The values d_1 and d_2 are corrected, when necessary, for natural leakage, that is, the current which passes under similar circumstances when no emanating material is present. This current is chiefly made up of a leakage due to conduction over the ebonite, as well as the current produced by the excited radioactivity which has collected on the negative electrode during the course of the day's experiments. It is generally very small, and the correction is only necessary when a specimen of substance almost free of emanation is being tested.

An example taken at random from the note-book will serve to illustrate the method of calculating the results, the emanating power of the comparison sample being considered 100 per cent.:

Dec. 7th, 11 *a.m.*—Natural leakage   .   10 divisions in 50″

                                            0.20   ,,   1″

5 grams comparison sample ThO_2 100   ,,   23.5″

3.6 ,, ThO_2 ignited 24 hours over Bunsen burner in platinum crucible 50   ,,   35.2″

$d_1 = 4.25$, corrected for nat. leakage $=$ . . .   4.05

$d_2 = 1.42 =$ 1.22

$$\frac{d_2 \, w_1}{d_1 \, w_2} = 0.42, \text{ or } 42 \text{ per cent.}$$

Comparison of Intensity of Straight Line Radiation

It was frequently of interest to obtain information about the intensity of the ordinary radiation correspondingly with measurement of emanating power. In order to do this rapidly and accurately, the following method was used. Fig. 2 shows the general arrangement. 0.1 gram of the compound to be tested was reduced to fine powder and uniformly sifted over a platinum plate 36 sq. cm. in area.

This plate was placed on a large metal plate connected to one pole of a battery of 300 volts, the other pole of which was earthed. An insulated parallel plate was placed about 6 cm. above it, and the whole apparatus enclosed in a metal box connected to earth, to prevent electrostatic disturbance. The shaded portions in the figure represented insulators. A door was made in the apparatus so that

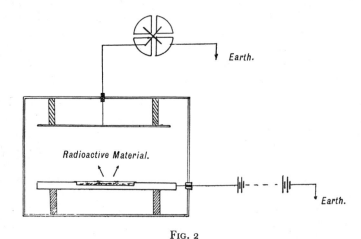

Fig. 2

the plate could be rapidly placed in position or removed. The current between the plates is observed in the usual way with the electrometer. The ratio of the currents for two substances is a comparative measure of their radioactivity. It is only possible to compare together with certainty substances of similar density and state of division—a light, floury material will tend to give lower values than a dense powder.

If a substance gives off an emanation, the current between the plates increases with time. Under these conditions when the thoria is exposed in thin layers with a maximum of radiating surface, all but 1 or 2 per cent. of the total effect is due to the straight line radiation; even when the effect due to the emanation has attained its maximum, this constitutes a very small percentage of the whole. This effect, however, may be to a large extent eliminated by taking the current between the electrodes immediately after the material is placed in the testing apparatus, or by passing a current of air between the electrodes to remove the emanation, and prevent it accumulating.

It is thus possible to compare intensity of radiations with an error not exceeding 1 or 2 per cent., and with great rapidity, and in these respects the electrical method is altogether superior to the photographic.

Comparison of Emanating Power.   The apparatus (Fig. 2) described for the comparison of radiations, can also be quite well employed for a comparison of emanating power.   In this case, a thick layer of thoria (several grams) is spread over the plate and covered with two thicknesses of ordinary paper.   This has been found almost completely to stop the straight line radiation, whilst allowing the emanation to pass through unimpeded.   The current is now measured when a steady state has been reached, due to the accumulation of the emanation.   This takes some time, and draughts of air must be guarded against.   For this reason, it is less convenient than the method first described, but the results obtained by the two methods are almost exactly the same.   Thus a sample of "de-emanated" thoria which gave 12 per cent. of the emanating power of the comparison sample by the first method gave 13 per cent. by the second method, whilst a sample of oxide prepared from thorium oxalate gave 37 per cent. and 39 per cent. by the two methods respectively.   The close agreement in the values by methods so completely different in character is a proof that the indications of the methods are worthy of a great degree of confidence.

The De-emanation of Thoria and the Regeneration of the Emanating Power

The emanating power of thoria, as has been stated, is destroyed to a large extent by intense ignition.   A closer study of this is the first step in the investigation of the phenomenon.   Previous experiments had not succeeded in completely de-emanating thoria, although a reduction to about 15 per cent. of its original value had been accomplished.   A sample of this preparation which had been kept for two years had not altered from this value.   An experiment was performed in which thoria was heated to the highest temperature which could be safely employed with platinum vessels: (1) in a thin layer in a large platinum dish, and (2) in bulk in a small platinum crucible placed inside the dish.   The two were heated together by means of a powerful gasoline furnace for one hour.   The temperature was such that the fireclay walls fused, and the pipeclay of a triangle showed signs of having been softened.   It was found that the sample that had been heated in a thin layer in the dish retained about 16 per cent. of its original emanating power, whilst the other sample retained about 8 per cent. There is thus no advantage in heating in thin layers, in fact rather the reverse, for the sample showing 16 per cent. again heated to a slightly lower temperature for half-an-hour in a small crucible was reduced to 12 per cent.

In a another experiment, a small platinum crucible filled with thoria was heated for half-an-hour in a small furnace by a large blow-pipe and powerful pair of bellows. Some asbestos wool had completely fused on the outside of the crucible, and the temperature was probably but little lower than in the previous experiment. This sample also retained about 8 per cent. of its emanating power. No further attempt has yet been made to completely destroy the emanating power.

A small quantity of thoria heated in a platinum crucible in the open over an ordinary small sized blowpipe and bellows for five minutes retained about 45 per cent. of its emanating power. The effect of time as well as of temperature was studied by heating about equal quantities in a platinum crucible over an ordinary Bunsen burner for different periods.

Heated 10 minutes	Emanating power	= 61 per cent.
,,　　1 hour	,,	= 59　,,
,,　　24 hours	,,	= 42　,,

It thus appears that there is a large and practically sudden decrease of emanating power for each temperature above a red heat, followed by a very gradual decrease with time when the temperature is maintained; thus five minutes on the blowpipe, whilst much more effective than the same time at the temperature of the Bunsen burner, produced rather less effect than 24 hours at the latter temperature.

Effect of Moisture. The next point to be examined was whether the loss of emanating power could be attributed to a loss of water and desiccation of the thoria by ignition. A sample of de-emanated thoria (retaining about 14 per cent.) was placed in the middle of a Jena glass tube, one end of which was closed and contained water, the other end being drawn out to a jet. This was supported in a powerful tube furnace in a sloping position, and the part containing the thoria heated to the highest possible temperature, while a slow current of steam from the water at the end was passed over it, escaping by the jet. When all the water had evaporated, the jet was drawn off and the tube allowed to cool in an atmosphere of steam free from air. The thoria, on testing, was found to have been lowered in emanating power to about 7 per cent. The further heating had thus reduced the emanating power without the steam having at all regenerated it.

In the next experiment, the reverse process was tried. Two

exactly parallel processes were carried out for ordinary thoria possessing the normal amount of emanating power. In the first, it was heated in a porcelain tube in the tube furnace for three hours, while about 500 c.c. of water were distilled over it from a retort. In the second, another quantity of thoria was heated in exactly the same way for the same time, only a current of well dried air was substituted for the steam. The result was conclusive: each sample had had its emanating power reduced to exactly the same amount, that is, about 50 per cent. of the original.

These experiments prove that water vapour exerts no influence either in de-emanating thoria or in effecting a recovery of its lost emanating power.

The Regeneration of the Emanating Power by Chemical Processes. The task of subjecting de-emanated thoria to a series of chemical changes to see if it would recover its lost emanating power was then undertaken.

It may first be mentioned that thoria which has been subjected to ignition has changed very materially in chemical and physical properties. The pure white colour changes at temperatures corresponding to the first stages of de-emanation to a light brown, and after subjection to the very highest temperatures to a pure pink. At the same time, as has been observed before, the solubility of the substance in sulphuric acid is greatly diminished. A part always obstinately refuses to dissolve, even after long and repeated boiling with the concentrated acid, although this part is diminished by each successive treatment and appears to be in no way different from the rest of the substance. No difference, however, occurs in the readiness with which chlorine attacks it when intimately mixed with carbon. The formation of the chloride by this method is the easiest way of dissolving ignited thoria.

Two quantities of the same de-emanated thoria were converted, the one into chloride and the other into sulphate, by the usual methods, and from each of these the oxalate was formed by precipitation of the acid solution with oxalic acid. Parts of the oxalates were then converted into oxides by heating over the Bunsen burner. In both cases there was a very marked recovery in emanating power; the oxide obtained from the sulphate had about 40 per cent., that from the chloride about 55 per cent., whereas the de-emanated thoria from which they were both produced had about 13 to 14 per cent. of the emanating power of thoria. The oxalates from which the oxides were formed each had about 11 per cent. of the power, and in converting them into oxides it was ascertained by a direct trial that too high a temperature had been employed and the thorium oxide had suffered partial de-emanation. At this time also, it was beginning to be realised that the emanating power was a quantity which varied, not only with the nature of the chemical compound, but also for the same compound very materially with its previous history. Thus the oxide from the oxalate does not possess as a rule so great an emanating power as that used for comparison, which would account for the above result. The following two exactly parallel experiments were therefore made, the one with ordinary, and the other with de-emanated thoria possessing 9 to 10 per cent. of the emanating power of the first. Each was converted to chloride in the ordinary way, by mixing with sugar solution, carbonising, and igniting the mixture of oxide and carbon so obtained in a current of dry chlorine. Each sample was then treated with water, the thorium precipitated as hydroxide with ammonia, and the hydroxides washed and dried at 110°. The hydroxide prepared from the de-emanated thoria possessed 128 per cent., that from the ordinary thoria 108 per cent. of the emanating power of ordinary thoria, when tested immediately after drying. Now a sample of hydroxide previously obtained had shown no less than three times the emanating power of ordinary thoria. The specimens were therefore tested again after having been kept for four days in loosely corked tubes. They now showed 157 per cent. and 139 per cent. respectively. The emanating power was thus increasing, so both specimens were exposed side by side in open watch glasses under a sheet of glass to keep off the dust. The result is again conclusive:

	From de-emanated ThO_2	From ordinary ThO_2
After nine days . .	253 per cent.	253 per cent.
After three more days	259 ,,	259 ,,

Thus the process of de-emanating thoria by ignition does not irretrievably destroy the emanating power, for after solution and re-precipitation no difference whatever exists in the emanating power between ordinary and de-emanated thoria.

The results also bring out another point—the marked effect of time and exposure to air in increasing the emanating power of thorium hydroxide. This will be examined more fully later.

A fair conclusion from these experiments is that the cause of the emanating power is not removed by ignition, but only rendered for the time being inoperative.

Radioactivity of De-emanated Thoria. The "straight line" radiation of thoria, de-emanated as completely as possible by ignition, was compared with that of ordinary thorium oxide by the method described. It was found that within the limits of error no difference whatever could be detected between them. This result serves to bring out the fact that the power of thoria to give an emanation is independent of its power to give a direct radiation.

Is the Emanating Power a Specific Property of Thorium?

Having shown that the de-emanation of thoria by the processes described consists rather in a temporary obliteration of the effect than in a removal of the cause producing it, the next question to be considered is whether it is possible to remove from thorium compounds by chemical methods any constituent to which the property of emanating power can be traced.

The thoria used in the investigation is that supplied by Messrs. Eimer and Amend of New York, and is obtained from monazite sand by a secret process. It, of course, does not consist of pure thoria, although from superficial investigation it appears to be of excellent quality. There is a small quantity of a substance present which can be precipitated by sodium phosphate after removal of the thorium as hydroxide by ammonia, the nature of which is at present under investigation. The most noticeable impurity is about 1 per cent of thorium sulphate. Careful washing completely removed this impurity, and the emanating power of the washed sample was identical with the ordinary. The impurity may therefore be disregarded for present purposes.

Emanating power is not confined to thorium from any particular source. Orangeite and thorite from Norway both possess it as well as monazite sand from Brazil. A specimen of thoria prepared from orangeite by the ordinary processes possessed about the same emanating power as that obtained from monazite sand by the secret process.

A quantity of thorium oxide was converted into the anhydrous sulphate and dissolved in iced water. The temperature was allowed to rise and the hydrated sulphate precipitated in four fractions, a fifth being obtained by evaporation of the mother liquor to dryness. These showed no marked difference in emanating power among themselves. The first fraction was dehydrated and again submitted to fractional precipitation as hydrated sulphate. The first fraction of the new series—designated fraction AA—was then compared in the following manner with the mother liquor fraction of the first series—designated as fraction E. Both were dehydrated, dissolved in water, and precipitated as hydroxide by ammonia, washed and dried under the same conditions, and compared together at regular intervals with a comparison sample of ordinary thoria.

	Fraction AA	Fraction E
At first	203 per cent.	200 per cent.
After 1 day . . .	240 ,,	249 ,,
After 13 days . .	316 ,,	321 ,,
After 43 days . .	352 ,,	372 ,,

The differences are too small to afford any indication of separation of the emanating material.

The straight line radiations of the two fractions tested in the apparatus (Fig. 2) also proved to be identical.

It was obviously useless trying any further fractionations by this method. Since there was no appreciable difference in either property in the fractions tried, there was nothing to be gained in a further repetition. These results completely accord with those of Sir William Crookes (*loc. cit.*), with which, however, we were not acquainted until after our own experiments had been performed.

Another method for the purification of thoria, employed by Dennis (*J. Amer. Chem. Soc.*, 1896, *18*, 947), the precipitation of the hydroxide by potassium azoimide, was next tried. The latter reagent was prepared by Thiele's method (*Annalen*, 1892, *270*, 1) from diazo-guanidine nitrate. Hydrazoic acid partially neutralised with potash precipitates thorium hydroxide from the boiling solution of a thorium salt. This hydroxide, compared with a sample which had been precipitated with ammonia in the ordinary way, showed similar emanating power.

These results, which fail to give any indication of a separation of the emanating material by chemical means, taken in conjunction with those already described in the preceding section on the regeneration of the emanating power in de-emanated thoria, certainly seemed to point to the conclusion that the power of giving an emanation is really a specific property of thorium. Recent results, which will be given in the last section (p. 109), put the question in a fresh light.

Effect of Conditions upon Emanating Power

Before any further work was undertaken, it was necessary to make a close study of the influence of conditions upon the emanating power of thorium compounds.

Effect of Temperature. The effect of increase of temperature on the emanating power of thoria has already been fully investigated by one of us (*Phys. Zeit.*, 1901, *2*, 429). The results stated briefly show that an increase in temperature up to a certain limit, in the neighbourhood of a red heat, correspondingly increases the emanating power. At the maximum, this is between three and four times the value at the ordinary temperature, and is maintained at this increased value for several hours without any sign of diminution with time. When the thoria is allowed to cool, the emanating power then returns to the neighbourhood of the normal value. If, however, the limit of temperature given is exceeded, de-emanation sets in, and even while the high temperature is maintained, the emanating power falls rapidly to a fraction of its former value.   On cooling, the substance is found to be more or less de-emanated.   It is of interest that no increase of emanating power is observed when de-emanation commences.

These experiments were extended to include the effects of cooling. The platinum tube which contained the thoria was surrounded with a felt jacket containing a mixture of solid carbon dioxide and ether. The emanating power immediately fell to 10 per cent. of its former value.   On removing the cooling agent, it again rose quickly to nearly its normal value.

In another experiment, some thoria was surrounded in a platinum crucible with a mixture of solid carbon dioxide and ether, and kept in a vacuum for several hours.   On removing it and allowing its temperature to rise, it possessed much the same value as an ordinary sample, and after standing some time in the air it was again tested and no difference could be detected between the two.

Thus changes in temperature produce very marked simultaneous changes in emanating power, but between the limits of $-110°$ and an incipient red heat no permanent alteration in the value occurs.

Effect of Moisture.   Dorn (*loc. cit.*) had noticed that moisture produced a moderate increase in the power of thoria of giving an emanation, and of exciting radioactivity on surrounding surfaces. We have confirmed and extended his results by the following experiments.

Two similar weights of ordinary thoria were exposed in jars sealed with wax, the one containing sulphuric acid and the other water, for a period of 4 days.   The desiccated sample showed 54 per cent. and the sample exposed to water vapour 134 per cent. of the original emanating power.   The experiment was repeated and the samples left for a week with much the same result: 70 per cent. and 141 per cent. respectively.   It was of interest to see if a more complete desiccation would further reduce the emanating power.   Five grams of thoria were sealed up in a tube containing phosphoric oxide, the two substances being separated by a plug of glass wool.   Before sealing, the tube was exhausted by a Töpler mercury pump.   After 26 days, the end of the tube was connected with a closely packed phosphoric oxide tube, the tip broken off inside the connection, and a slow stream of dried air thus allowed to enter.   The other end was connected to the testing cylinder, and arrangements were made to send a stream of air through into the cylinder.   When all was ready, this end of the tube was broken inside the connection, and the emanating power measured.   A similar experiment made with an ordinary sample of thoria, using the same arrangement, showed that the desiccated sample possessed 79 per cent. of the emanating power of the ordinary sample tested under the same conditions.

A sample of thoria sprayed with water gave 125 per cent. of its original emanating power.   If completely flooded with water, however, the value is much reduced, as would be expected from the reduction of surface.

Another trial was made, in which thoria was flooded with concentrated sulphuric acid.   Hardly any emanation was observed so long as the mixture remained undisturbed, but when vigorously shaken it gave nearly one-half of the original emanation.

These experiments show that the presence of water, although producing a marked increase, is not apparently essential for the production of the phenomena.   It must be mentioned, however, that thoria only ceases to lose weight after prolonged ignition with the blowpipe, that is, under conditions which nearly destroy its emanating power.   This, with analogous points, will be taken up, however, in a separate communication on the more purely chemical side of the question.

The results of some experiments on the effects of other conditions may be shortly tabulated.   In each case the sample was exposed to the conditions given for 4 days.   The emanating power is that possessed at the end of this period, compared with that of the first sample, which is regarded as 100 per cent.:

1. Kept in sealed test-tube enclosed completely in lead tube . . . .   100 per cent.
2. Taken from tightly stoppered stock bottle containing the main quantity   100   ,,
3. Sealed up in test-tube and exposed to bright, all-day sun   100   ,,
4. Exposed to the air of the laboratory in open watch glass   105   ,,
5. Kept in a continuous stream of ordinary air   . .   88   ,,

The last experiment was made at a different time from the other four, and therefore is not strictly comparable.   The most useful result attained is that thoria does not change in emanating power when kept in closed vessels under different conditions, but when exposed to the air the emanating power varies within comparatively narrow limits.

Thorium Hydroxide.   The effect of time on the emanating power of the freshly prepared hydroxide already mentioned is one of the most striking observations in this connection.   The following additional experiments have been made on this point.   A quantity of hydroxide was prepared, and separate portions subjected to different drying temperatures and subsequent conditions, as follows:

Emanating power

1. Dried at 110° and exposed some hours to the air   .   264 per cent.
2. Dried as before at 110° and kept in desiccator until
   tested   226   ,,
3. Dried at 200° and kept in desiccator   220   ,,
4. Dried at 250° and kept in desiccator   219   ,,

From this, it appears that the additional loss of water caused by exposure to increasing temperatures is without effect on the emanating power.

A similar experiment to that described for thorium oxide was performed with the hydroxide.   Two quantities were exposed in closed bottles to the action of moist air and of air dried with sulphuric acid respectively, and showed, after 4 days, emanating powers of 394 per cent. and 307 per cent.   After having been exposed to the air for 24 hours, these samples showed 350 per cent. and 324 per cent. respectively.

The next experiment was designed to include the effect of carbon dioxide, which the hydroxide absorbs from the air to the extent of 2 per cent. of its weight.   A quantity of hydroxide was tested immediately after preparation, and possessed 140 per cent. emanating power.   A sample was sealed up in a test-tube, while another similar sample was tested in the following manner.   It was exposed to a current of moist carbon dioxide for an hour, and then possessed an emanating power of 156 per cent.   It was then left exposed to the air of the laboratory and tested at intervals:

After   2 days .   .   .   .   Emanating power 263 per cent.
  ,,   6   ,, ...   ,,   325   ,,
  ,,   10   ,, ...   ,,   300   ,,
  ,,   11   ,, ...   ,,   341   ,,
  ,,   16   ,, ...   ,,   362   ,,

On the last day, the sealed up specimen was opened and examined, and was found to possess an emanating power of 298 per cent.   These experiments show that if the air is fundamental in producing the increase of emanating power with time, a very limited quantity of it is effective.   For the present, it is perhaps better to consider it as an effect of time simply, hastened no doubt by the presence of water vapour.

On the Chemical Nature of the Emanation

The following work has reference to the emanation itself and not to the material producing it, and was designed to see whether the emanation possesses chemical properties which would identify it with any known kind of matter. It had been noticed at the time of its discovery that it passed unchanged through concentrated sulphuric acid. The same holds true of every reagent that has been investigated.

The effect of temperature was first tried. The air containing the emanation, obtained in the usual way by passage over thoria, was led through the platinum tube heated electrically to the highest attainable temperature, and also through the tube cooled by solid carbon dioxide and ether. The tube was then filled with platinum black, and the emanation passed through in the cold, and with gradually increasing temperatures, until the limit was reached. The effect of the intense heat was to convert the platinum black completely into platinum sponge. In another experiment, the emanation was passed through a layer of red hot lead chromate in a glass tube. The current of air was replaced by a current of hydrogen and the emanation sent through red hot magnesium powder, and red hot palladium black, and, by using a current of carbon dioxide, through red hot zinc dust. In every case, the emanation passed without sensible change in the amount. If anything, a slight increase occurred, owing to the time taken for the gas current to pass through the tubes when hot being slightly less than when cold, the decay *en route* being consequently less. It will be noticed that the only known gases capable of passing in unchanged amount through all the reagents employed are the recently discovered gases of the argon family.

But another interpretation may be put upon the results. If the emanation were the manifestation of excited radioactivity on the surrounding atmosphere, then since from the nature of the experiments it was necessary to employ in each case, as the atmosphere, a gas not acted on by the reagent employed, the result obtained might be explained. Red hot magnesium would not retain an emanation consisting of radioactive hydrogen, or red hot zinc dust an emanation consisting of radioactive carbon dioxide. The correctness of this explanation was tested in the following way. Carbon dioxide was passed over thoria, then through a T-tube, where a current of air met and mixed with it, both passing on to the testing cylinder. But between this and the T-tube, a large soda-lime tube was introduced, and the current of gas thus freed from its admixed carbon dioxide before being tested in the cylinder for emanation. The amount of emanation found was quite unchanged, whether carbon dioxide was sent over thoria in the manner described, or whether an equally rapid current of air was substituted for it, keeping the other arrangements as before. The theory that the emanation may consist of the surrounding medium rendered radioactive is thus excluded, and the interpretation of the experiments must be that the emanation is a chemically inert gas analogous in nature to the members of the argon family.

It is perhaps early to discuss these results from a theoretical point of view, although it appears certain that an explanation of the nature of the emanation must precede, as a necessary step, any hypothesis put forward to account for emanating power. The explanation already advanced and disproved being left out of the question, two other views of the origin and nature of the emanation are still possible. It may be that one of the inert constituents of the atmosphere is rendered radioactive in the presence of thoria and so constitutes the emanation. The actual amount being probably extremely small, and air being a constant impurity in all gases as ordinarily prepared, it is of course no argument against this view that emanating power is independent of the gaseous medium surrounding the emanating material. An experiment is in progress, however, to ascertain whether emanating power persists in a current of gas as free from air as present methods of preparation allow. The other alternative is to look upon the emanation as consisting of a gas emitted by the thorium compound. It is not necessary that such should contain thorium, it might conceivably be an inert gas continuously emitted in the radioactive state.

In the present state of knowledge, it would be premature to attempt to choose between these two alternatives. But in any decision of this point, the work already given on the regeneration of the emanating power of thoria de-emanated by ignition, the continuous loss of emanating power by successive ignition at increasing temperatures, and the increase in the chemical activity of thorium hydroxide with time, must be taken into consideration.

Concentration of the Radioactive Material

Since the preceding account was written, developments have been made in the subject which completely alter the aspect of the whole question of emanating power and radioactivity. The first has reference to thorium nitrate, which in the solid state hardly possesses any emanating power. In a careful determination, using 20 grams of the finely powdered commercial salt, this worked out to be only 1.8 per cent. of the emanating power of thoria. Dissolved in water, however, and tested for emanation by bubbling a current of air through it, it gives about three times as much emanation as thorium oxide.

That is, solution in water increases the emanating power of thorium nitrate nearly 200 times. The emanating power, as in the case of solids, is proportional to the weight of substance present, and within the limits tried is not much affected by dilution, for a solution of 10 grams made up to 25 c.c. in volume possessed a similar value when diluted four times.

Solutions of thorium chloride also give a large amount of emanation.

In these experiments, the cylinder *C* (Fig. 1) is replaced by a Drechsel bottle. A drying tube of calcium chloride is inserted between it and the testing cylinder to prevent the moisture destroying the insulation of the latter. In this connection, the method of testing the insulation by varying the voltage is invaluable. The air current under these circumstances cannot of course be kept so constant as when working with solid substances, and the results are not strictly comparable in consequence, but the arrangement works well enough for a first approximation.

Simultaneously with this observation of the latent emanating power of thorium nitrate, it was noticed that preparations of thorium carbonate varied enormously in emanating power according to their method of preparation. A sample prepared from the nitrate by complete precipitation with sodium carbonate showed an emanating power of 370 per cent. of that of the ordinary oxide, and this value remained fairly constant with time. In another experiment, the precipitated carbonate was partially redissolved in nitric acid, and the redissolved fraction completely reprecipitated with ammonia as hydroxide. The result was remarkable: the carbonate had an emanating power of only 6 per cent., the hydroxide one of 1225 per cent. of that of the ordinary oxide. On repeating the experiments, both fractions proved almost equally inactive, the carbonate showing 14 per cent. and the hydroxide 19 per cent. of the emanating power of thoria. An even greater difference between these two similar experiments was observed in the effects of time on the different preparations. In the first, the carbonate did not alter in value in 7 days, whilst the hydroxide steadily decreased:

	Hydroxide	Carbonate
Original	1225 per cent.	6.2 per cent.
After 1 day	1094 ,,	8.4 ,,
After 4 days	696 ,,	4.8 ,,
After 7 days	614 ,,	4.7 ,,
After 14 days	473 ,,	— ,,

In the second experiment, the emanating power of both the carbonate and hydroxide had increased many fold when tested 11 days later, and the former now possessed 109 per cent., the latter, 273 per cent. (originally 14 per cent. and 19 per cent. respectively).

The straight line radioactivity of the carbonate from the first experiment which possessed such a low emanating power is of interest. It proved to be similar to that of a specimen of hydroxide of normal emanating power, which it resembled in density and state of division. After having been kept 7 days without showing any sign of recovering its emanating power, it was redissolved in nitric acid, and reprecipitated with ammonia as hydroxide. The latter now possessed, when first made, an emanating power of 65 per cent., and after 24 hours 145 per cent., from which value it did not much alter.

These results throw a new light on the question of emanating power. In the first experiment, which we have so far not succeeded in repeating, by an accident in the conditions apparently, two fractions were separated from thorium which varied in their emanating power in the ratio of 200 to 1. The active fraction diminished to nearly a third of its original value in 14 days spontaneously, whilst the activity of the inactive fraction was, to a large extent, regenerated by solution and reprecipitation, in an exactly analogous manner to the behaviour of thoria de-emanated by ignition. Attempts to repeat this result have so far led to the production of two more or less completely de-emanated fractions, which, however, spontaneously increase in activity with time, as in the second experiment, and this seems to be generally the case, whether incomplete precipitation is effected as in the experiment given by re-solution of the carbonate in acid, or by using a deficiency of sodium carbonate in the first instance.

The production of preparations of such low emanating power led naturally to an examination being made of the filtrates and washings for radioactivity. It was found that these possess when concentrated both emanating power and radioactivity in considerable amounts, although from the nature of their production they should be chemically free from thorium. The behaviour is quite general, a dilute solution of thorium nitrate, after the thorium has been precipitated as hydroxide with ammonia, shows when concentrated an emanating power of from one-third to two-thirds that of the original nitrate in solution. It does not matter whether the thorium is precipitated with ammonia directly, or after preliminary partial precipitation as carbonate—either by adding insufficient sodium carbonate in the first place, or by precipitating completely and dissolving part of the precipitate in nitric acid—the thorium-free filtrate invariably possessed emanating power, and when evaporated to dryness exhibited straight line radioactivity also in amounts very much greater than possessed by the same weight of thoria.

The result of a careful chemical investigation of the active filtrates produced under the various conditions described was to show that these contained no thorium, or at most only a minute trace, but another substance in very appreciable quantities which can be precipitated with sodium phosphate, and which, so prepared, is a white substance possessing both emanating power and radioactivity, often many hundred-fold greater than thoria. It has not yet been obtained in sufficiently large quantities for an exhaustive chemical investigation, and it is impossible at present to say what it may prove to be.

We may at once state, however, that we do not incline to the view that it is ThX, either in the sense of the radioactive or emanating constituent of thorium. The evidence of a long series of experiments in two directions, of which the final steps can only find place here, is quite definite on this point, and in our opinion admits of only one conclusion. There seems little doubt of the actual existence of a constituent ThX to which the properties of radioactivity and emanating power of thorium must be ascribed, but in all probability it is present in altogether minute amount, and must therefore be possessed of these qualities to a correspondingly intense degree.

But before the reasons for this view are put forward, it is necessary to discuss more nearly the meaning of the experiments already given on the emanating power. It has been shown that this is a most uncertain quantity, similar experiments often giving preparations of very varying value, as is clearly shown in the results given, as well as in many others in the same direction. The most pregnant fact is that although, as has been shown, precipitation with ammonia invariably leaves behind considerable emanating material in the filtrate which is lost, this seems to exert little influence on the emanating power of the precipitates. These, prepared under different conditions, often by a different number of precipitations, in which therefore varying amounts of the emanating material are lost, show a surprising uniformity in this property, especially after they have attained their maximum power by keeping. It is only necessary to quote the experiment on the almost completely de-emanated carbonate, which gained in emanating power thirty times by conversion into the hydroxide, although during the process much emanating material must have been lost, to show that the value of the emanating power alone furnishes no criterion of the amount of emanating material present.

It may safely be said that three things must be carefully distinguished between in considering the nature of the property possessed by thoria of giving out a radioactive emanation. First, the nature of the emanation itself, secondly, the nature of the emanating power, and thirdly, the nature of the emanating material.   The first, the emanation itself, we have shown to possess the negative properties of a chemically inert gas, whose radioactivity is unaffected by any conditions, apparently, except lapse of time.   With regard to the second, the emanating power or *rate* at which the emanation is produced per unit weight of substance, it is certain that this does not depend only, or even mainly, on the quantity of emanating material present.   The regeneration of the emanating power of thoria de-emanated by ignition, the enormous variation with time in the emanating power of the hydroxide and carbonate under certain conditions, and the comparatively constant maximum which these substances ultimately attain, although prepared under conditions where different amounts of the emanating material are lost, make this point perfectly clear.   These considerations, taken in conjunction with the effect of temperature, moisture, &c., on emanating power, and the nature of the emanation itself, make the property appear rather as the result of a dynamical change, possibly in the nature of a chemical reaction where the active mass of emanating material is a constant, than as the property of a peculiar kind of matter in the static state, additive with regard to mass.

It is, however, neither the emanation itself nor the emanating power with which we are concerned in these experiments, but the third conception, the emanating material, that is, the substance, whether thorium or not, which is responsible for the activity.   It has been shown that it is difficult to follow, by means of the value of the emanating power, the progress of the removal of the active material. When this was realised, attention was directed to the straight line radioactivity, which is generally unaffected by these changes of conditions and previous history which produce such profound alteration in the former property.   The two phenomena are un-doubtedly connected.   The intensely radioactive preparations obtained from thorium in different ways always show correspondingly great emanating power when the conditions are favourable for the manifestation of the latter.   Solution appears to be the most generally favourable condition.   The experiments we had been engaged in were therefore repeated in a form which would allow a close study of the total radioactivity, in the hope that this value would prove a more suitable indication of the amount of active material present than the emanating power alone.

Seventy grams of thorium nitrate were dissolved in four litres of boiling water, and precipitated with ammonia added cautiously in very dilute solution in excess.   The filtrates and washings were evaporated to about 60 c.c. and then possessed as much emanating power as 146 grams of thoria.   On evaporating the solution to dryness and removing the ammonium salts by ignition the residue weighed 0.0583 gram. The emanating power of this residue in solution was thus about 2500 times that of ordinary thoria. In the solid state, however, the value fell to one-fiftieth. But its total radiation was equivalent to at least 23.6 grams of thoria, that is, was about 400 times as great. It was dissolved in hydrochloric acid, and ammonia added in excess, when a precipitate weighing 0.0015 gram was thrown down. This contained all the thorium present besides iron in appreciable quantity which had been introduced during the evaporation. It equalled in radioactivity 2.73 grams of thoria, the ratio in this case being thus no less than 1800 times. Sodium phosphate precipitated 0.0225 gram of white substance the activity of which was equivalent to 4.4 grams of thoria, that is, 200 times. The sodium salts freed from ammonium still possessed a radioactivity equivalent to 3.6 grams of thorium oxide. In other experiments, however, these had been obtained quite free from activity, and this result is due to the solubility of the phosphate in water, so that some was dissolved during the washing (which the subsequent determination of the weight rendered necessary) and appeared in the filtrate.

The radioactive residue obtained in the first place from the filtrate by evaporation and ignition, before it was redissolved, had, however, been tested to determine the penetrative power of the radiations emitted. If the rays from various radioactive substances are made to pass through successive layers of aluminium foil, each additional layer of foil cuts down the radiation to a fraction of its former value, and a curve can be plotted with the thickness of metal penetrated as abscissæ, and the intensity of the rays after penetration as ordinates, expressing at a glance the penetrative power of the rays being examined (compare Rutherford, *Phil. Mag.*, 1899, [v], 47, 122). The curves so obtained are quite different for different radioactive substances. The radiations from uranium, radium, thorium, each give distinct and characteristic curves, whilst that of the last named again is quite different from that given by the excited radioactivity produced by the thorium emanation. The examination in this way of the penetrative power of the rays from the radioactive residue showed that the radiations emitted were in every respect identical with the ordinary thorium radiation. In another experiment, the nature of the emanation from a similar intensely active thorium-free residue was submitted to examination. The rate of decay was quite indistinguishable from that of the ordinary thorium emanation. That is, substances chemically free from thorium have been prepared possessing thorium radioactivity in an intense degree.

The main quantity of thorium hydroxide in the last experiment was redissolved in nitric acid, and the previous round of operations repeated twice, the filtrates from each operation being mixed and then examined exactly as in the former case.   The emanating power of the concentrated solution was only equal to that of 8 grams of thoria in this instance, and the radioactivity of the residue to that of 3 grams.

From this only a small quantity of the phosphate precipitate was obtained (0.001 gram) the radioactivity of which was equal to that of 0.3 gram of thoria (ratio 200:1).

The *emanating power* of the main quantity of the hydroxide when first so prepared was 73 per cent. that of thoria, that is, about one-half of its usual value.   The hydroxide was converted into oxide by ignition, and its *radioactivity* compared with that of the oxide from the original nitrate prepared in the same way.   It was found to be only about one-third as active, the exact ratio being 0.36:1.

Only one conclusion seems possible from this series of experiments. There is no longer any room for doubt that a part of the radioactive constituent ThX has been separated from thorium, and obtained in a very concentrated form, in one instance 1800 times more powerful in its actions.   This result, taken into account with the reduction of the radioactivity and emanating power of the main quantity of thorium compound, and the identity of the radiations of the active thorium-free preparations with those of the ordinary thorium radiation, warrant the conclusion that ThX is a distinct substance, differing from thorium in its chemical properties and so capable of separation therefrom.   The manner in which it makes its appearance, associated with each precipitate formed in its concentrated solution, resembles the behaviour of Crookes' UrX, which he found was dragged down by precipitates when no question of insolubility is involved, and suggests the view that it is really present in minute quantity.   Even in the case of the most active preparations, these probably are composed of some ThX associated with accidental admixtures probably large in proportion.

These results receive confirmation from observations made in a different method of separating ThX.   The experiment was tried of washing thoria with water repeatedly, and seeing if the radioactivity was thereby affected.   In this way, it was found that the filtered washings, on concentration, deposited small amounts of material, with an activity often of the order of a thousand times greater than that of the original sample.   In one experiment, 290 grams of thoria were shaken for a long time with nine quantities, each of 2 litres, of distilled water.   The first washing, containing most of the sulphate already referred to, was rejected, the rest concentrated to different stages, and filtered at each stage.   One of the residues so obtained weighed 6.4 mg. and was equivalent in radioactivity to 11.3 grams of the original thoria, and was therefore no less than 1800 times more radioactive. It was examined chemically, and gave, after conversion into sulphate, the characteristic reaction of thorium sulphate, being precipitated from its solution in cold water by warming. *No other substance than thorium could be detected by chemical analysis*, although of course the quantity was too small for a minute examination. But the absence of the substance precipitable as phosphate, noticed in the other experiments, confirms the opinion that this is an accidental admixture without influence on the qualities of radioactivity and emanating power. The penetrative power of the radiation from this substance again established its identity with the ordinary thorium radiation. In another experiment, a small quantity of thoria was shaken many times with large quantities of water. In this case, the radioactivity of the residue was examined and found to be about 20 per cent. less radioactive than the original sample.

There remains only one step to prove beyond doubt that the radioactivity and emanating power of thorium are not specific properties of the thorium molecule—the preparation of thoria free from these properties—and on this problem we are now engaged. To sum up briefly what has already been accomplished, two different methods have effected a concentration of the activity many hundred-fold in one fraction, and a corresponding diminution of activity in the remainder, but in each case the character of the radiation is not thereby affected. In one method, the active fraction appears to consist only of thorium, so far as examination has been possible, whilst in the other case radioactivity and emanating power appear to be manifested indiscriminately in all the products, without reference to their chemical nature. The simplest explanation of this behaviour, on the present view, is that so far the active constituent of thorium has only been obtained in relatively minute quantity, and therefore does not answer to any definite analytical reactions.

Macdonald Physics Building.
Macdonald Chemistry and Mining Building.
McGill University, Montreal.

[Quite independently of Crookes and at almost the same time, Becquerel succeeded in partially separating uranium and uranium X by the methods he describes in the next paper. That the radioactivity could be taken away from uranium was a solid scientific fact, but it was thoroughly incongruous in the face of all the studies he, the Curies, and others had made on radioactive uranium. It was a happy circumstance that when Becquerel saw this he had ready to his hand all the preparations from his earlier work.   They needed no more than testing, and in every test they verified his logical conclusions: the purified uranium had regained its radioactivity, and what Crookes had called uranium X was non-radioactive.

Pierre Curie had found it difficult to accept Rutherford's material explanation of the temporary radioactivities.   To him radioactivity was one of the characteristics of a chemical element and therefore permanent.   From a true radioactive substance, however, energy might be transferred to other bodies in the neighborhood, and the longer or shorter emission of rays which occurred while this energy was being dissipated he called an induced radio-activity.[3]   This was an elastic idea which accounted for both the short-lived elements deposited by the radioactive emanations and the entrainments which occurred when ordinary salts were precipitated from radioactive solutions.   It was hardly useful for Becquerel's present discovery, however, and his explanations are happier when he leaves "auto-induction" and goes over to his ionic model.—A. R.]

9

Henri Becquerel

On the Radioactivity of Uranium

[Translation of "Sur la radio-activité de l'uranium," *Comptes rendus de l'Académie des Sciences, Paris*, 1901, *133*: 977–980 (9 December).]

Since I announced the spontaneous and permanent radioactivity of uranium and of the salts of this metal, it has been observed that, under certain conditions, the radiation property of these substances did not remain constant.   In particular, Giesel has shown that after certain treatments preparations of uranium became less active, and Sir W. Crookes, by fractional crystallizations, has obtained an inactive nitrate of uranium.

I shall also recall the experiments I did in 1900[4] on the same question, using a method indicated by Debierne.   If an insoluble sulfate is precipitated in an active solution, it entrains an active

---

[3] P. Curie and A. Debierne, "Sur la radioactivité induite provoquée par les sels de radium," *C. R. Acad. Sci., Paris*, 1901, *132*: 548–551; "Sur la radioactivité et les gaz activés par le radium," *ibid.*, 768–770; "Sur la radioactivité des sels de radium," *ibid.*, *133*: 276–279.

[4] *Comptes rendus*, Vol. 130, p. 1584, and Vol. 131, p. 137.

product with the precipitate.   The experiments concerned solutions of uranium chloride into which a little barium chloride was introduced.   The barium was then precipitated as the sulfate; the precipitate was strongly radioactive and, according to the proportions of uranium and barium, it might be made considerably more active than the uranium.   At the same time, the uranium salt recovered from the filtrate had become less active.   After eighteen successive operations, I obtained a uranium salt with very little activity.   The progressive weakening of the products was determined either by their action on an electrometer or by the photographic exposure produced through a slip of thin glass.   The photographic action appeared to decrease more rapidly than the influence on the electrometer did. The preparations have all been preserved, either as chlorides or as oxides, a state in which they are more active.

The observations of Sir W. Crookes, and those I have just referred to, would lead to the idea that the activity of uranium is perhaps due to a small quantity of a very active compound, and that pure uranium would be inactive.

Nevertheless, the fact that the radioactivity of a particular salt of uranium purchased on the market is the same, whatever the origin of the metal and whatever previous treatments it has undergone, makes this hypothesis less probable.   Since its radioactivity may well have been weakened, we had to conclude that the salts of uranium recovered their original radioactivity with time.

Another consideration allows us to think that this must be so. The radioactive substances produce the phenomena of induced radioactivity, so well studied by the Curies and by Debierne.   This effect should be produced equally well in a mixture of active and of inactive substances, so that by induction on itself the mixture should spontaneously increase its activity over a period of time, up to a maximum.   It is known, also, that solid preparations of radium-bearing barium increase their radioactivity considerably over a period of time following their precipitation.

Experience confirms for uranium the predictions set forth above. I have resumed the study of the progressively weakened specimens I had prepared eighteen months ago, and, as I expected, I have found that all these specimens are nearly identical with one another.   They were compared with one another either by the electrometer, by the rapidity with which they allow charge to be communicated to an insulated conductor, or by photographic exposure through a slip of thin glass on a plate of silver bromide in gelatine.

Thus the lost activity has been spontaneously regained.   In contrast, the precipitated barium sulfate, formerly more active than the uranium, is now completely inactive.   The loss of activity, which is the characteristic of active or induced substances, shows that the barium did not entrain the essentially active and permanent part of the uranium. This gives us a strong presumption of the existence of an activity belonging to the uranium, even though it has not been shown that this metal is not intimately associated with another very active substance not separated in the preceding operations.

By what mechanism does the substance regain its temporarily weakened activity? The hypothesis of an auto-induction would apply to a mixture and even to a chemical combination of molecules, some active and others inactive; for a pure substance, this would be equivalent to a molecular transformation.

Perhaps it is not without interest to sketch a hypothesis which has guided me so far and which does not seem in disagreement with the majority of the observed facts. I have already expressed the idea that if the emission of the deviable rays, which are identical with the cathode rays, was the cause of the emission of the nondeviable radiation, which has such an analogy to the x-rays, this spontaneous emission being comparable to the evaporation of an odorous substance, radioactivity would be brought nearer to a recognized phenomenon. The energy dissipated would be obtained from the active substance itself, but the corresponding loss in weight would be too small to be observed.

According to a hypothesis of J. J. Thomson, there should be two kinds of particles of different magnitudes, one kind about a thousand times smaller than the other. In separating, the smaller would carry negative charges and pick up enormous velocities, which would permit them to penetrate bodies. The others, larger, whose masses would be of the order of electrolytic ions, would move at much lower velocities. They would not penetrate bodies, and would behave like a sort of gas, forming on every body, except on those that were positively electrified, a material deposit which would explain the phenomena of induced radioactivity and the identity of the induction on various solid substances, whatever their nature.

This material deposit in turn would be capable of dividing into smaller particles which would penetrate the glass, giving the deviable and nondeviable rays observed with induced substances, and because of this molecular subdivision the induced radioactivity would be dissipated, even through an envelope of glass.

One might even invoke the phenomenon of the liberation of ions from a part of the molecules in solution to explain the increase in the power of induction of certain active substances when dissolved.

Nevertheless, one should not compare the emanation which produces the induced radioactivity to an ordinary gas, since according to Curie's experiments the equilibrium established in a closed vessel between the active matter and the induction on the walls is a function of the quantity of active matter and does not show any phenomenon analogous with a maximum vapor tension.

Finally, I shall recall in ending this Note that, following experiments made at the temperature of liquid air, I concluded that the radiation of uranium was not altered at this low temperature.[5]

The small amount of liquid air then available having been exhausted, I could not directly verify the exactness of this conclusion. Thanks to the kindness of our colleague M. d'Arsonval, who has again given me liquid air, I have been able to repair that gap. I have discovered, by electrometric measures like those described in the Note cited above, that at the temperature of liquid air the intensity of that part of the uranium radiation which penetrates a sheet of aluminum 0.1 mm thick remains practically the same as at ordinary temperatures, or at least undergoes a decrease no greater than 0.01 of its value, and that this difference in any case is attributable to experimental errors. The air which condenses around the refrigerated uranium, as indicated, stops the more easily absorbed portion of the radiation.

[Pierre Curie was of a temperament very different from Becquerel's. More abstract and more intellectual, he was ruled by ideas rather than observations. To argue that Becquerel's chemical operations had removed a radioactive substance from the uranium seemed to him excessively speculative, for he saw clearly that the changes involved here would have to be not the molecular rearrangements of ordinary chemistry, but changes in the atoms themselves. Together with Marie Curie he drafted the critical reply given below, reasserting their claim that true radioactivity must be permanent and their conviction that the only fruitful way of investigating radioactivity was to study its energy.

Beginning with the discovery of polonium, Becquerel had presented all of the Curies' papers to the *Académie des Sciences*. This was the last paper for which he performed that service.—A. R.]

---

[5] *Comptes rendus*, Vol. 133, p. 199.

10

P. Curie and Mme. S. Curie

On Radioactive Substances

[Translation of "Sur les corps radio-actifs," *Comptes rendus de l'Académie des Sciences, Paris*, 1902, *134*: 85–87 (13 January).]

In a recent Note, Becquerel has made certain hypotheses on the nature of radioactive phenomena. We shall explain here the ideas which have guided us in our research.

We think there is an advantage in giving a very general form to the hypotheses necessary in any physical research.

Since the beginning of our research, we have taken radioactivity to be an *atomic property* of substances. This assumption is sufficient for creating the method of research on radioactive elements.[6]

Each atom of a radioactive substance functions as a *constant source of energy*. From this hypothesis we can draw greatly varied consequences to be submitted to the control of experience without our having to specify precisely where the radioactive substance obtains that energy.

Experiments over several years show that for uranium, thorium, radium, and probably also for actinium, the radiant activity is rigorously the same every time the radioactive substance is brought back to the same chemical and physical state, and that this activity does not vary with the time.[7]

Certain experiments if badly interpreted might lead to the assumption of a partial destruction of the power of radium. When a radium-bearing salt is dissolved and then restored to the dry state, a considerable lowering of its radiant activity is noted, but little by little the activity resumes its original value at the end of a longer or shorter period, according to the conditions of the experiment (twenty days, for example).

Also, when a radium-bearing salt is held for a long time at red heat and then brought back to room temperature, one notes that the radiant activity is less than before heating, but little by little the salt spontaneously recovers its original activity (in ten days, for example).

---

[6] Mme. Curie, *Revue générale des Sciences*, January 30, 1899.

[7] Polonium by contrast is an exception. Its activity decreases slowly with time. This substance is a species of active bismuth; it has not yet been proved that it contains a new element. Polonium differs from several points of view from the other radioactive substances: it does not give rays deviable by a magnetic field and it does not excite induced radioactivity.

In the two cases, the temporary lowering of the radiation bears principally on the penetrating rays.

A salt of radium which has been made red hot loses to a large extent the property of producing induced radioactivity, but to restore this property it is necessary only to pass it through the dissolved state.

A great number of studies still have to be made on this subject. We have no notion of the magnitude of the energy brought into play in the phenomena of radioactivity, we know neither by what laws it is dissipated nor whether it varies with the physical and chemical state of the radiating bodies.

If we seek to fix the origin of the energy of radioactivity, we may make various assumptions, which group around two quite general hypotheses: (1) each radioactive atom possesses in the form of potential energy the energy it releases; (2) the radioactive atom is a mechanism which at each instant draws in from outside itself the energy it releases.

According to the first hypothesis, the potential energy of radioactive substances should at length exhaust itself, although the experience of several years has shown us no variation up to the present. If, indeed, one grants with Crookes and J. J. Thomson that radiation of the cathode type is material, one may conceive that radioactive atoms are in the process of transformation. Experiments made so far to verify this have given negative results. After four months no variation can be observed in the weights of radium-bearing substances nor any variation in the state of the spectrum.

The theories advanced by Perrin and Becquerel are likewise theories of atomic transformation.[8] Perrin likens each atom to a planetary system from which certain negatively charged particles could escape. Becquerel explains induced radioactivity by a progressive and complete dismemberment of the atoms.

The hypotheses of the second group mentioned above are those according to which radioactive substances are transformers of energy.

This energy might be borrowed, in violation of Carnot's principle, from the heat of the surrounding medium, which would undergo cooling. It might again be borrowed from unknown sources, for example from radiations unknown to us. It is indeed probable that we know little about the medium that surrounds us, since our knowledge is limited to phenomena which can affect our senses, directly or indirectly.

In studying unknown phenomena we can make quite general hypotheses and advance step by step in concordance with experience.

---

[8] J. Perrin, *Revue scientifique*, February, 1901. H. Becquerel, *Comptes rendus*, December 9, 1901.

PIERRE CURIE (1859-1906)

MARIE CURIE (MME. S. CURIE) (1867-1934)

This sure, methodical progress is necessarily slow. In contrast, we can make bold hypotheses in which the mechanism of phenomena is specified. This procedure has the advantage of suggesting certain experiments and above all of facilitating the thought process, making it less abstract by the use of an image. On the other hand, we cannot hope to imagine a priori a complex theory which agrees with experience. Precise hypotheses almost certainly contain a portion of error along with a portion of truth. This latter portion, if it exists, alone becomes a part of some more general proposition to which it will be necessary to return some day.

[At McGill before Christmas 1901, Soddy had been troubled by the impurity of the thorium nitrate, which gave a white precipitate with sodium phosphate. Crookes in his paper on uranium X had mentioned an exceptionally pure thorium nitrate from Germany, and Rutherford had written him early in December to ask how it might be obtained. The same season had also brought Crookes a letter from Becquerel about his uranium preparations and the recovery of their radioactivity. In neighborly style, as he forwarded Rutherford's order to Berlin, Crookes had passed Becquerel's news along to Montreal.[9]

When Rutherford and Soddy returned to their laboratories in the first days of 1902, they found everything waiting: the German nitrate, Crookes's letter, and Becquerel's paper [No. 9 in this volume] fresh from the press. All they had to do was set to work.

They had just convinced themselves that the release of emanations was a thoroughly complicated phenomenon which depended on all sorts of special circumstances. Their new experiments then would be done with the ionizing rays, and, since they would involve the growth and decay of radioactivity, they would be patterned on those Rutherford had carried out two years before.

On that pattern, there was only one interpretation of their results. Thorium X was being produced from thorium at a steady rate, and once produced it began to lose its radioactivity by an exponential law of decay. That being established, it was necessary to suppose that the thorium X came into being by a transmutation of the thorium. When they saw that, Rutherford and Soddy had only to convince the world that it was true, handicapped as they were by operating from the wrong side of the Atlantic Ocean and against the firmly expressed opinion of the Curies.

The result was the following paper—thorough in its experimental work, thorough in facing up to the peculiarities of the situation, assured in tone, and constructed with enormous care. When, in April, it was finished after a bare four months of work, and sent off to London for publication,

---

[9] A. S. Eve, *Rutherford* (New York: Macmillan, 1939), p. 79.

Rutherford wrote again to Crookes, asking his help in case its radical doctrines should cause any delay.[10]—A. R.]

11

E. Rutherford and Frederick Soddy

The Radioactivity of Thorium Compounds
II. The Cause and Nature of Radioactivity

[From *Journal of the Chemical Society, Transactions*, 1902, *81*: 837–860. This is the second paper of a series. The first appears as Paper 8 in this volume.—A. R.]

At the close of the first paper on this subject (this vol., p. 87), it was shown that a constituent responsible for part of the radioactivity of thorium could be separated from its compounds by chemical means. Two methods were given. In one, a thorium solution was precipitated by ammonia, and the thorium hydroxide precipitate showed only about one-third of the normal activity, whilst the filtrate, on evaporation and removal of the ammonium salts by ignition, left a very active residue—in some cases more than a thousand times as active as an equal weight of thoria. In the other method, thorium oxide was washed repeatedly with large quantities of water. The washings, on evaporation, deposited very active residues, whilst the radioactivity of the thoria was appreciably diminished by the process.

In both these methods, the active residues are extremely small, and the view was put forward that even the most active specimens consisted largely of accidental impurities, ThX, the active constituent of thorium, being only present in minute amount. By the kindness of Dr. Knöfler, of Berlin, who in the friendliest manner placed at our disposal a large specimen of his purest thorium nitrate, we were at once able to confirm this opinion. This specimen, which had been purified by many processes, did not contain any of the impurity precipitable by sodium phosphate after the removal of the thorium with ammonia, which was present in the commercial nitrate previously used. The radioactivity and emanating power of Dr. Knöfler's specimen were, however, at least as great as any other in our possession,

---

[10] N. Feather, *Lord Rutherford* (London and Glasgow: Blackie, 1940), p. 88.

and the residues obtained from the filtrate after precipitating with ammonia were no less active.

I. *Scope of the Present Paper*

In the present communication, the results of a further detailed investigation of the radioactivity and emanating power of thorium compounds are given, and these have led to a theoretical interpretation of the processes involved which give rise to the phenomenon of natural radioactivity.

The Influence of Time on the Activity of Thorium and ThX.   The preparations employed in our previous experiments were allowed to stand over during the Christmas vacation.   On examining them about three weeks later it was found that the thorium hydroxide, which originally possessed only about 36 per cent. of its normal activity, had almost completely recovered the usual value.   The active residues, on the other hand, prepared by both methods had almost completely lost their original activity.   The chemical separation effected was thus not permanent in character.   At this time, M. Becquerel's paper (*Compt. rend.*, 1901, *133*, 977) came to hand, in which he shows that the same phenomena of recovery and decay are presented by uranium after it has been partially separated from its active constituent by chemical treatment.

A long series of observations was at once started to determine:

1. The rate of recovery of the activity of thorium rendered less active by removal of ThX,
2. The rate of decay of the activity of the separated ThX,

in order to see how the two processes were connected.   The results led to the view that may at once be stated.   The radioactivity of thorium at any time is the resultant of two opposing processes:

1. The production of fresh radioactive material at a constant rate by the thorium compound.
2. The decay of the radiating power of the active material with time.

The normal or constant radioactivity possessed by thorium is an equilibrium value, where the rate of increase of radioactivity due to the production of fresh active material is balanced by the rate of decay of radioactivity of that already formed.   It is the purpose of the present paper to substantiate and develop this hypothesis.

II. *The Rates of Recovery and Decay of Thorium Radioactivity*

A quantity of the pure thorium nitrate was separated from ThX in the manner described by several precipitations with ammonia.

The radioactivity of the hydroxide so obtained was tested at regular intervals to determine the rate of recovery of its activity. For this purpose, the original specimen of 0.5 gram was left undisturbed throughout the whole series of measurements on the plate over which it had been sifted, and was compared always with 0.5 gram of ordinary de-emanated thorium hydroxide spread similarly on a second plate and also left undisturbed. The emanation from the hydroxide was prevented from interfering with the results by a special arrangement for drawing a current of air over it during the measurements.

The rate of increase of emanating power of the same preparation was determined at the same time (see section VII). The methods and apparatus employed have been described in the previous paper.

The active filtrate from the preparation was concentrated and made up to 100 c.c. in volume. One-fourth was evaporated to dryness, the ammonium nitrate expelled by ignition in a platinum dish, and the radioactivity of the residue tested at the same intervals as the hydroxide to determine the rate of decay of its activity. The comparison in this case was made with a standard sample of uranium oxide kept undisturbed on a metal plate, which repeated work has shown to be a perfectly constant source of radiation. The remainder of the filtrate was used for other experiments (sections V and VII).

The following table gives an example of one of a numerous series of observations made with different preparations at different times. The maximum value attained by the hydroxide and the original value of the ThX are taken as 100:

Time in days	Activity of hydroxide	Activity of ThX
0	44	100
1	37	117
2	48	100
3	54	88
4	62	72
5	68	—
6	71	53
8	78	—
9	—	29.5
10	83	25.2
13	—	15.2
15	—	11.1
17	96.5	—
21	99	—
28	100	—

Fig. 1 (below) shows the curves obtained by plotting the radio-activities as ordinates, and the time in days as abscissæ. Curve II illustrates the rate of recovery of the activity of thorium, curve I the rate of decay of activity of ThX. It will be seen that neither of the curves is regular for the first two days. The activity of the hydroxide

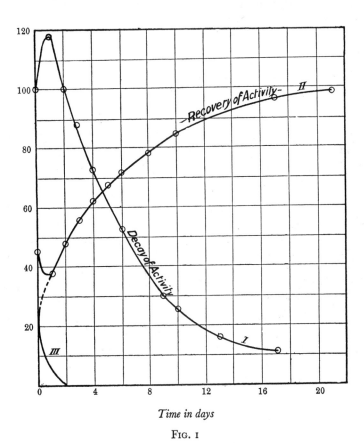

Time in days

FIG. 1

at first actually diminished, and had about the same value after two days as when first prepared. The activity of the ThX, on the other hand, at first increases, and does not begin to fall below its original value until after the lapse of two days (compare section VIII). These results cannot be ascribed to errors of measurement, for they have been regularly observed whenever similar preparations have been tested. The activity of the residue obtained from thorium oxide by the second method of washing decayed very similarly to that of ThX, as shown by the above curve.

If for present purposes the initial periods of the curve are disregarded and the latter portions only considered, it will be seen at once that the time taken for the hydroxide to recover one-half of its lost activity is about equal to the time taken by the ThX to lose half its activity, namely, in each case about 4 days, and speaking generally the percentage proportion of the lost activity regained by the hydroxide over any given interval is approximately equal to the percentage proportion of the activity lost by the ThX during the same interval. If the recovery curve is produced backwards in the normal

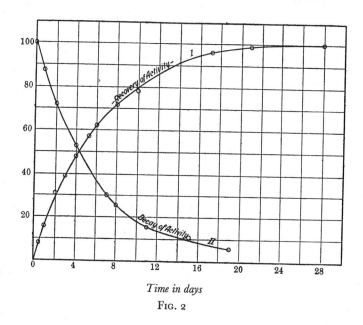

Time in days

Fig. 2

direction to cut the vertical axis it will be seen to do so at a minimum of about 25 per cent., and the above result holds even more accurately if the recovery is assumed to start from this constant minimum, as indeed it has been shown to do under suitable conditions (fig. 4, p. 141). This is brought out by figure 2, which represents the recovery curve in which the percentage amounts of activity recovered, reckoned from this 25 per cent. minimum, are plotted as ordinates. In the same figure, the decay curve after the second day is shown on the same scale.

The activity of ThX decreases very approximately in a geometrical progression with the time, that is, if I_0 represent the initial activity, and I_t the activity after time t

$$\frac{I_t}{I_0} = e^{-\lambda t} \qquad . \quad . \quad . \quad . \quad . \quad . \quad (1)$$

where λ is a constant and e the base of natural logarithms.

The experimental curve obtained with the hydroxide for the rate of rise of its activity from a minimum to a maximum value will therefore be approximately expressed by the equation

$$\frac{I_t}{I_0} = 1 - e^{-\lambda t} \qquad . \quad . \quad . \quad . \quad . \quad (2)$$

where I_0 represents the amount of activity recovered when the maximum is reached, and I_t the activity recovered after time t, λ being the *same constant as before*.

Now this last equation has been theoretically developed (Rutherford, *Phil. Mag.*, 1900, [v], *49*, 10, 181) to express the rise of activity to a constant maximum of a system consisting of radiating particles in which

(i) The rate of supply of fresh radiating particles is constant,
(ii) The activity of each particle dies down geometrically with the time according to equation (1).

It therefore follows that if the initial irregularities of the curves are disregarded and the residual activity of thorium is assumed to possess a *constant* value, the experimental curve obtained for the recovery of activity will be explained if two processes are supposed to be taking place:

1. That the active constituent ThX is being produced at a constant rate.
2. That the activity of the ThX decays geometrically with time.

Without at first going into the difficult questions connected with the initial irregularities and the residual activity, the main result that follows from the curves given can be put to experimental test very simply. The primary conception is that the major part of the radioactivity of thorium is not due to the thorium at all, but to the presence of a non-thorium substance in minute amount which is being continuously produced.

III. *Chemical Properties of* ThX

The fact that thorium, on precipitation from its solutions by ammonia, leaves the major part of its activity in the filtrate does not

of itself prove that a material *constituent* responsible for this activity
has been chemically separated.   It is possible that the matter constituting the non-thorium part of the solution is rendered temporarily
radioactive by its association with thorium, and this property is
retained through the processes of precipitation, evaporation, and
ignition, and manifests itself finally in the residue remaining.

This view, however, can be shown to be quite untenable, for
according to it any precipitate capable of removing thorium completely from its solution should yield active residues similar to those
obtained from ammonia.   Quite the reverse, however, holds.

When thorium nitrate is precipitated by sodium or ammonium
carbonate, the residue from the filtrate, after evaporation and ignition, is free from activity, and the thorium carbonate obtained
possesses the normal value for its activity.

The same holds true when oxalic acid is used as the precipitant.
This reagent, even in strongly acid solution, precipitates almost all
the thorium.   When the filtrate is rendered alkaline by ammonia,
filtered, evaporated, and ignited, the residue obtained is inactive.

In the case where sodium phosphate is used as the precipitant in
ordinary acid solution, the part that comes down is more or less free
from ThX.   On making the solution alkaline with ammonia, the
remainder of the thorium is precipitated as phosphate and carries
with it the whole of the active constituent, so that the residue from the
filtrate is again inactive.

In fact, ammonia is the only reagent of those tried capable of
separating ThX from thorium.

The result obtained by Sir William Crookes with uranium, which
we have confirmed by the electrical method, may here be mentioned.
UrX is completely precipitated by ammonia together with the
uranium, and the residue obtained by the evaporation of the filtrate
is quite inactive.

There can thus be no question that both ThX and UrX are
distinct types of matter with definite chemical properties.   Any
hypothesis that attempts to account for the recovery of activity of
thorium and uranium with time must of necessity start from this
primary conception.

IV. *The Continuous Production of* ThX

If the recovery of the activity of thorium with time is due to the
production of ThX, it should be possible to obtain experimental
evidence of the process.   The first point to be ascertained is how far
the removal of ThX by the method given reduces the total radioactivity of thorium.   A preliminary trial showed that precipitation

in hot dilute solutions by dilute ammonia is the most favourable condition for the separation. Five grams of thorium nitrate, as obtained from the maker, were precipitated by ammonia, the precipitate being redissolved in nitric acid, and reprecipitated under the same conditions successively *without lapse of time*. The removal of ThX was followed by a measurement of the activity of the residues obtained from the successive filtrates. The activity of the ThX from the first filtrate was equivalent to that of 4.23 grams of thoria, from the second to 0.33 gram, and from the third to 0.07 gram. It will be seen that by two precipitations the whole of the ThX is removed. The radioactivity of the separated hydroxide was 48 per cent. of that of the standard de-emanated sample of thoria.

Rate of Production of ThX. A quantity of thorium nitrate solution which had been freed from ThX about a month before was again subjected to the same process. The activity of the residue from the filtrate, in an experiment in which 10 grams of this nitrate had been employed, was equivalent to that of 8.3 grams of thorium oxide. This experiment was performed on the same day as the one recorded above, in which 5 grams of the new sample of nitrate had been employed, and it will be seen that there is no difference in the activity of the filtrates in the two cases. In one month, the activity of the ThX in a thorium compound again reaches its maximum value.

If a period of 24 hours is allowed to elapse between the successive precipitations, the activity of the ThX formed during that time corresponds to about one-sixth of the maximum activity of the total thorium employed. In three hours, the activity of the amount produced is about one-thirtieth. The rate of production of ThX worked out from these figures well agrees with the form of the curve obtained for the recovery of activity of thorium if the latter is taken to express the continuous production of ThX at a constant rate and diminution of the activity of the product in geometrical progression with the time.

By using the Dolezalek electrometer, on which the radioactivity of 1 mg. of thoria produces a measurable effect, the course of production of ThX can be followed after extremely short intervals. Working with 10 grams of thorium nitrate, the amount produced in the minimum time taken to carry out the successive precipitations is as much as can be conveniently measured. If any interval is allowed to elapse, the effect is beyond the range of the instrument, unless the sensitiveness is reduced to a fraction of its ordinary value by the introduction of capacities into the system. Capacities of 0.01 and 0.02 microfarad, which reduce the sensitiveness to less than one-hundredth and one two-hundredth of the normal, were frequently employed in dealing with these active residues. For ordinary work with 0.25 to 0.5 gram of thorium compound, 0.001 microfarad was necessary. Most of the measurements in the course of the present paper were made with this instrument, and a range from that represented by 1 milligram of thoria to any desired maximum could readily be obtained. Of course, the greatest care is necessary in working with so sensitive an instrument to prevent electrostatic disturbances of every kind.

The process of the production of ThX is continuous, and no alteration was observed in the amount produced in a given time after repeated separations. In an experiment carried out for another purpose (section VIII), after twenty-three successive precipitations extending over 9 days, the amount formed during the last interval was, so far as could be judged, no less than that produced at the beginning of the process.

The phenomenon of radioactivity, by the aid of the electrometer as its measuring instrument, thus enables us to detect and measure changes occurring in matter after a few minutes' interval which have never yet been detected by the balance or suspected to take place.

V. *Influence of Conditions on the Changes occurring in Thorium*

It has been shown that in thorium compounds the decay of radioactivity with time is balanced by a continuous production of fresh active material. The change which produces this material must be chemical in nature, for the products of the action are different in chemical properties from the thorium from which they are produced. The first step in the study of the nature of this change is to examine the effect of conditions upon its rate of production.

Effect of Conditions on the Rate of Decay. Since the activity of the products affords the means of measuring the amount of change, the influence of conditions on the rate of decay must first be found. It was observed that, like all other types of temporary radioactivity, the rate of decay is not altered by any known agency. It is not affected by ignition or chemical treatment, and the material responsible for it can be dissolved in acids and reobtained by the evaporation of the solution without affecting the activity. The following experiment shows that the activity decays at the same rate in solutions as in the solid state. The remainder of the solution that had been used to determine the decay curve of ThX (Fig. 1) was allowed to stand, and at the end of 12 days a second fourth part was evaporated to dryness and ignited, and its activity compared with that of the first, which had been left since evaporation in its original platinum dish. The activities of the two specimens so compared with each other were the same, showing that, in spite of the very different conditions, the two fractions had decayed at equal rates.   After 19 days, a third fourth part was evaporated, and the activity, now very small, was indistinguishable from that of the fraction first evaporated.   Resolution of the residue after the activity had decayed does not regenerate it. The activity of ThX thus decays at a rate independent of the chemical and physical condition of the molecule.

The rate of recovery of activity under different conditions in thorium compounds therefore affords a direct measure of the rate of production of ThX under these conditions.   The following experiments were performed.

One part of thorium hydroxide, newly separated from ThX, was sealed up in a vacuum obtained by a good Töpler pump, and the other part exposed to air.   On comparing the samples 12 days later, no difference could be detected between them either in their radioactivity or emanating power.

In the next experiment, a quantity of hydroxide freed from ThX was divided into two equal parts; one was exposed for 20 hours to the heat of a Bunsen burner in a platinum crucible and then compared with the other.   No difference in the activities was observed.   In a second experiment, one-half was ignited for 20 minutes over the blowpipe and then compared with the other with the same result.   The difference of temperature and the conversion of thorium hydroxide into oxide thus exercised no influence on the activity.

Some experiments that were designed to test in as drastic a manner as possible the effect of the chemical condition of the molecule on the rate of production of ThX brought to light small differences, but these are almost certainly to be accounted for in another way.   It will be shown later (section VIII) that about 21 per cent. of the normal radioactivity of thorium oxide under ordinary conditions consists of a secondary activity excited on the mass of the material. This portion is, of course, a variable, and since it is divided among the total amount of matter present, the conditions of aggregation, &c., will affect the value of this part.   This effect of excited radioactivity in thorium makes a certain answer to the question difficult, and on this account the conclusion that the rate of production of ThX is independent of the molecular conditions is not final.   The following experiment, however, makes it extremely probable that this is the case.

A quantity of thorium nitrate, as obtained from the maker, was converted into oxide in a platinum crucible by treatment with sulphuric acid and ignition to a white heat.   The de-emanated oxide so obtained was spread on a plate, and any change in radioactivity with time, which under these circumstances could certainly be detected, was looked for during the week following the preparation. None whatever was observed, whereas if the rate of production of

ThX in thorium nitrate is different from that in the oxide, the equilibrium point, at which the decay and increase of activity balance each other, will be altered in consequence of the treatment. There should have therefore occurred a logarithmic rise or fall from the old to the new value. As, however, the radioactivity remained constant, it appears very probable that the changes involved are independent of the molecular condition. It will be seen that the assumption is here made that the proportion of excited radioactivity in the two compounds is the same, and for this reason compounds were chosen which possess but low emanating power (compare section VII, last paragraph).

Uranium is a far simpler example of a radioactive element than thorium, as the phenomena of excited radioactivity and emanating power are here absent. The separation of UrX and the recovery of the activity of the uranium with time appear, however, analogous to these processes in thorium, and the rates of recovery and decay of activity in uranium are at present under investigation. It is proposed to test the influence of conditions on the rate of change more thoroughly in the case of uranium, as here secondary changes do not interfere.

VI. *The Cause and Nature of Radioactivity*

The foregoing conclusions enable a generalisation to be made in the subject of radioactivity. Energy considerations require that the intensity of radiation from any source should die down with time unless there is a constant supply of energy to replace that dissipated. This has been found to hold true in the case of all known types of radioactivity with the exception of the "naturally" radioactive elements, to take the best established cases, thorium, uranium, and radium. In their first paper on the present subject, the authors showed that the radioactivity of the emanation produced by thorium compounds decayed geometrically with the time under all conditions, and was not affected by the most drastic chemical and physical treatment. The same has been shown by one of us (Rutherford, *Phil. Mag.*, 1900, [v], *49*, 161) to hold for the excited radioactivity produced by the thorium emanation. This decays at the same rate whether on the wire on which it is originally deposited, or in solution of hydrochloric or nitric acid. The excited radioactivity produced by the radium emanation appears analogous. All these examples satisfy energy considerations. In the case of the three naturally occurring radioactive elements, however, it is obvious that there must be a continuous replacement of the dissipated energy, and no satisfactory explanation has yet been put forward to account for this.

The nature of the process becomes clear in the light of the foregoing results. The material constituent responsible for the radioactivity, when it is separated from the thorium which produces it, behaves in the same way as the other typically radioactive substances cited. Its activity decays geometrically with the time, and the rate of decay is independent of the molecular conditions. The normal radioactivity is, however, maintained at a constant value by a chemical change which produces fresh radioactive material at a rate also independent of the conditions. The energy required to maintain the radiations will be accounted for if we suppose that the energy of the system after the change has occurred is less than it was before.

The work of Crookes and of Becquerel on the separation of UrX and the recovery of the activity of the uranium with time makes it appear extremely probable that the same explanation holds true for this element. The work of M. and Mme. Curie, the discoverers of radium, goes to show that this substance easily suffers a temporary decrease of its activity by chemical treatment, the normal value being regained after the lapse of time, and this can be well interpreted on the new view. All known types of radioactivity can thus be brought into the same category.

VII. *The Place of Emanating Power in the Radioactivity of Thorium*

Turning from radioactive solids to gases which manifest this property, many of the very puzzling results obtained in the investigation of the radioactive emanation produced by thorium compounds can now also be simply explained. This section is devoted to the purpose and to further work which has been carried out in order to determine more exactly the place of emanating power in the radioactivity of thorium.

It was shown that the solutions from which thorium hydroxide had been precipitated by ammonia possessed about as much emanating power as the solutions from which they were prepared, whilst the precipitated hydroxide in all cases but one was more or less completely de-emanated, but spontaneously regained its normal value with lapse of time. In one solitary instance that could not be repeated (this vol., p. 110) the hydroxide had an abnormally *high* emanating power, decaying to nearly normal value in 14 days; this can now be explained. The thorium was first partly precipitated as thorium carbonate by means of sodium carbonate, and nitric acid added to redissolve a part. Under these circumstances, all the ThX remained in solution, and on adding ammonia the thorium only should be precipitated, which, as always occurred when the experiment was repeated, ought to be more or less free from emanating power. But if, as apparently happened in this case, care was not taken to boil off all the carbon dioxide produced before adding ammonia, the latter would re-form a carbonate which completely precipitated both ThX and thorium. Hence the small hydroxide fraction contained all the ThX originally present, and possessed a high emanating power decaying to normal value with time. The fact that the carbonate fraction in this same experiment behaved abnormally and did *not* recover its emanating power is more difficult to explain and the point will be reverted to later.

In further explanation of the results then obtained it is only necessary to point out that since emanating power and not radio-activity was the first object of the investigation, any measurements of the latter, especially in the earlier part of the paper, were, as a rule, performed long after the specimens had been prepared, that is, after they had regained their normal values. In some cases, if these measurements had been made immediately after preparation the results would have doubtless been different.

The conclusion was arrived at that emanating power was the manifestation of a dynamical change of the nature of a chemical reaction rather than a function of matter in the static state, even before it was known that the emanating material ThX was being continuously reproduced. The latter discovery, however, enables a fairly complete explanation of the phenomenon to be given.

On resuming the work after the Christmas vacation, it was found on the one hand that some concentrated filtrates possessing high emanating power originally had completely lost it with lapse of time, and on the other, that the emanating power of almost all of the numerous samples of thorium hydroxide and carbonate prepared had regained about the same value, namely, between three and four times that of thorium oxide. The rate of decay of the emanating power of ThX and the recovery of this property by the thorium from which it had been separated were then investigated in parallel with the similar experiments on radioactivity already described. One-fourth of the concentrated filtrate used for the latter purpose was taken, and the decrease of its emanating power with time measured. The increase of emanating power of the thorium hydroxide from which it had been prepared was also measured. The curves (Fig. 3, p. 138) express the results. The decay curve is merely approximate, for it is not easy to determine accurately the emanating power of a liquid without special arrangements to ensure the constancy of the air current and the shaking of the solution. The experiments, although merely approximate, bear out the conclusion that emanating power decays and recovers according to the same law as the radioactivity of ThX, and that it is therefore one of the properties of the latter and not of thorium.   If care be taken to remove the ThX, the thorium almost entirely loses its emanating power.   The small fraction that remains, often only a few per cent. of the maximum, can be accounted for by the reproduction of ThX during the time taken to dry the precipitate.   The decay curve given, so far as it can be relied on, shows that the emanating power of ThX at any instant is proportional to its radioactivity.

It was shown in the first paper that the emanation consisted of a chemically inert gas continuously emitted from thorium compounds. The results therefore find their simplest expression on the view that just as a chemical change is proceeding in thorium whereby a non-thorium material is produced, so the latter undergoes a further transformation, giving rise to a gaseous product which in the radioactive state constitutes the emanation.

It will be seen at once that this secondary change is of a different kind from the primary, for it is affected apparently by the conditions in a very marked manner.   It was shown that moisture, the state of aggregation, and temperature influenced the value of emanating power.   From $-80°$ to a red heat, the latter regularly increases in the ratio of $1:40$ in the case of thorium oxide, whilst the ratio between the values for thorium nitrate in the solid state and in solution is as $1:200$.   The secondary reaction appears therefore at first sight much more nearly allied to ordinary chemical reaction than the primary. It must not be forgotten, however, that the laws controlling the manifestation of the two phenomena, radioactivity and emanating power, are of necessity very different.   In the former, we deal with the intensity of radiations emitted by a solid, in the latter with the rate of escape of a gas into the surrounding air from either a solid or a liquid. Since this gas is detected by its radioactivity, and this decays extremely rapidly with time, a very slight delay in the rate of its escape will enormously affect the experimental value obtained for emanating power.   It is possible that this cause is sufficient to account for the results obtained at different temperatures and with solids and liquids. De-emanation by ignition, on this view, would mean that at a certain temperature the crystalline form of thoria is permanently altered in such a way that the emanation is delayed in its escape.

On the other hand, it is now well established by experiment that sometimes thorium compounds de-emanated chemically by removal of ThX do not recover their normal emanating power with time, but remain constant at a lower value.   The carbonate mentioned in the last paper and already referred to is an example of this, for it possessed hardly any emanating power until it was again dissolved and precipitated.   On one occasion, two samples of hydroxide, prepared from different nitrates, were tested together for rise of emanating power.

That of the one rose normally to its maximum (as in Fig. 3), which was twenty times the minimum. The other started from the same minimum, but rose to a maximum only one-fourth as great. When the experiment was repeated under the same conditions, using the same sample of nitrate, the compound behaved normally. It thus appears that the emanation can be almost entirely prevented from escaping in the radioactive state in some cases, and partially prevented in others where no visible peculiarity of physical condition

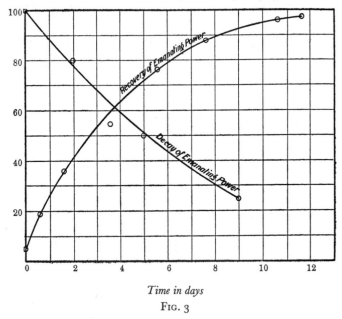

Time in days

FIG. 3

exists and where other preparations similarly prepared behave normally.

The question is further complicated by the property possessed by the emanation of exciting radioactivity on *all* surfaces with which it comes into contact. This process must be going on in the matter of the thorium compound itself, and it will be shown (section VIII) that this effect contributes an important quota to the total radioactivity of the compound. It seemed reasonable to suppose that the effect will be the greater the less the extent to which emanation succeeds in escaping in the radioactive state, and therefore that de-emanated compounds should possess a greater proportion of excited radioactivity than those with high emanating power. This conclusion was tested by converting a specimen of thorium carbonate with an emanating power five times that of ordinary thoria into oxide and de-emanating it by intense ignition. The energy that before escaped in the form of emanation is now, all but a few per cent., prevented from escaping. The radioactivity of the oxides so prepared rose in the first three days to about 30 per cent. of its original amount, and there thus seem to be grounds for the view that the excited radioactivity will contribute a much greater effect in a non-emanating thorium compound than in one having great emanating power. Additional confirmation of this view is to be found in the nature of the radiations emitted by the two classes of compounds (section X).

It will be seen that the phenomenon is too complicated to allow of an answer at the present stage to the question whether the secondary change which produces the emanation is, like the primary, independent of the conditions or not.

VIII. *The Initial Portions of the Curves of Decay and Recovery*

The curves of the recovery and decay of the activities of thorium and ThX with time suggested the explanation that the radioactivity of thorium was being maintained by the production of ThX at a constant rate. Before this can be considered rigidly established, two outstanding points remain to be cleared up. (1) What is the meaning of the early portion of the curves? The recovery curve drops before it rises, and the decay curve rises before it drops. (2) Why does not the removal of ThX render thorium completely inactive? A large proportion of the original radioactivity remains after the removal of ThX.

A study of the curves (Fig. 1) shows that in each case a double action is probably at work. It must be supposed that the normal decay and recovery are taking place, but are being masked by a simultaneous rise and decay from causes unknown. From what is known of the radioactivity of thorium, it was surmised that an action might be taking place similar to that effected by the emanation of exciting radioactivity on surrounding inactive matter. On this view, the residual activity of thorium might consist in whole or part of a secondary or excited radioactivity produced on the whole mass of the thorium compound by its association with the ThX. The drop in the recovery curve on this view would be due to the decay of this excited radioactivity proceeding simultaneously with, and at first reversing the effect of, the regeneration of ThX. The rise of the decay curve would be the increase due to the ThX exciting activity on the matter with which it is associated, the increase from this cause being greater than the decrease due to the decay of the activity of the ThX. It is easy to put this hypothesis to experimental test. If the

ThX is removed from the thorium as soon as it is formed over a sufficient period, the former will be prevented from exciting activity on the latter, and that already excited will decay spontaneously. The experiment was therefore performed.   A quantity of nitrate was precipitated as hydroxide in the usual way to remove ThX, the precipitate redissolved in nitric acid, and again precipitated after a certain interval.   From time to time a portion of the hydroxide was removed and its radioactivity tested.   In this way, the thorium was precipitated in all 23 times in a period of 9 days, and the radioactivity reduced to a constant minimum.   The following table shows the results:

	Activity of hydroxide
After precipitations:	
At three intervals of 24 hours	39 per cent.
At three more intervals each of 24 hours, and	
three more each of 8 hours	22 ,,
At three more each of 8 hours	24 ,,
At six more each of 4 hours	25 ,,

The constant minimum thus attained—about 25 per cent. of the original activity—is thus about 21 per cent. below that obtained by two successive precipitations without an interval, which has been shown to remove all the ThX separable by the process.   The rate of recovery of this hydroxide precipitated 23 times was then measured (Fig. 4).   It will be seen that it is now quite normal and the initial drop characteristic of the ordinary curve is absent.   It is, in fact, almost identical with the ordinary curve (Fig. 1) produced back to cut the vertical axis, and there is thus no doubt that there is a residual activity of thorium unconnected apparently with ThX, and constituting about one-fourth of the whole.

The decay curves of several of the fractions of ThX separated in this experiment after varying intervals of time were taken for the first few days.   All of them showed the initial rise of about 15 per cent. at the end of 18 hours, and then a normal decay to zero.   The position is thus proved that the initial irregularities are caused by the secondary radiation excited by ThX upon the surrounding matter.   By suitably choosing the conditions, the recovery curve can be made to rise normally from a constant minimum, and the decay curve be shown to consist of two curves, the first the rate of production of excited radioactivity, and the second the rate of decay of the activity as a whole.   It is a significant fact that exactly similar curves have already been obtained by one of us (*Phys. Zeit.*, 1902, *3*, 254) for the excited radioactivity produced by the thorium emanation under very similar conditions.   If a negatively charged wire be exposed *for a few minutes only* to the thorium emanation, the excited radioactivity produced at first increases to several times its value for the first few hours after the exciting cause is removed, and then commences to decay, exactly as in the case of ThX.

So far nothing has been stated as to whether the excited radioactivity which contributes about 21 per cent. of the total activity of thorium is the same or different from the known type produced by the

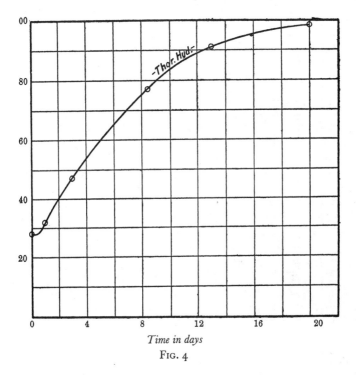

Time in days

Fig. 4

thorium emanation.   All that has been assumed is that it should follow the same general law, that is, the effect should increase with the time of action of the exciting cause, and decrease with time after the cause is removed.   If the rate of increase of the excited activity be worked out from the curves given (Fig. 5) it will be found to agree with that of the ordinary excited activity, that is, it rises to half the value in about 12 hours.   Curve I is the observed decay curve for ThX, curve II is the theoretical curve, assuming that it decreases geometrically with the time and falls to half value in four days. Curve III is obtained by plotting the difference between these two,

and therefore constitutes the curve of excited activity.   Curve IV is
the experimental curve obtained for the rise of the excited radioactivity from the thorium emanation when the exciting cause is
constant.   But the exciting cause (ThX) in the present case is not
constant, but is itself falling to half value in 4 days, and hence the
difference curve, at first almost on the other, drops away from it as
time goes on, and finally decays to zero.   Curve III, Fig. 1, represents
a similar difference curve for *the decay* of excited activity, plotted from
the recovery curve of thorium.   There is thus no reason to doubt that the

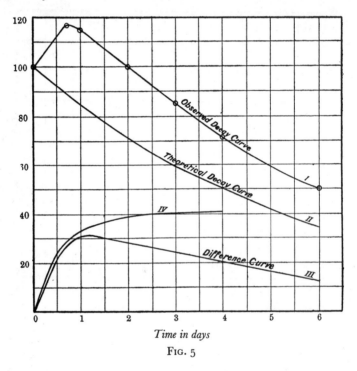

Time in days

Fig. 5

effect is the same as that produced by the thorium emanation, which
is itself a secondary effect of ThX.

IX. *The Non-separable Radioactivity of Thorium*

It has not yet been found possible by any means to free thorium
from its residual activity, and the place of this part in the scheme of
radioactivity of thorium remains to be considered.   Disregarding the
view that it is a separate phenomenon and not connected with the
major part of the activity, two hypotheses can be brought forward

capable of experimental test, and in accordance with the views advanced on the nature of radioactivity, to account for the existence of this part. First, if there was a second type of excited activity produced by ThX, similar to that known, but with a very slow rate of decay, it would account for the existence of the non-separable activity. If this is true, it will not be found possible to free thorium from this activity by chemical means, but the continuous removal of ThX over a very long period would, as in the above case, cause its spontaneous decay.

Secondly, if the change which gives rise to ThX produces a second type of matter at the same time, that is, if it is of the type of a decomposition rather than a depolymerisation, the second type would also in all probability be radioactive, and would cause the residual activity. On this view, the second type of matter should also be amenable to separation by chemical means, although it is certain from the failure of the methods already tried that it resembles thorium much more closely than ThX. But until it is separated from the thorium producing it, its activity will not decay spontaneously. Thus what has already been shown to hold for ThX will be true for the second constituent if methods are found to remove it from the thorium.

It is shown in the following communication by one of us[11] that uranium also possesses a non-separable radioactivity extremely analogous to that possessed by thorium, and whatever view is taken of the one will in all probability hold also for the other. This consideration makes the second hypothesis that the residual activity is caused by a second non-thorium type of matter produced in the original change the more probable of the two.

X. *The Nature of the Radiations from Thorium and* ThX

It has recently been found (Rutherford and Grier, *Phys. Zeit.*, 1902, *3*, 385) that thorium compounds, in addition to a type of easily absorbed Röntgen rays, non-deviable in the magnetic field, emit also rays of a very penetrating character deviable in the magnetic field. The latter are therefore similar to cathode rays, which are known to consist of material particles travelling with a velocity approaching that of light. But thorium, in comparison with uranium and radium, emits a much smaller proportion of deviable radiation.

From the view of radioactivity put forward, it necessarily follows that the total radioactivity of thorium is altered neither in character nor amount by chemical treatment. This conclusion can be tested by comparing the radiations of thorium and ThX with the mixture

---

[11] [F. Soddy, "The Radioactivity of Uranium", *Journal of the Chemical Society*, 1902, *81*: 860–865.—A. R.]

which constitutes the thorium radiation. It must, however, be pointed out that it is difficult to make any absolute measurement of radioactivity on account of the different extents in different cases to which the radiations are absorbed in the material of the substance emitting them. The total radioactivity of the original thorium is derived from a small quantity of the substance in the form of powder, whilst the radiations from ThX are produced by a very thin film of the material on the platinum dish. The radiation from thorium is absorbed to the extent of one-half by aluminium foil 0.0004 cm. thick, and as thorium oxide is far denser than aluminium, it is probable that the radiation in this case is confined to a surface layer only 0.0001 cm. deep. In the ThX, on the other hand, there is probably but little absorbed in the substance itself. The difficulty can be overcome to some extent by taking for the comparison the radioactivity of a thin film of a soluble thorium salt produced by evaporating a solution to dryness over a large metal plate. Compared in this way, the radio-activity of ThX when first separated is almost exactly equal to the activity of the nitrate from which it is produced, whilst the hydroxide retains about two-fifths of this amount. The difference is in the expected direction, for it is certain that more absorption takes place in the nitrate than in the products into which it is separated. The requirements of the hypothesis can thus be said to be satisfied, but the example illustrates the difficulty of making absolute measurements of radioactivity. These throughout have almost completely been avoided. It is possible to trace with great accuracy the *change* of radioactivity of any preparation by leaving it undisturbed on its original plate and comparing it always with the same comparison sample; but to express the radioactivity of one body like ThX in terms of that of another like thoria, except for the purposes of com-parison, is misleading, as the above consideration shows.

Similar difficulties stand in the way of an answer to the second question, whether the nature of the radiations is affected by chemical treatment, for it has been observed experimentally that the penetrat-ing power of these radiations decreases with the thickness of material traversed. The character of the radiations from ThX and thorium have, however, been compared by the method of penetrative power. A large number of comparisons justifies the view that the character of thorium radioactivity is unaltered by chemical treatment and the separation of ThX, although the different types are unequally dis-tributed among the separated products.

The determination of the proportion between the deviable and non-deviable rays affords a new means of approaching the question. The general result is that the radiations from ThX and the excited radiation it produces both comprise deviable and non-deviable radiation.   But in the experiment in which the excited radiation was allowed to decay spontaneously by removing the ThX as formed, the final product, after 23 precipitations, was found to be quite free from deviable radiation.   This, as will be shown in the following paper,[12] is one of the most striking resemblances between the non-separable radioactivities of uranium and thorium.

Finally, it may be mentioned that the proportion of deviable and non-deviable radiation is different for different compounds of thorium.   The nitrate and ignited oxide, compounds which hardly possess any emanating power, have a higher proportion of deviable radiation than compounds with great emanating power.   This is indirect evidence of the correctness of the view already put forward (section VII), that when the emanation is prevented from escaping it augments the proportion of excited radioactivity of the compound.

XI.   *Summary of Results*

The foregoing experimental results may be briefly summarised. The major part of the radioactivity of thorium—ordinarily about 54 per cent.—is due to a non-thorium type of matter, ThX, possessing distinct chemical properties, which is temporarily radioactive, its activity falling to half the value in about four days.   The constant radioactivity of thorium is maintained by the production of this material at a constant rate.   Both the rate of production of the new material and rate of decay of its activity appear to be independent of the physical and chemical condition of the system.   The ThX is undergoing a further change, and one of the products is gaseous and in the radioactive state constitutes the emanation produced by thorium compounds.   The ThX further possesses the property of exciting radioactivity on surrounding inactive matter, and about 21 per cent. of the total activity under ordinary circumstances is derived from this source.   Its rate of decay and other considerations make it probable that it is the same as the excited radioactivity produced by the thorium emanation, which has been shown to be produced by ThX.   There is evidence that if by any means the emanation is prevented from escaping in the radioactive state, the energy of its radiation goes to augment the proportion of excited radioactivity in the compound.

Thorium can be freed by suitable means from both ThX and the excited radioactivity which the latter produces, and then possesses an activity about 25 per cent. of its original value, below which it has not been reduced.   This residual radiation consists entirely of rays

---

[12] [See reference 11.—A. R.]

non-deviable by the magnetic field, whereas the other two components comprise both deviable and non-deviable radiation. Most probably this residual activity is caused by a second non-thorium type of matter produced in the same change as the ThX, and it should therefore prove possible to separate it by chemical methods.

XII. *General Theoretical Considerations*

Turning from the experimental results to their theoretical interpretation, it is necessary first to consider the generally accepted view of the nature of radioactivity. It is well established that this property is the function of the atom and not of the molecule. Uranium and thorium, to take the most definite cases, possess the property in whatever molecular condition they occur, and the former also in the elementary state. So far as the radioactivity of different compounds of different density and states of division can be compared together, the intensity of the radiation appears to depend only on the quantity of active element present. It is not dependent on the source from which the element is derived or the process of purification to which it has been subjected, provided sufficient time is allowed for the equilibrium point to be reached. It is not possible to explain the phenomena by the existence of impurities associated with the radioactive elements, even if any advantage could be derived from the assumption, for these impurities must necessarily be present always to the same extent in different specimens derived from the most widely different sources, and moreover they must persist *in unaltered amount* after the most refined processes of purification. This is contrary to the accepted meaning of the term impurity.

All the most prominent workers in this subject are agreed in considering radioactivity an atomic phenomenon. M. and Mme. Curie, the pioneers in the chemistry of the subject, have stated (*Compt. rend.*, 1902, *134*, 85) that this idea underlies their whole work from the beginning and created their methods of research. M. Becquerel, the original discoverer of the property for uranium, in his announcement of the recovery of the activity of the same element after the active constituent had been removed by chemical treatment, points out the significance of the fact that uranium is giving out cathode rays. These, according to the hypothesis of Sir William Crookes and Professor J. J. Thomson, are *material* particles of mass one-thousandth that of the hydrogen atom.

The present researches had as their starting point the facts that had come to light with regard to the emanation produced by thorium compounds and the property it possesses of exciting radioactivity on surrounding objects. In each case, the radioactivity appeared as the manifestation of *a special kind of matter* in minute amount.   The emanation behaved in all respects like a gas, and the excited radio-activity it produces as an invisible deposit of intensely active material independent of the nature of the substance on which it was deposited, and capable of being removed by rubbing or the action of acids.

The position is thus reached that radioactivity is at once an atomic phenomenon and the accompaniment of a chemical change in which new kinds of matter are produced.   The two considerations force us to the conclusion that radioactivity is a manifestation of subatomic chemical change.

There is not the least evidence for assuming that uranium and thorium are not as homogeneous as any other chemical element, in the ordinary sense of the word, so far as the action of *known* forces is con-cerned.   The idea of the chemical atom in certain cases spontane-ously breaking up with evolution of energy is not of itself contrary to anything that is known of the properties of atoms, for the causes that bring about the disruption are not among those that are yet under our control, whereas the universally accepted idea of the stability of the chemical atom is based solely on the knowledge we possess of the forces at our disposal.

The changes brought to knowledge by radioactivity, although undeniably material and chemical in nature, are of a different order of magnitude from any that have before been dealt with in chemistry. The course of the production of new matter which can be recognised by the electrometer, by means of the property of radioactivity, after the course of a few hours or even minutes, might possibly require geological epochs to attain to quantities recognised by the balance. It is true that the well-defined chemical properties of both ThX and UrX are not in accordance with the view that the actual amounts involved are of this extreme order of minuteness, yet, on the other hand, the existence of radioactive elements at all in the earth's crust is an *a priori* argument against the magnitude of the change being anything but small.

It is a significant fact that the radioactive elements are all at the end of the periodic table.   If we suppose that radium is the missing second higher homologue of barium, then the known examples— uranium, thorium, radium, polonium (bismuth), and lead are the five elements of heaviest atomic weight.   Nothing can yet be stated of the mechanism of the changes involved, but whatever view is ultimately adopted it seems not unreasonable to hope that radio-activity affords the means of obtaining information of processes occurring within the chemical atom.

Macdonald Physics Building,   ⎱ McGill
Macdonald Chemistry and Mining Building,⎰   University.

[As soon as the studies on thorium X were going well, Soddy had started parallel experiments with uranium to see whether it could be brought under the same theory. He had trouble repeating Crookes's work, however, until he discovered that Rutherford's two different radiations from uranium were differently affected by chemical treatment. The alpha rays, of high ionizing power and low penetration, remained with the uranium; only the penetrating but low-ionizing beta rays were carried off with uranium X. This was confirmed by A. G. Grier (a young electrical engineer doing research under Rutherford that winter), who added the information that the last residual radioactivity which no chemical treatment had yet removed from thorium also consisted of alpha rays alone.[13]

All this Rutherford and Soddy knew in April when they finished their paper on the transformation theory, but the full meaning did not sink into their minds until summer was well along. Meanwhile, they had been busy making their work available to physicists.

For Soddy's sake, the two joint papers (Papers 8 and 11 in this volume) had gone to The Chemical Society in London, which was printing them in its *Journal*. Since few physicists would read them there, they were both redrafted for *The Philosophical Magazine*, the leading physical journal in English. As the more important, the new version of the second paper was sent off first;[14] the early material on the emanation was presented in a publication which soon followed. By now their ideas had matured, and at the end of their last-mentioned paper they attached a quite separate section (Section IX, given below as Paper 12), in which their earlier theory was magnificently altered.

The change was seemingly slight. It consisted in postulating that the energy of the rays was released at the instant of transformation instead of streaming away gradually over minutes or hours or days. But the improvement made thereby was enormous, as their tightly packed paragraph shows. What was more, as we can now see, this was a decisive step in the development of atomic conceptions in physical science. In their earlier version, radiation had been a continuous process. The single burst they imagined was now a discrete event, as sharply defined and isolated in time as the transforming atoms themselves were isolated in space.—A. R.]

---

[13] F. Soddy, "The Radioactivity of Uranium," *Journal of the Chemical Society*, 1902, *81*: 860–865.

E. Rutherford and A. G. Grier, "Magnetische Ablenkbarkeit der Strahlen von Radioaktiven Substanzen," *Physikalische Zeitschrift*, 1901–1902, *3*: 385–390 (*Phys. Z.*); "Deviable Rays of Radioactive Substances," *Phil. Mag.* [6], 1902, *4*: 315–330.

[14] E. Rutherford and F. Soddy, "The Cause and Nature of Radioactivity, Part I," *Phil. Mag.* [6], 1902, *4*: 370–396.

12

E. Rutherford and Frederick Soddy

The Cause and Nature of Radioactivity, Part II

Section IX. Further Theoretical Considerations

[From *The London, Edinburgh, and Dublin Philosophical Magazine and Journal of Science* [6], 1902, 4: 584–585.]

Enough has been brought forward to make it clear that in the radioactivity of thorium, and, by analogy, of radium, we are witnessing the effect of a most complex series of changes, each of which is accompanied by the continuous production of a special kind of active matter. The complexity of the phenomenon gives rise to an important question concerning the fundamental relation between the changes which occur and radioactivity. So far it has been assumed, as the simplest explanation, that the radioactivity is *preceded* by chemical change, the products of the latter possessing a certain amount of available energy dissipated in the course of time. A slightly different view is at least open to consideration, and is in some ways preferable. Radioactivity may be an *accompaniment* of the change, the amount of the former at any instant being proportional to the amount of the latter. On this view the non-separable radioactivites of thorium and uranium would be caused by the primary change in which ThX and UrX are produced. The activity of ThX would be caused by the secondary change producing the emanation, the activity of the emanation by a tertiary change in which the matter causing the excited activity is produced, the activity of the latter being derived from still further changes. The law of the decay of the activity with time (equation 1 first part) in all cases but the primary then appears as the expression of the simple law of chemical change, in which one substance only alters at a rate proportional to the amount remaining. In the primary change the amount remaining is infinitely great compared with the amount that alters in short time, and therefore the velocity of reaction is constant. This view certainly affords an explanation of why the emanating power of ThX is proportional to the radioactivity. So long as the latter is considered a consequence of what has occurred there is no reason why this should be so.   But if it is considered the accompaniment of the change in which the emanation is formed the result follows naturally.   Further and more exact determinations of the rate of rise and decay of emanating power are therefore called for.

In the case of uranium the changes so far as they can be followed by the radioactivity appear to be at an end with that which causes the activity of UrX.   It is of interest that this substance gives only cathode-rays, and that it continues to do so for many weeks after its separation from uranium.   This gives rise to the question whether any connexion can be established between the nature of the radiation and the kind of change producing it.

The only consideration which is opposed to this view is the existence of polonium.   The radiations of this body resemble closely the non-separable radioactivity of uranium, both in penetrating power and the absence of deviable rays.   But all attempts (Soddy, *loc. cit.*)[15] have so far failed to separate polonium from uranium, and until this is done its existence does not of itself affect the present question.

It seems as if a more satisfactory explanation of the residual activities common to both uranium and thorium, and of the con-nexion between the emanating power and radioactivity of ThX, is obtained on the modified view.   But further work, both on this latter point and on the nature of polonium, must be awaited before the connexion between radioactivity and chemical change can be considered exactly determined.

Macdonald Physics Building,
Macdonald Chemistry and Mining Building,
McGill University, Montreal.

---

[15] [F. Soddy, "The Radioactivity of Uranium," *Proceedings of the Chemical Society*, 1902, *18*: 121–122. This is the abstract of the paper cited in footnote 13. —A. R.]

V. The Energy of Radioactivity

[Up until this moment the alpha rays had seemed relatively unimportant. Becquerel had shown that beta rays were streams of high-speed electrons,[1] and the alpha rays could plausibly be a secondary radiation they produced. Now that Rutherford and Soddy knew that the primary transformations of uranium and thorium each involved the emission of an alpha ray, and now that they believed that this ray appeared in the very instant of the transformation, the alpha rays became enormously interesting. By mid-November, 1902, Rutherford had shown that they too were streams of particles, enormously larger than the beta-ray electrons, probably as heavy as atoms, and carrying positive rather than negative charges.[2]

Through the winter that followed, Rutherford and Soddy continued to test their ideas. They followed the growth and decay of the radioactivities of uranium and uranium X and found them exactly matched to those of thorium and thorium X, though extending over a longer period of time. That meant that uranium was steadily transforming itself into uranium X. With McGill's new liquid-air machine, they managed to condense the emanations from both radium and thorium and to estimate the temperatures at which they liquefied, thus conferring on those two substances another of the properties of ordinary gases. They found an exponential law of decay for the radioactivity of radium emanation and showed that, like thorium emanation, it had the chemical properties of an inert gas. They settled a plaguing doubt by proving that radium produced its emanation at a steady rate; the variations in "emanating power" which had seemed to set this apart from the other transformations represented therefore only variations in the speed with which the emanation could escape before the next transformation ended its gaseous state.[3]

In the spring of 1903 Soddy obtained a position in Sir William Ramsay's

---

[1] H. Becquerel, "Note sur quelques propriétés du rayonnement de l'uranium et des corps radio-actifs," *C. R. Acad. Sci., Paris*, 1899, *128*: 771–777; "Influence d'un champ magnétique sur le rayonnement des corps radio-actifs," *ibid.*, *129*: 996–1001; "Contribution a l'étude du rayonnement du radium," *ibid.*, 1900, *130*: 206–211; "Sur la dispersion du rayonnement du radium dans un champ magnétique," *ibid.*, 372–376; "Déviation du rayonnement du radium dans un champ électrique," *ibid.*, 809–815.

[2] E. Rutherford, "Die magnetische und elektrische Ablenkung der leicht absorbierbaren Radiumstrahlen," *Phys. Z.*, 1902–1903, *4*: 235–240; "The Magnetic and Electric Deviation of the Easily Absorbed Rays from Radium," *Phil. Mag.* [6], 1903, *5*: 177–187.

[3] E. Rutherford and F. Soddy, "The Radioactivity of Uranium," *Phil. Mag.* [6], 1903, *5*: 441–445; "A Comparative Study of the Radioactivity of Radium and Thorium," *ibid.*, 445–457; "Condensation of the Radioactive Emanations," *ibid.*, 561–576.

laboratory at University College, London. It was an advance he had
earned, and to close their busy partnership, Rutherford and Soddy drew up
a last, joint paper, setting out their theory in detail and summarizing the
evidence they had collected in its support. That paper, which is printed
next, is interesting in part for this summary, in part also for the struggle with
ideas which occupies its middle portion. The short-lived radioactive substances, Rutherford and Soddy thought, cannot quite be elements. They
proposed to call them "metabolons" instead, and they established a firm
distinction between elements with a permanent radioactivity and the metabolons which have only a temporary existence in each particular atomic
form. Yet by the end of the paper, radium, which they introduced as "one
of the best defined and most characteristic of the chemical elements," has
become by implication a metabolon with a life of only a few thousand years.
More interesting still is the closing section in which Rutherford and Soddy
turned to arithmetic and reached quite amazing conclusions about the
internal energy of atoms by simple calculations with very imperfectly known
numbers.—A. R.]

13

E. Rutherford and Frederick Soddy

Radioactive Change

[From *The London, Edinburgh, and Dublin Philosophical Magazine and
Journal of Science* [6], 1903, *5*: 576–591.]

§ 1. *The Products of Radioactive Change and their Specific Material Nature*

In previous papers it has been shown that the radioactivity of the
elements radium, thorium and uranium is maintained by the continuous production of new kinds of matter which possess temporary
activity. In some cases the new product exhibits well-defined
chemical differences from the element producing it, and can be
separated by chemical processes. Examples of this are to be found
in the removal of thorium X from thorium and uranium X from
uranium. In other cases the new products are gaseous in character,
and so separate themselves by the mere process of diffusion, giving
rise to the radioactive emanations which are produced by compounds
of thorium and radium. These emanations can be condensed by
cold and again volatilized; although they do not appear to possess
positive chemical affinities, they are frequently occluded by the substances producing them when in the solid state, and are liberated by

solution; they diffuse rapidly into the atmosphere and through porous partitions, and in general exhibit the behaviour of inert gases of fairly high molecular weight. In other cases again the new matter is itself non-volatile, but is produced by the further change of the gaseous emanation; so that the latter acts as the intermediary in the process of its separation from the radioactive element. This is the case with the two different kinds of excited activity produced on objects in the neighbourhood of compounds of thorium and radium respectively, which in turn possess well-defined and characteristic material properties. For example, the thorium excited activity is volatilized at a definite high temperature, and redeposited in the neighbourhood, and can be dissolved in some reagents and not in others.

These various new bodies differ from ordinary matter, therefore, only in one point, namely, that their quantity is far below the limit that can be reached by the ordinary methods of chemical and spectroscopic analysis. As an example that this is no argument against their specific material existence, it may be mentioned that the same is true of radium itself as it occurs in nature. No chemical or spectroscopic test is sufficiently delicate to detect radium in pitchblende, and it is not until the quantity present is increased many times by concentration that the characteristic spectrum begins to make its appearance. Mme. Curie and also Giesel have succeeded in obtaining quite considerable quantities of pure radium compounds by working up many tons of pitchblende, and the results go to show that radium is in reality one of the best defined and most characteristic of the chemical elements. So, also, the various new bodies, whose existence has been discovered by the aid of their radioactivity, would no doubt, like radium, be brought within the range of the older methods of investigation if it were possible to increase the quantity of material employed indefinitely.

§ 2. *The Synchronism between the Change and the Radiation*

In the present paper the nature of the changes in which these new bodies are produced remains to be considered. The experimental evidence that has been accumulated is now sufficiently complete to enable a general theory of the nature of the process to be established with a considerable degree of certainty and definiteness. It soon became apparent from this evidence that a much more intimate connexion exists between the radioactivity and the changes that maintain it than is expressed in the idea of the production of active matter. It will be recalled that all cases of radioactive change that have been studied can be resolved into the production by one substance of one other (disregarding for the present the expelled rays). When several changes occur together these are not simultaneous but successive. Thus thorium produces thorium X, the thorium X produces the thorium emanation, and the latter produces the excited activity. Now the radioactivity of each of these substances can be shown to be connected, not with the change in which it was itself produced, but with the change in which it in turn produces the next new type. Thus after thorium X has been separated from the thorium producing it, the radiations of the thorium X are proportional to the amount of emanation that it produces, and both the radioactivity and the emanating power of thorium X decay according to the same law *and at the same rate*. In the next stage the emanation goes on to produce the excited activity. The activity of the emanation falls to half-value in one minute, and the amount of excited activity produced by it on the negative electrode in an electric field falls off in like ratio. These results are fully borne out in the case of radium. The activity of the radium emanation decays to half-value in four days, and so also does its power of producing the excited activity.

Hence it is not possible to regard radioactivity as a *consequence* of changes that have already taken place. The rays emitted must be an *accompaniment* of the change of the radiating system into the one next produced.

Non-separable activity. This point of view at once accounts for the existence of a constant radioactivity, non-separable by chemical processes, in each of the three radio-elements. This non-separable activity consists of the radiations that accompany the primary change of the radio-element itself into the first new product that is produced. Thus in thorium about 25 per cent. of the α radiation accompanies the first change of the thorium into thorium X. In uranium the whole of the α radiation is non-separable and accompanies the change of the uranium into uranium X.

Several important consequences follow from the conclusion that the radiations accompany the change. A body that is radioactive must *ipso facto* be changing, and hence it is not possible that any of the new types of radioactive matter—*e.g.*, uranium X, thorium X, the two emanations, &c.—can be identical with any of the known elements. For they remain in existence only a short time, and the decay of their radioactivity is the expression of their continuously diminishing quantity. On the other hand, since the ultimate products of the changes cannot be radioactive, there must always exist at least one stage in the process beyond the range of the methods of experiment. For this reason the ultimate products that result from the changes remain unknown, the quantities involved being unrecognizable, except by the methods of radioactivity. In the naturally occurring minerals containing the radio-elements these changes must have been proceeding steadily over very long periods, and, unless they succeed in escaping, the ultimate products should have accumulated in sufficient quantity to be detected, and therefore should appear in nature as the invariable companions of the radio-elements. We have already suggested on these and other grounds that possibly helium may be such an ultimate product, although, of course, the suggestion is at present a purely speculative one. But a closer study of the radioactive minerals would in all probability afford further evidence on this important question.

§ 3. *The Material Nature of the Radiations*

The view that the ray or rays from any system are produced at the moment the system changes has received strong confirmation by the discovery of the electric and magnetic deviability of the α ray. The deviation is in the opposite sense to the β or cathode-ray, and the rays thus consist of positively charged bodies projected with great velocity (Rutherford, *Phil. Mag.*, Feb. 1903). The latter was shown to be of the order of 2.5×10^9 cms. per second. The value of e/m, the ratio of the charge of the carrier to its mass, is of the order 6×10^3. Now the value of e/m for the cathode-ray is about 10^7. Assuming that the value of the charge is the same in each case, the apparent mass of the positive projected particle is over 1000 times as great as for the cathode-ray. Now $e/m = 10^4$ for the hydrogen atom in the electrolysis of water. The particle that constitutes the α ray thus behaves as if its mass were of the same order as that of the hydrogen atom. The α rays from all the radio-elements, and from the various radioactive bodies which they produce, possess analogous properties, and differ only to a slight extent in penetrating power. There are thus strong reasons for the belief that the α rays generally are projections and that the mass of the particle is of the same order as that of the hydrogen atom, and very large compared with the mass of the projected particle which constitutes the β or easily deviable ray from the same element.

With regard to the part played in radioactivity by the two types of radiation, there can be no doubt that the α rays are by far the more important. In all cases they represent over 99 per cent. of the energy radiated,[4] and although the β rays on account of their penetrating power and marked photographic action have been more often studied, they are comparatively of much less significance.

---

[4] In the paper in which this is deduced (*Phil. Mag.* Sept. 1902, p. 329) there is an obvious slip of calculation. The number should be 100 instead of 1000.

It has been shown that the non-separable activity of all three radio-elements, the activity of the two emanations, and the first stage of the excited activity of radium, comprise only α rays.   It is not until the processes near completion in so far as their progress can be experimentally traced that the β or cathode-ray makes its appearance.[5]

In light of this evidence there is every reason to suppose, not merely that the expulsion of a charged particle accompanies the change, but that this expulsion actually *is* the change.

§ 4. *The Law of Radioactive Change*

The view that the radiation from an active substance accompanies the change gives a very definite physical meaning to the law of decay of radioactivity.   In all cases where one of the radioactive products has been separated, and its activity examined independently of the active substance which gives rise to it, or which it in turn produces, it has been found that the activity under all conditions investigated falls off in a geometrical progression with the time.   This is expressed by the equation

$$\frac{I_t}{I_0} = \epsilon^{-\lambda t}$$

where I_0 is the initial ionization current due to the radiations, I_t that after the time t, and λ is a constant.   Each ray or projected particle will in general produce a certain definite number of ions in its path, and the ionization current is therefore proportional to the number of such particles projected per second.   Thus

$$\frac{n_t}{n_0} = \epsilon^{-\lambda t},$$

where n_t is the number projected in unit of time for the time t and n_0 the number initially.

If each changing system gives rise to one ray, the number of systems N_t which remain unchanged at the time t is given by

$$N_t = \int_t^\infty n_t . dt = \frac{n_0}{\lambda} \epsilon^{-\lambda t}.$$

---

[5] In addition to the α and β rays the radio-elements also give out a third type of radiation which is extremely penetrating.   Thorium as well as radium (Rutherford, *Phys. Zeit.* 1902) gives out these penetrating rays, and it has since been found that uranium possesses the same property.   These rays have not yet been sufficiently examined to make any discussion possible of the part they play in radioactive processes.

The number N_0 initially present is given by putting $t = 0$.

$$N_0 = \frac{n_0}{\lambda}$$

and

$$\frac{N_t}{N_0} = \epsilon^{-\lambda t}.$$

The same law holds if each changing system produces two or any definite number of rays.

Differentiating

$$\frac{dN}{dt} = -\lambda N_t,$$

or, the rate of change of the system at any time is always proportional to the amount remaining unchanged.

The law of radioactive change may therefore be expressed in the one statement—the proportional amount of radioactive matter that changes in unit time is a constant.   When the total amount does not vary (a condition nearly fulfilled at the equilibrium point where the rate of supply is equal to the rate of change) the proportion of the whole which changes in unit time is represented by the constant λ, which possesses for each type of active matter a fixed and characteristic value. λ may therefore be suitably called the "radioactive constant."   The complexity of the phenomena of radioactivity is due to the existence as a general rule of several different types of matter changing at the same time into one another, each type possessing a different radioactive constant.

§ 5. *The Conservation of Radioactivity*

The law of radioactive change that has been deduced holds for each stage that has been examined, and therefore holds for the phenomenon generally.   The radioactive constant λ has been investigated under very widely varied conditions of temperature, and under the influence of the most powerful chemical and physical agencies, and no alteration of its value has been observed.   The law forms in fact the mathematical expression of a general principle to which we have been led as the result of our investigations as a whole. Radioactivity, according to present knowledge, must be regarded as the result of a process which lies wholly outside the sphere of known controllable forces, and cannot be created, altered, or destroyed. Like gravitation, it is proportional only to the quantity of matter involved, and in this restricted sense it is therefore true to speak of the principle as the conservation of radioactivity.[6] Radioactivity differs of course from gravitation in being a special and not necessarily a universal property of matter, which is possessed by different kinds in widely different degree. In the processes of radioactivity these different kinds change into one another and into inactive matter, producing corresponding changes in the radioactivity. Thus the decay of radioactivity is to be ascribed to the disappearance of the active matter, and the recovery of radioactivity to its production. When the two processes balance—a condition very nearly fulfilled in the case of the radio-elements in a closed space—the activity remains constant. But here the apparent constancy is merely the expression of the slow rate of change of the radio-element itself. Over sufficiently long periods its radioactivity must also decay according to the law of radioactive change, for otherwise it would be necessary to look upon radioactive change as involving the creation of matter. In the universe therefore the total radioactivity must, according to our present knowledge, be growing less and tending to disappear. Hence the energy liberated in radioactive processes does not disobey the law of the conservation of energy.

It is not implied in this view that radioactivity, considered with reference to the quantity of matter involved, is conserved under all conceivable conditions, or that it will not ultimately be found possible to control the processes that give rise to it. The principle enunciated applies of course only to our present state of experimental knowledge, which is satisfactorily interpreted by its aid.

The general evidence on which the principle is based embraces the whole field of radioactivity. The experiments of Becquerel and Curie have shown that the radiations from uranium and radium respectively remain constant over long intervals of time. Mme. Curie put forward the view that radioactivity was a specific property of the element in question, and the successful separation of the element

---

[6] Apart from the considerations that follow, this nomenclature is a convenient expression of the observed facts that the total radioactivity (measured by the radiations peculiar to the radio-elements) is for any given mass of radio-element a constant under all conditions investigated. The radioactive equilibrium may be disturbed and the activity distributed among one or more active products capable of separation from the original element. But the sum total throughout these operations is at all times the same.

For practical purposes the expression "conservation," applied to the radioactivity of the three radio-elements, is justified by the extremely minute proportion that can change in any interval over which it is possible to extend actual observations. But *rigidly* the term "conservation" applies only with reference to the radioactivity of any definite quantity of radioactive matter, whereas in nature this quantity must be changing spontaneously and continually growing less. To avoid possible misunderstanding, therefore, it is necessary to use the expression only in this restricted sense.

radium from pitchblende was a direct result of this method of regarding the property. The possibility of separating from a radio-element an intensely active constituent, although at first sight contradictory, has afforded under closer examination nothing but confirmation of this view. In all cases only a part of the activity is removed, and this part is recovered spontaneously by the radio-element in the course of time. Mme. Curie's original position, that radioactivity is a specific property of the element, must be considered to be beyond question. Even if it should ultimately be found that uranium and thorium are admixtures of these elements with a small *constant* proportion of new radio-elements with correspondingly intense activity, the general method of regarding the subject is quite unaffected.

In the next place, throughout the course of our investigations we have not observed a single instance in which radioactivity has been created in an element not radioactive, or destroyed or altered in one that is, and there is no case at present on record in which such a creation or destruction can be considered as established. It will be shown later that radioactive change can only be of the nature of an atomic disintegration, and hence this result is to be expected, from the universal experience of chemistry in failing to transform the elements. For the same reason it is not to be expected that the rate of radioactive change would be affected by known physical or chemical influences. Lastly, the principle of the conservation of radioactivity is in agreement with the energy relations of radioactive change. These will be considered more fully in § 7, where it is shown that the energy changes involved are of a much higher order of magnitude than is the case in molecular change.

It is necessary to consider briefly some of the apparent exceptions to this principle of the conservation of radioactivity. In the first place it will be recalled that the emanating power of the various compounds of thorium and radium respectively differ widely among themselves, and are greatly influenced by alterations of physical state. It was recently proved (*Phil. Mag.* April 1903, p. 453) that these variations are caused by alterations in the rate at which the emanations escape into the surrounding atmosphere. The emanation is produced at the same rate both in de-emanated and in highly emanating thorium and radium compounds, but is in the former stored up or occluded in the compound. By comparing the amount stored up with the amount produced per second by the same compound dissolved, it was found possible to put the matter to a very sharp experimental test which completely established the law of the conservation of radioactivity in these cases. Another exception is the apparent destruction of the thorium excited activity deposited on a platinum wire by ignition to a white heat. This has recently been examined in this laboratory by Miss Gates, and it was found that the excited activity is not destroyed, but is volatilized at a definite temperature and redeposited in unchanged amount on the neighbouring surfaces.

Radioactive "Induction." Various workers in this subject have explained the results they have obtained on the idea of radioactive "induction" in which a radioactive substance has been attributed the power of inducing activity in bodies mixed with it, or in its neighbourhood, which are not otherwise radioactive. This theory was put forward by Becquerel to explain the fact that certain precipitates (notably barium sulphate) formed in solutions of radioactive salts are themselves radioactive. The explanation has been of great utility in accounting for the numerous examples of the presence of radioactivity in non-active elements, without the necessity of assuming in each case the existence of a new radio-element therein, but our own results do not allow us to accept it.

In the great majority of instances that have been recorded the results seem to be due simply to the *mixture of active matter with the inactive element.* In some cases the effect is due to the presence of a small quantity of the original radio-element, in which case the "induced" activity is permanent. In other cases, one of the disintegration products, like uranium X or thorium X, has been dragged down by the precipitate, producing temporary, or, as it is sometimes termed, "false" activity. In neither case is the original character of the radiation at all affected. It is probable that a re-examination of some of the effects that have been attributed to radioactive induction would lead to new disintegration products of the known radio-elements being recognized.

Other Results. A number of cases remain for consideration, where, by working with very large quantities of material, there have been separated from minerals possible new radio-elements, *i.e.* substances possessing apparently permanent radioactivity with chemical properties different from those of the three known radio-elements. In most of these cases, unfortunately, the real criteria that are of value, viz., the nature of the radiations and the presence or absence of distinctive emanations, have not been investigated. The chemical properties are of less service, for even if a new element were present, it is not at all necessary that it should be in sufficient quantity to be detected by chemical or spectroscopic analysis. Thus the radio-lead described by Hoffmann and Strauss and by Giesel cannot be regarded as a new element until it is shown that it has permanent activity of a distinctive character.

In this connexion the question whether polonium (radiobismuth) is a new element is of great interest. The polonium discovered by Mme. Curie is not a permanent radioactive substance, its activity decaying slowly with the time. On the view put forward in these papers, polonium must be regarded as a disintegration product of one of the radio-elements present in pitchblende. Recently, however, Marckwald (*Ber. der D. Chem. Gesel.* 1902, pp. 2285 & 4239), by the electrolysis of pitchblende solutions, has obtained an intensely radioactive substance very analogous to the polonium of Curie. But he states that the activity of his preparation does not decay with time, and this, if confirmed, is sufficient to warrant the conclusion that he is not dealing with the same substance as Mme. Curie. On the other hand, both preparations give only α rays, and in this they are quite distinct from the other radio-elements. Marckwald has succeeded in separating his substance from bismuth, thus showing it to possess different chemical properties, and in his latest paper states that the bismuth-free product is indistinguishable chemically from tellurium. If the permanence of the radioactivity is established, the existence of a new radio-element must be inferred.

If elements heavier than uranium exist it is probable that they will be radioactive. The extreme delicacy of radioactivity as a means of chemical analysis would enable such elements to be recognized even if present in infinitesimal quantity. It is therefore to be expected that the number of radio-elements will be augmented in the future, and that considerably more than the three at present recognized exist in minute quantity. In the first stage of the search for such elements a purely chemical examination is of little service. The main criteria are the permanence of the radiations, their distinctive character, and the existence or absence of distinctive emanations or other disintegration products.

§ 6. *The Relation of Radioactive Change to Chemical Change*

The law of radioactive change, that the rate of change is proportional to the quantity of changing substance, is also the law of monomolecular chemical reaction. Radioactive change, therefore, must be of such a kind as to involve one system only, for if it were anything of the nature of a combination, where the mutual action of two systems was involved, the rate of change would be dependent on the concentration, and the law would involve a volume-factor. This is not the case. Since radioactivity is a specific property of the element, the changing system must be the chemical atom, and since only one system is involved in the production of a new system and, in addition, heavy charged particles, in radioactive change the chemical atom must suffer disintegration.

The radio-elements possess of all elements the heaviest atomic weight. This is indeed their sole common chemical characteristic. The disintegration of the atom and the expulsion of heavy charged particles of the same order of mass as the hydrogen atom leaves behind a new system lighter than before, and possessing chemical and physical properties quite different from those of the original element. The disintegration process, once started, proceeds from stage to stage with definite measurable velocities in each case. At each stage one or more α "rays" are projected, until the last stages are reached, when the β "ray" or electron is expelled. It seems advisable to possess a special name for these now numerous atom-fragments, or new atoms, which result from the original atom after the ray has been expelled, and which remain in existence only a limited time, continually undergoing further change. Their instability is their chief characteristic. On the one hand, it prevents the quantity accumulating, and in consequence it is hardly likely that they can ever be investigated by the ordinary methods. On the other, the instability and consequent ray-expulsion furnishes the means whereby they can be investigated. We would therefore suggest the term *metabolon* for this purpose. Thus in the following table the metabolons at present known to result from the disintegration of the three radio-elements · have been arranged in order.

Uranium	Thorium	Radium
↓	↓	↓
Uranium X	Thorium X	Radium Emanation
↓	↓	↓
?	Thorium Emanation	Radium-Excited Activity I
	↓	↓
	Thorium-Excited Activity I	ditto II
	↓	↓
	ditto II	ditto III
	↓	↓
	?	?

The three queries represent the three unknown ultimate products. The atoms of the radio-elements themselves form, so to speak, the common ground between metabolons and atoms, possessing the properties of both. Thus, although they are disintegrating, the rate is so slow that sufficient quantity can be accumulated to be investigated chemically. Since the rate of disintegration is probably a million times faster for radium than it is for thorium or uranium, we have an explanation of the excessively minute proportion of radium in the natural minerals. Indeed, every consideration points to the conclusion that the radium atom is also a metabolon in the full sense of having been formed by disintegration of one of the other elements present in the mineral. For example, an estimation of its "life" goes to show that the latter can hardly be more than a few thousand years (see § 7). The point is under experimental investigation by one of us, and a fuller discussion is reserved until later.

There is at present no evidence that a single atom or metabolon ever produces more than one new kind of metabolon at each change, and there are no means at present of finding, for example, either how many metabolons of thorium X, or how many projected particles, or "rays," are produced from each atom of thorium. The simplest plan therefore, since it involves no possibility of serious error if the nature of the convention is understood, is to assume that each atom or metabolon produces one new metabolon or atom and one "ray."

§ 7. *The Energy of Radioactive Change, and the Internal Energy of the Chemical Atom*

The position of the chemical atom as a very definite stage in the complexity of matter, although not the lowest of which it is now possible to obtain experimental knowledge, is brought out most clearly by a comparison of the respective energy relations of radio-active and chemical change. It is possible to calculate the order of the quantity of energy radiated from a given quantity of radio-element during its complete change, by several independent methods, the conclusions of which agree very well among themselves. The most direct way is from the energy of the particle projected, and the total number of atoms. For each atom cannot produce less than one "ray" for each change it undergoes, and we therefore arrive in this manner at a minimum estimate of the total energy radiated. On the other hand, one atom of a radio-element, if completely resolved into projected particles, could not produce more than about 200 such particles at most, assuming that the mass of the products is equal to the mass of the atom. This consideration enables us to set a maximum limit to the estimate. The α rays represent so large a proportion of the total energy of radiation that they alone need be considered.

Let m = mass of the projected particle,
v = the velocity,
e = charge.

Now for the α ray of radium

$$v = 2.5 \, 10^9,$$

$$\frac{e}{m} = 6 \, 10^3.$$

The kinetic energy of each particle

$$\tfrac{1}{2}mv^2 = \frac{1}{2}\frac{m}{e}v^2 e = 5 \, 10^{14}e.$$

J. J. Thomson has shown that

$$e = 6 \, 10^{-10} \text{ E.S. Units} = 2 \, 10^{-20} \text{ Electromagnetic Units.}$$

Therefore the kinetic energy of each projected particle = 10^{-5} erg. Taking 10^{20} as the probable number of atoms in one gram of radium, the total energy of the rays from the latter = 10^{15} ergs = $2.4 \, 10^7$ gram-calories, on the assumption that each atom projects one ray. Five successive stages in the disintegration are known, and each stage corresponds to the projection of at least one ray. It may therefore be stated that the total energy of radiation during the disintegration of one gram of radium cannot be less than 10^8 gram-calories, and may be between 10^9 and 10^{10} gram-calories. The energy radiated does not necessarily involve the whole of the energy of disintegration and may be only a small part of it. 10^8 gram-calories per gram may therefore be safely accepted as the least possible estimate of the energy of radioactive change in radium. The union of hydrogen and oxygen liberates approximately $4 \, 10^3$ gram-calories per gram of water produced, and this reaction sets free more energy for a given weight than any other chemical change known. The energy of radioactive change must therefore be at least twenty-thousand times, and may be a million times, as great as the energy of any molecular change.

The rate at which this store of energy is radiated, and in consequence the life of a radio-element, can now be considered. The order of the total quantity of energy liberated per second in the form of rays from 1 gram of radium may be calculated from the total number of ions produced and the energy required to produce an ion. In the solid salt a great proportion of the radiation is absorbed in the material, but the difficulty may be to a large extent avoided by determining the number of ions produced by the radiation of the emanation, and the proportionate amount of the total radiation of radium due to the emanation. In this case most of the rays are absorbed in producing ions from the air. It was experimentally found that the maximum current due to the emanation from 1 gram of radium, of activity 1000 compared with uranium, in a large cylinder filled with air, was $1.65 \, 10^{-8}$ electromagnetic units. Taking $e = 2 \, 10^{-20}$, the number of ions produced per second = $8.2 \, 10^{11}$. These ions result from the collision of the projected particles with the gas in their path. Townsend (*Phil. Mag.* 1901, vol. i.), from experiments on the production of ions by collision, has found that the minimum energy required to produce an ion is 10^{-11} ergs. Taking the activity of pure radium as a million times that of uranium, the total energy radiated per second by the emanation from 1 gram of pure radium = 8200 ergs. In radium compounds in the solid state, this amount is about .4 of the total energy of radiation, which therefore is about

$$2 \ 10^4 \text{ ergs per second,}$$
$$6.3 \ 10^{11} \text{ ergs per year,}$$
$$15{,}000 \text{ gram-calories per year.}$$

This again is an under-estimate, for only the energy employed in producing ions has been considered, and this may be only a small fraction of the total energy of the rays.

Since the α radiation of all the radio-elements is extremely similar in character, it appears reasonable to assume that the feebler radiations of thorium and uranium are due to these elements disintegrating less rapidly than radium. The energy radiated in these cases is about 10^{-6} that from radium, and is therefore about .015 gram-calorie per year. Dividing this quantity by the total energy of radiation, $2.4 \ 10^7$ gram-calories, we obtain the number $6 \ 10^{-10}$ as a maximum estimate for the proportionate amount of uranium or thorium undergoing change per year. Hence in one gram of these elements less than a milligram would change in a million years. In the case of radium, however, the same amount must be changing per gram *per year*. The "life" of the radium cannot be in consequence more than a few thousand years on this minimum estimate, based on the assumption that each particle produces one ray at each change. If more are produced the life becomes correspondingly longer, but as a maximum the estimate can hardly be increased more than 50 times. So that it appears certain that the radium present in a mineral has not been in existence as long as the mineral itself, but is being continually produced by radioactive change.

Lastly, the number of "rays" produced per second from 1 gram of a radio-element may be estimated. Since the energy of each "ray" $= 10^{-5}$ ergs $= 2.4 \ 10^{-13}$ gram-calories, $6 \ 10^{10}$ rays are projected every year from 1 gram of uranium. This is approximately 2000 per second. The α radiation of 1 milligram of uranium in one second is probably within the range of detection by the electrical method. The methods of experiment are therefore almost equal to the investigation of a single atom disintegrating, whereas not less than 10^4 atoms of uranium could be detected by the balance.

It has been pointed out that these estimates are concerned with the energy of radiation, and not with the total energy of radioactive change. The latter, in turn, can only be a portion of the internal energy of the atom, for the internal energy of the resulting products remains unknown. All these considerations point to the conclusion that the energy latent in the atom must be enormous compared with that rendered free in ordinary chemical change. Now the radio-elements differ in no way from the other elements in their chemical and physical behaviour. On the one hand they resemble chemically their inactive prototypes in the periodic system very closely, and on the other they possess no common chemical characteristic which could be associated with their radioactivity. Hence there is no reason to assume that this enormous store of energy is possessed by the radio-elements alone. It seems probable that atomic energy in general is of a similar, high order of magnitude, although the absence of change prevents its existence being manifested. The existence of this energy accounts for the stability of the chemical elements as well as for the conservation of radioactivity under the influence of the most varied conditions. It must be taken into account in cosmical physics. The maintenance of solar energy, for example, no longer presents any fundamental difficulty if the internal energy of the component elements is considered to be available, *i.e.* if processes of sub-atomic change are going on. It is interesting to note that Sir Norman Lockyer has interpreted the results of his spectroscopic researches on the latter view (Inorganic Evolution, 1900) although he regards the temperature as the cause rather than the effect of the process.

McGill University, Montreal.

[Rutherford and Soddy could hardly have finished the manuscript of this last paper when Pierre Curie published the one which is printed next. In it he details measurements of an easily perceptible amount of heat produced by radium which he made with a young assistant named Albert Laborde. To compare their measurements with Rutherford and Soddy's estimates, one must bear in mind that 100 gram calories each hour become 880,000 gram calories in a year.—A. R.]

14

P. Curie and A. Laborde

On the Heat Spontaneously Released by the Salts of Radium

[Translation of "Sur la chaleur dégagée spontanément par les sels de radium," *Comptes rendus de l'Académie des Sciences, Paris*, 1903, *136*: 673–675 (16 March).]

We have discovered that the salts of radium constantly release heat.

An iron-constantan thermo-electric couple, whose junctions are surrounded, one by radium-bearing barium chloride and the other by pure barium chloride, in fact shows a difference in temperature between the two substances.

We performed the experiment with two identical small bulbs, putting in one 1 g. of radium-bearing barium chloride containing about one-sixth of its weight in radium chloride, and in the other 1 g. of pure barium chloride. The junctions of the thermo-electric couple were placed respectively in the center of each bulb and in the middle of the material which filled them. These bulbs were isolated in the air in the middle of two small, identical vessels, themselves located in a third, which was thermally insulated and in which the temperature was substantially uniform. Variations in the temperature of the surroundings under these conditions would be felt in the same way at both junctions and would not affect the indications of the couple.

We have thus determined a difference in temperature of $1.5°$ between the radium-bearing barium chloride and the pure barium chloride, the radium-bearing salt having the higher temperature. As a control, we repeated the experiment under the same conditions with two bulbs, both of which contained pure barium chloride. The differences in temperature observed then were only of the order of magnitude of a hundredth of a degree.

We have attempted a quantitative evaluation of the heat developed by radium in a given time.

For that purpose, we first compared this heat with that developed by an electric current of known intensity in a wire of known resistance.

A bulb containing the radium was enclosed in a metal block to which it communicated its heat. One of the junctions of the thermo-electric couple was located in a hollow sunk in the block; the other junction was located in a second similar block which did not contain radium. When a steady state was established the block received from the radium, in a given time, as much heat as it lost outside by conduction and radiation. The couple then showed a definite difference in temperature between the two blocks.

Once this experiment had been performed, we substituted for the bulb containing the radium a bulb in which there was a fine, platinum-iridium wire heated by the passage of a current. The intensity of the current was altered until in a steady state the difference in temperature between the two blocks was the same as in the preceding experiment. The heat developed by the radium in the first experiment was then equal to that developed during the same time by the current in the second experiment. This last quantity is easy to calculate.

We again evaluated the heat developed by the radium by making direct measurements in a Bunsen calorimeter.

Before making the experiment we first determined that the level of the mercury in the stem of the calorimeter would remain perfectly fixed. The bulb containing the radium stood during this time in a tube maintained at zero by melting ice. At a given moment the bulb was introduced into the calorimeter and it was found that the mercury moved along the stem with a perfectly uniform velocity (at the rate of 2.5 cm per hour, for example, with the specimen mentioned above). When we withdrew the bulb containing the radium, the mercury stopped at once.

One g. of the radium-bearing barium chloride with which we made most of these experiments developed about 14 small calories per hour, but the composition of this specimen is not exactly known. According to its radiant activity it should contain about one-sixth of its weight as pure radium chloride. We also made a few measurements with a specimen of 0.08 g. of pure radium chloride. The measurements made by the two methods led to results of the same order of magnitude, without their being in exact agreement. We intended in these first investigations only to demonstrate indisputably the existence of a heat development under various conditions, and to give the order of magnitude of the phenomenon.

One g. of radium develops a quantity of heat of the order of 100 small calories per hour.

One gram-atom of radium (225 g.) would develop each hour 22,500 calories, a number comparable to that for the heat developed by the burning in oxygen of a gram-atom of hydrogen.

The continuing development of such a quantity of heat cannot be explained by an ordinary chemical transformation. If we seek the origin of the production of heat in an internal transformation, this transformation must be of a more profound nature and must be due to a modification of the atom of radium itself. Nevertheless, such a transformation, if it exists, proceeds with extreme slowness. Indeed, the properties of radium do not show any considerable variation over several years, and Demarçay has observed no difference in the spectrum of the same sample of radium chloride on making two examinations at an interval of five months. If the preceding hypothesis were accurate, then the energy put into play in the transformation of atoms would be extraordinarily great.

The hypothesis of a continuous modification of the atom is not the only one compatible with the development of heat by radium. This development of heat may still be explained by supposing that the radium makes use of an external energy of unknown nature.

VI. Transmutation Beyond Doubt

[The brief note which is reprinted next appears little more than a nice verification of a prediction by Rutherford and Soddy. Actually the document had an enormous contemporary impact. If what it said was true—and Ramsay's name guaranteed that—i.e. if helium could be obtained from radium, then Rutherford and Soddy's transformation theory would begin to be credible to the scientific world in general.

This was not the crucial experiment, of course; the theory was firmly established without it. The real evidence for the transformation theory lay in the tissue of experiment and argument which Rutherford and Soddy had elaborated during the previous eighteen months. The structure which justified the theory had to be taken as a whole, however, and for those who had not worked through it this new experiment was so direct, so neat and self-contained as to be thoroughly convincing.

Sir William Ramsay (1852–1916), who performed it with Soddy, was Professor of Chemistry at University College, London. He was justly famous for having isolated, identified, and established as elements one complete section of the Periodic Table, the column of the inert gases. He had begun in 1894 on argon as a collaborator with Lord Rayleigh, and by 1900 he had added helium, neon, krypton, and xenon.[1] To this family Rutherford and Soddy assigned the emanations from thorium and radium after a handful of chemical tests, and Ramsay, who had a strong proprietary feeling for any research field he entered, was anxious to make his own investigation of the properties of these Canadian gases.

His chance came in the summer of 1903. Radium had become relatively cheap; Friedrich Giesel, chemist for *Buchler und Compagnie*, a quinine manufacturer in Braunschweig, had developed an effective method of concentrating it, and his firm had now put pure radium bromide on the market.[2] With this German material, with the special knowledge Soddy had brought from Montreal, and with his own experience, Ramsay saw the way clear.

He intended to begin with the spectrum of the emanation. Few of the atoms of emanation which formed within the body of radium bromide crystals were ever able to escape; when these crystals are dissolved in water, a quantity of imprisoned emanation should be released at once. It was necessary, therefore, to build an apparatus in which the emanation could be

---

[1] Sir William Ramsay, *The Gases of the Atmosphere* (4th ed., London: Macmillan, 1915).

[2] F. Giesel, "Über Radiumbromid und sein Flammenspektrum," *Phys. Z.*, 1901–1902, *3*: 578–579.

released, retained, purified, and delivered to an electric discharge tube where its spectrum would be excited.

What upset all these carefully laid plans was the radioactivity of the emanation. As Giesel had already pointed out, the rays from radium carried enough energy to decompose water, so that as his radium bromide crystallized from solution it occluded a fair amount of free hydrogen and oxygen. In Ramsay's apparatus the rays from the emanation attacked the stopcock grease at the joints and flooded everything with carbon dioxide. When liquid air was brought in to freeze the carbon dioxide gas, the emanation condensed too, and nothing was left to form a spectrum but helium.

Yet this was a good ending. Helium formed no compounds. It could be occluded in radium bromide only if it had been formed within the solid structure of the crystals, and the only plausible substance from which it could have been formed was radium itself. Radium was an element, as Marie Curie had proved.[3] Ramsay's own work had established helium. Beyond any doubt, out of one element a totally different one had been produced, and transmutation was a reality.—A. R.]

15

William Ramsay and Frederick Soddy

Gases Occluded by Radium Bromide

[From *Nature*, 1903, *68*: 246.]

RUTHERFORD AND SODDY (*Phil. Mag.*, 1902, p. 582; 1903, p. 453 and 579) pointed out that the almost invariable presence of helium in minerals containing uranium indicated that that gas might be one of the ultimate products of the disintegration of the radio-elements. Rutherford, moreover, determined the mass of the projected particle which constitues the "α-ray" of radium (*Phil. Mag.*, 1903, p. 177) to be approximately twice as great as that of the hydrogen atom, an observation which points in the same direction. These α-particles are readily absorbed by solids, and should accumulate in the solid salts of radium and in the radio-active minerals.

We have been engaged for some months in examining the spectrum of the "radio-active emanation" from radium, and during this work the opportunity presented itself of examining the gases occluded by 20 mgrs. of radium bromide which had been kept for some time in

---

[3] Mme. Curie, "Sur le poids atomique du radium," *C. R. Acad. Sci.*, *Paris*, 1902, *135*: 161–163.

the solid state. These gases, which are continuously generated, have already been partially examined by their discoverer, Giesel, and by Bodländer (*Ber. deutsch. chem. Ges.*, 36, p. 347), and found to consist mainly of hydrogen and some oxygen. We have found that after removing hydrogen and oxygen from the gases evolved from 20 mgrs. of radium bromide, the spectrum showed the presence of carbon dioxide. On freezing out the carbon dioxide, and with it, a large proportion of the radium "emanation," the residue gave unmistakably the D_3 line of helium. This was confirmed by sealing off the tube, and comparing its spectrum with that of a helium tube. The coincidence of the two lines may be taken to be at least within 1/10th of the distance between D_1 and D_2, or say 0.5 of an Ångström unit.

This observation, if confirmed, substantiates the theory already mentioned, and brings ordinary methods to bear on the changes occurring in radio-active bodies.

WILLIAM RAMSAY
FREDERICK SODDY

July 10

P.S. (July 13).—We have repeated the experiment with 30 mgrs. of fresh radium bromide, kindly placed at our disposal by Prof. Rutherford, which had probably been kept for several months in the solid state. Entirely new apparatus was constructed for the purpose, and better precautions were taken to exclude from the spectrum tube carbon dioxide and the emanation. The spectrum was practically that of pure helium, with the addition of two new lines. The lines identified are:—

Red 6677	Green-blue . . . 4932
Yellow (D_3) . . . 5876	Blue 4713
Green 5016	Violet 4472

The additional lines are one in the red and one in the green; these we have been unable to identify.

SIR WILLIAM RAMSAY (1852-1916)
[From *Famous Chemists, The Men and Their Work* by Sir William
A. Tilden, London: George Routledge & Sons, Ltd.; New York:
E. P. Dutton & Co., 1921.]

VII. Transmutations in Detail

[Rutherford found the discrepancy between the estimate he had made with Soddy of the heat produced by radium and the actual measurements by Curie and Laborde rather uncomfortable. It was possible that the estimates had been overconservative, and it was possible also that he still misunderstood radioactivity.

As the theory stood now, the energy of radioactivity was internal energy from the atoms, released in the instant of transformation and carried off by the rays. More precisely it was carried off by the moving particles which made up the rays, and each single atomic transformation probably shot a single particle into the beam. On this basis, every substance which gave out rays must also produce heat, and its heat production would stand in strict proportion to the intensity of its rays.

The alternative, which the Curies had always preferred, was the hypothesis that an atom of radium drew in its energy steadily from outside. A part of this energy would maintain the rays, but if a surplus remained, the major part of it would go into heat by some other process of transfer. On this basis, the rate of heat production would probably not be proportional to the rate of ray production.

In one form, the hypothesis of an outside source was already untenable, as J. J. Thomson had recently pointed out.[1] In the Bunsen calorimeter which Curie and Laborde had used, the radium melted ice while it was entirely surrounded by it. If the energy of the radium was drawn from its immediate surroundings, then the ice had supplied the heat to melt itself. It was still possible, however, that the radium received energy from some unrecognized penetrating radiation which (in common with uranium and thorium) it had a special power to absorb.

In the fall of 1903 Rutherford enlisted the help of H. T. Barnes (1873–1950), a specialist in the heat measurements for which McGill was celebrated. Together they took a specimen of Giesel's radium bromide which Rutherford had bought that summer and measured its heat production. Then they extracted the emanation and from hour to hour measured in alternation the heat produced by the radium-without-emanation and the emanation-without-radium. The two varied in a complicated way, very much as the radioactivity of the two specimens was known to vary, but the sum of the separate quantities of heat was steadily at the level the radium had maintained before its emanation was removed.[2] This was precisely the behavior which the transformation theory called for. To match it on the hypothesis of an outside source would call for a series of special assumptions in which Rutherford saw little value.

---

[1] J. J. Thomson, "Radium," *Nature*, 1902–1903, *67*: 601–602.

[2] E. Rutherford and H. T. Barnes, "Heating Effect of the Radium Emanation," *Nature*, 1903, *68*: 622; *Phil. Mag.* [6], 1904, 7: 202–219.

These experiments brought sharply before him something he had known for a long time, that the radium atom passed rather swiftly through a whole series of transformations.   Starting as radium, a chemically active element which formed solid compounds, it turned first into the emanation, a gas which formed no compounds whatever.   The emanation transmuted again to a solid substance—at least the product was deposited on solid surfaces in its neighborhood—and within that deposit the atom went through at least three more changes.

The transformation theory was competent to deal with all this quantitatively, and during the winter of 1903–1904 Rutherford busied himself with the necessary mathematics.   Then in January came an invitation from London to deliver the annual Bakerian Lecture before the Royal Society that spring.   By May, when he gave the lecture, his analysis of the rapid changes was well advanced; by August, when he had rewritten it for publication, still more details were worked in.

With this lecture, the transformation theory had come of age.   It took account of what was known, explaining every variation in radioactivity which experiments could create.   It established, although tacitly, a new principle for the future, that a radioactive element could be identified by its period of half transformation, or, in modern terms, its half life.   There were still many problems to be worked out.   The chain from radium would extend to radium F before Rutherford completed his study of it;[3] there were complexities in thorium to be unraveled; and the necessary link between radium and uranium was still undiscovered.   All of this would require and thereby help to prove the transformation theory.   But it would be chemical rather than physical work,[4] and therefore the account of the predominantly physical side of the discovery of radioactive transmutations may stop here.—A. R.]

---

[3] E. Rutherford, "Slow Transformation Products of Radium," *Nature*, 1904–1905, *71*: 341–342; *Phil. Mag.* [6], 1905, *10*: 290–306.

[4] See the volume *Radiochemistry and the Discovery of Isotopes* in this same Dover series of *Classics of Science*.

16

E. Rutherford

The Succession of Changes in Radioactive Bodies[5]

[From *Philosophical Transactions of the Royal Society of London*, A, 1905, *204*: 169–219.]

1. In previous papers by RUTHERFORD and SODDY[6] it has been shown that the radioactivity of the radio-elements is always accompanied by the production of a series of new substances with some distinctive physical and chemical properties. For example, thorium produces from itself an intensely radioactive substance, ThX, which can be separated from the thorium in consequence of its solubility in ammonia. In addition, thorium gives rise to a gaseous product, the thorium emanation, and also to another substance which is deposited on the surface of bodies in the neighbourhood of the thorium, where it gives rise to the phenomenon known as 'excited activity.'

A close examination of the origin of these products shows that they are not produced simultaneously, but arise in consequence of a succession of changes originating in the radio-element. Thorium first of all gives rise to the product ThX. The ThX produces from itself the thorium emanation, and this in turn is transformed into a non-volatile substance. A similar series of changes is observed in radium, with the exception that there is no product in radium corresponding to the ThX in the case of thorium. Radium first of all produces an emanation, which, like thorium, is transformed into a non-volatile substance. In uranium only one product, UrX, has been observed, for uranium does not give off an emanation and does not in consequence produce excited activity on bodies.

2. As a typical example of the evidence, from which it is deduced that one substance is the parent of another, we will consider the connection of the two products ThX and the thorium emanation. After the separation of ThX from a thorium solution, by precipitation with ammonia, the precipitated thorium hydroxide has lost to a large extent its power of emanating. This cannot be ascribed to a prevention of escape of the emanation produced in it, for very little emanation is observed when a current of air is drawn through the hydroxide

---

[5] Bakerian Lecture, delivered May 19, 1904.
[6] *Phil. Mag.*, Sept., Nov., 1902; April and May, 1903.

in a state of solution, when most of the emanation present would be carried off. On the other hand, the solution containing the ThX gives off a large quantity of emanation, showing that the power of giving an emanation belongs to the product ThX. Now it is found that the quantity of emanation given off by the separated ThX decreases according to an exponential law with the time, falling to half value in four days. The rate of production of emanation thus falls off according to the same law and at the same rate as the activity of the ThX measured in the ordinary manner by the α rays. Now this is exactly the result to be expected if the ThX is the parent of the emanation, for the activity of ThX at any time is proportional to its rate of change, *i.e.*, to the rate of production of the secondary type of matter by the emanation in consequence of a change in it. Since the rate of change of the emanation (half transformed in 1 minute) is very rapid compared with the rate of change of ThX, the amount of emanation present will be practically proportional to the activity of the ThX at any instant, *i.e.*, to the amount of unchanged ThX present. The observed fact that the hydroxide regains its power of emanating in the course of time is due to the production of fresh ThX by the thorium, which in turn produces the emanation.

In a similar way, excited activity is produced on bodies over which the emanation is passed, and in amount proportional to the activity of the emanation, *i.e.*, to the amount of the emanation present. This shows that the active deposit, which gives rise to the phenomenon of excited activity, is itself a product of the emanation. The evidence thus seems to be conclusive that ThX is the parent of the emanation and that the emanation is the parent of the deposited matter.

3. Each of these radioactive products is marked by some distinctive chemical and physical properties which differentiate it from the preceding and succeeding products. For example, ThX behaves as a solid and is soluble in ammonia, while thorium is not. The thorium emanation behaves as a chemically inert gas and condenses at a temperature of $-120°$ C The active deposit from the emanation behaves as a solid and is readily soluble in sulphuric and hydrochloric acids and is only slightly soluble in ammonia. The two emanations and the products, UrX and ThX, lose their activity according to an exponential law with the time, and at a rate that is independent—as far as observation has gone—of the chemical and physical agents at our disposal. The time taken for the radioactivity of each of these products to fall to half its value is thus a definite physical constant, which serves to distinguish it from all other products.

On the other hand, the 'excited activity' produced in bodies by exposure in the presence of the thorium and radium and actinium emanations does not decay according to a simple exponential law. The variation of the excited activity with time is very complicated, especially in the case of radium, and is dependent on the time of exposure of the body in the presence of the emanation.

It will be shown in the paper that the complicated rate of decay of the excited activity of the thorium, radium, and actinium is due to the fact that the deposited matter undergoes two successive changes in thorium and actinium and at least four successive changes in radium.

The changes occurring present several points of interest and importance and will be considered in some detail. In the course of this paper the following subjects will be considered:—

(1) Nomenclature;

(2) Rate of decay of the excited activity of thorium and radium for different times of exposure to the emanation, and for the different types of radiation;

(3) Mathematical theory of successive changes;

(4) Application of the theory to explain the changes in (*a*) thorium, (*b*) actinium, (*c*) radium;

(5) Matter of slow rate of change produced by radium: comparison of the matter with the radio-tellurium of MARCK-WALD;

(6) Apparent radioactivity of ordinary matter, due in part to an active deposit of slow rate of change from the atmosphere;

(7) Comparison of the successive changes in uranium, thorium, actinium, and radium;
Table of active products;

(8) Discussion of the significance of 'rayless' changes in the radio-elements;

(9) Radiations from the active products;
Significance of the appearance of β and γ rays in the last rapid change in the radio-elements;

(10) Difference between radioactive and chemical change;

(11) Discussion of experiments made to measure the charge carried off by the α rays;

(12) Magnitude of the changes occurring in the radio-elements;

(13) Origin of the radio-elements.

4. *Nomenclature.* The nomenclature to be applied to the numerous radioactive products is a question of great importance and also one of considerable difficulty. Since there are at least six distinct substances produced from radium, and probably five from thorium and actinium, it is neither advisable nor convenient to give each a special name. At the same time, it is becoming more and more necessary that each product should be labelled in such a way as to

indicate its place in the succession of changes. This difficulty is especially felt in discussing the numerous changes in the active deposits from the different emanations. Many of the names attached to the products were given at the time of their discovery, before their position in the scheme of changes was understood. In this way the names UrX, ThX were applied to the active residues obtained by chemical treatment of uranium and thorium. Since, in all probability, these products are the first products of the two elements, it may be advisable to retain these names, which certainly have the advantage of brevity. The name 'emanation' was originally given to the radioactive gas from thorium, and has since been applied to the similar gaseous products of radium and actinium.

Finding the name 'radium emanation' somewhat long and clumsy, Sir WILLIAM RAMSAY[7] has recently suggested 'ex-radio' as an equivalent. This name is certainly brief and is also suggestive of its origin; but at least four other ex-radios, whose parentage is as certain as that of the emanation, remain unnamed. A difficulty arises in applying the corresponding names ex-thorio, ex-actinio to the other gaseous products, for, unlike radium, the emanations of thorium and actinium are probably the second and not the first disintegration product of the radio-elements in question. Another name thus has to be applied to the first product in these cases. It may be advisable to give a special name to the emanation, as it so far has been the product most investigated and the first to be chemically isolated; but, on the other hand, the name 'radium emanation' is historically interesting, and suggests a type of volatile or gaseous matter. Since the term 'excited' or 'induced' activity refers only to the radiations from the active body, a name is required for the radiating matter itself. The writer some time ago suggested the name 'emanation X.'[8] This title was given from analogy to the names UrX and ThX, to indicate that the active matter was product of the emanation. The name, however, is not very suitable, and, in addition, can only be applied to the initial product deposited, and not to the further products of its decomposition. It is very convenient in discussing mathematically the theory of successive changes to suppose that the deposited matter called A is changed into B, B into C, C into D, and so on. I have therefore discarded the name emanation X, and have used the terms radium A, radium B, and so on, to signify the successive products of the decomposition of the emanation of radium. A similar nomenclature is applied to thorium and actinium. This system of notation is elastic and simple, and I have found it of great

---

[7] *Proc. Roy. Soc.*, p. 470, June, 1904; *Comptes Rendus*, 138, June 6, 1904.
[8] *Phil. Mag.*, February, 1904.

convenience in the discussion of successive products.   In speaking generally of the active matter, which causes excited activity, without regard to its constituents, I have used the term 'active deposit.'   The scheme of nomenclature employed in the paper is clearly shown below:—

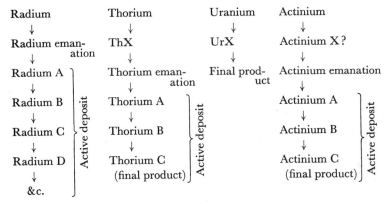

Each product on this scheme is the parent of the product below it. Since only two products have been observed in the active deposit of thorium and actinium, thorium C and actinium C respectively refer to their final inactive products.

5. *Decay of the Excited Activity of Thorium.*   If a body is exposed for several days in the presence of a constant supply of thorium emanation, the activity imparted to it reaches a constant value.   On removal, the activity is found to decay very approximately according to an exponential law with the time, falling to half value in 11 hours. If, however, the body is only exposed for a few minutes in the presence of the emanation, the activity after removal increases, during the course of about 3 hours, to 5 to 6 times the initial value, passes through a maximum, and then decays approximately according to the normal rate, *i.e.*, the activity falls to half value in about 11 hours.[9]

The curve of increase of activity with time (measured by the α rays) for a rod exposed 10 minutes in the presence of the thorium emanation is shown graphically in fig. 1, curve C.   The rod was made active by charging it negatively to 100 volts in a closed vessel.[10]

---

[9] RUTHERFORD, *Phil. Mag.*, January, 1903.

[10] It is important that the air in the vessel should be dust-free, for Miss BROOKS has found that the carriers of 'excited activity' in dusty air adhere to the dust particles, and remain anchored in the gas for several days.   On the application of an electric field, some of the dust particles are conveyed to the negative electrode. The presence of old radioactive matter in the rod masks, to a large extent, the rise observed for the radioactive matter which has just been formed.

With increasing times of exposure, the rise of the excited activity after removal becomes less and less marked, and is almost inappreciable after 6 hours.

I have discussed elsewhere in some detail ('Treatise on Radio-activity,' p. 258) the explanation of this remarkable effect, and have shown that it can be accounted for completely on the supposition that there are two successive changes occurring in the matter deposited by the emanation, viz.:—

(1) A 'rayless' change, in which the matter undergoes a trans-formation according to the same law as the radioactive changes, but which is not accompanied by the appearance of either α or β rays.

(2) A second change which gives rise to all three types of rays.

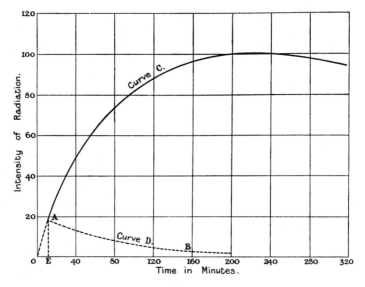

FIG. 1

It will be shown later (section 13) that the matter in the two changes is half transformed in 55 minutes and 11 hours, respectively; but without further physical data it is not possible to deduce directly from the experimental curves whether the first change has the period 55 minutes, or 11 hours. It is supposed that the matter A, deposited from the emanation, changes into the matter B, and this in turn changes into C. The change from A to B is not accompanied by any observable radiation, while the change from B to C is accompanied by all three types of rays. The matter C is either inactive or active to such a slight extent that its radioactivity cannot be detected.

The theory of these numerous changes will be considered in detail, later, together with the corresponding changes in radium and actinium.

6. *Decay of the Excited Activity of Radium.*   Miss Brooks and the writer [11] showed that the curves of decay of the excited activity of radium were very complicated in character and varied greatly with the time of exposure.   It was later pointed out that this was probably due to a triple change in the deposited matter.   P. Curie and Danne [12] recently determined the curves of decay of the excited

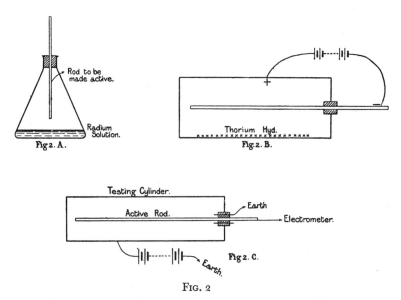

FIG. 2

activity of radium for different times of exposure.   A discussion of their results will be given later.

The shape of the decay curves of the excited activity of radium depends not only on the time of exposure, but also on which of the types of radiation is used as a means of measurement.   The curves of decay of excited activity are quite different for the α and for the β rays.

In the experiments a radium solution was placed in a closed glass vessel (see fig. 2, A).   The emanation then collected in the air space above the solution.   The rod to be made active was introduced through an opening in the stopper and exposed in the presence of the emanation for a definite interval.   For experiments on the excited

[11] *Phil. Mag.*, July, 1902.
[12] *Comptes Rendus*, 136, p. 364, 1903.

activity of thorium, some highly emanating thorium hydroxide was
placed inside a closed cylinder (see fig. 2, B). The central rod,
which was to be made active, was connected to the negative pole of
a battery of about 100 volts. If the decay of activity was to be
measured by the α rays, the rod was made the central electrode in a
cylindrical vessel (see fig. 2, C). A saturating voltage was applied,
and the current between the cylinders measured by means of an
electrometer with a suitable capacity in parallel. A current of dust-
free air was continuously circulated through the cylinder in order to
remove any emanation which might have adhered to the wire. For
experiments on the β or γ rays it was found advisable to use an electro-

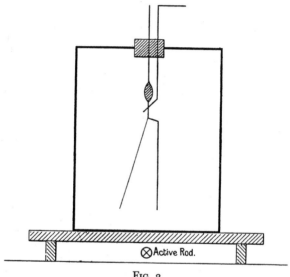

FIG. 3

scope instead of an electrometer. The gold-leaf system was insulated
inside of a metal vessel by means of a sulphur bead, after the method
first employed by C. T. R. WILSON (see fig. 3). The rate of movement of the leaves was determined through mica windows by means
of a microscope provided with a micrometer eye-piece. For
measurements with the β rays, the active rod was placed under the
electroscope, and, before entering into the vessel, passed through a
sheet of metal of sufficient thickness to absorb all the α rays. For
measurements with the γ rays, the electroscope was placed on a lead
plate 0.6 centim. thick, and the active rod placed under the lead
plate. The α and β rays were completely stopped by the lead, and
the discharge in the electroscope was then due to the γ rays alone.

The electroscope is very advantageous for measurements of this character, and accurate observations can be simply and readily made. It, however, cannot be used with advantage to follow very rapid changes in activity.

7. The curve of decay of activity, measured by the α rays, for an exposure of 1 minute in the presence of the radium emanation is shown in fig. 4, curve BB.

The curve exhibits three stages:—

(1) A rapid decay in the course of 15 minutes to less than 10 per cent. of the value immediately after removal;

(2) A period of 30 minutes in which the activity varies very little;

(3) A gradual decrease almost to zero.

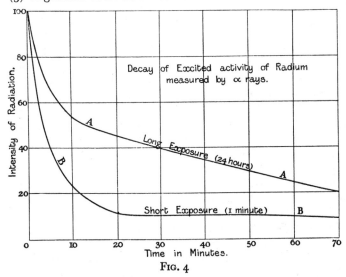

FIG. 4

The initial drop decays very approximately according to an exponential law with the time, falling to half value in about 3 minutes. Three or 4 hours after removal the activity again decays according to an exponential law with the time, falling to half value in about 28 minutes. These results thus indicate:—

(1) An initial change in which half the matter is transformed in 3 minutes;

(2) A final change in which half the matter is transformed in 28 minutes.

Before considering the explanation of the intermediate portion of the curve further experimental results will be considered.

The curve of decay of the excited activity for a long exposure (24 hours) is shown graphically in fig. 4, curve AA. There is at first a rapid decrease for the first 15 minutes to about 50 per cent. of the initial value, then a slower decay, and after an interval of about 4 hours a gradual decay nearly to zero, according to an exponential law with the time, falling to half value in 28 minutes.

The curves of variation with time of the excited activity when measured by the β rays are shown graphically in figs. 5 and 6.

Fig. 5 is for a short exposure of 1 minute. Fig. 6 shows the decay for a long exposure of about 24 hours.

The curves obtained for the β rays are quite different from those obtained for the α rays. For a short exposure, the activity measured by the β rays is at first small, then passes through a maximum about 36 minutes after removal. There is then a gradual decrease, and after several hours the activity decays according to an exponential law, falling, as in the other cases, to half value in 28 minutes.

The curve shown in fig. 6 for the β rays is very similar in shape to the corresponding curve, fig. 4, curve AA, for the α rays, with the exception that the rapid initial drop observed for the α-ray curve is quite absent. The later portions of the curve are similar in shape, and, disregarding the first 15 minutes after removal, the activity decays at exactly the same rate in both cases.

The curves obtained by means of the γ rays are identical with those obtained for the β rays. This shows that the β and γ rays always occur together and in the same proportion.

For increase of the time of exposure from 1 minute to 24 hours the curves obtained are intermediate in shape between the two representative limiting curves, figs. 5 and 6.

The results obtained by Curie and Danne for the decay of the excited activity of radium for different times of exposure are shown graphically in fig. 7. The ordinates represent the logarithm of the activity and the abscissæ time in hours. A comparison of the curves obtained by myself and those obtained by Curie and Danne at once discloses some marked differences.

The lowest curve for a short exposure of 20 seconds is very similar in shape to the corresponding curve, fig. 4, curve B, where the activity was measured by the α rays. On the other hand, the upper curve A of fig. 7 does not show the initial drop found by me (see fig. 4, curve A), where the activity is measured by the α rays. If the activity is supposed to be measured by the β rays, the upper curve A, fig. 7, is similar to that shown in fig. 6. The lower curve of fig. 7 is, however, again different from the corresponding β-ray curve shown in fig. 5.

I think the difference between the results of Curie and Danne and those obtained by myself lies in the fact that the former did not take into account that the shape of the curves depended on whether the α or β rays were used as a means of measurement. Curie and

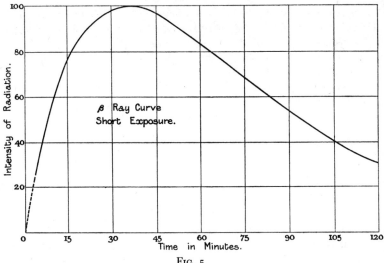

FIG. 5

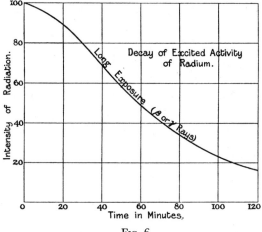

FIG. 6

DANNE do not state, or give any evidence to show, which of the types of rays they employed for measurement, but I think there is no doubt that the lower curve (fig. 1) was obtained by means of the α rays, while the four upper curves (fig. 7) were obtained by means of the β rays. The intermediate curves, for an exposure of 1 minute and 5 minutes, do not agree with the results obtained by me for either the α or β rays, but appear to be a mixture of both.

The sudden initial drop is a characteristic of the α-ray curve, but I have only observed the rise to a maximum, as in fig. 5, where measurements are made by the β or γ rays.

Miss BROOKS, working in the laboratory, has re-determined the cause of decay of the excited activity of radium for different times of exposure, separately for both the α and β rays, and the results will be published shortly.[13]

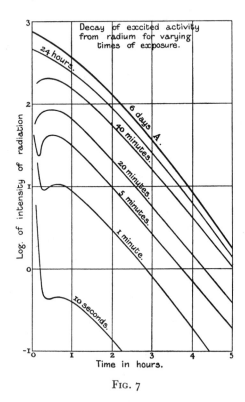

FIG. 7

8. *Explanation of the Curves.* It has been pointed out that the rapid initial drop for curves A and B, fig. 4, is due to a change giving rise to α rays, in which half of the matter is transformed in about 3 minutes. The absence of the drop in the corresponding curves, when measured by the β rays, shows that the first 3-minute change does not give rise to β rays; for if it gave rise to β rays, the activity should fall off at the same rate as the corresponding α-ray curve.

---

[13] [Since published, *Phil. Mag.*, September, 1904.]

It has been shown that the activity several hours after removal decays in all cases according to an exponential law with the time, falling to half value in 28 minutes. This is the case whether for a short or long exposure, or whether the activity is measured by the α, β, or γ rays. This indicates that the final 28-minute change gives rise to all three types of rays.

It will be shown that these results can be completely explained on the supposition that three successive changes occur in the deposited matter of the following character [14]:—

(1) A first change of the matter deposited in which half of the matter is transformed in about 3 minutes, and which gives rise only to α rays;

(2) A second 'rayless' change in which half the matter is transformed in 21 minutes;

(3) A third change in which half the matter is transformed in 28 minutes, and which gives rise to α, β, and γ rays.

9. *Theory of Successive Changes.* Before considering the evidence from which these changes are deduced, the general theory of successive changes of radioactive matter will be considered. It is supposed that the matter A deposited by the emanation changes into B, B into C, C into D, and so on.

Each of these changes is supposed to take place according to the same law as a monomolecular change in chemistry, *i.e.*, the number N of particles unchanged after a time t is given by $N = N_0 e^{-\lambda t}$, where N_0 is the initial number and λ the constant of the change.

---

[14] The view that the complicated rates of decay of the excited activity produced by radium and thorium were due to a double change in the deposit from thorium and a treble change in that of radium was first suggested in 1902 (RUTHERFORD, *Physik. Zeitsch.*, 3, p. 254, 1902), and discussed later in *Phil. Mag.*, Jan., 1903, and also by RUTHERFORD and SODDY, *Phil. Mag.*, April and May, 1903. In 1903, CURIE and DANNE (*Comptes Rendus*, 136, p. 364, 1903) found that the decay curve of the excited activity of radium (measured by the β rays) for a long exposure to the emanation could be empirically expressed by the differences of two exponentials. The first definite statement of the changes occurring in the active deposit of radium and the existence of a rayless change occurs in a paper by RUTHERFORD and BARNES, *Phil. Mag.*, Feb., 1904. A discussion of the evidence on which these conclusions were based was reserved for a later paper. A brief account of the theory of successive changes and the evidence of the existence of a rayless change in both radium and thorium was given in 'Radioactivity,' pp. 268–274. Somewhat later CURIE and DANNE (*Comptes Rendus*, 138, p. 683, 1904), using the hypothesis of successive changes advanced by RUTHERFORD and SODDY, arrived at a similar conclusion in regard to the changes in radium. In a later paper (*Comptes Rendus*, 138, p. 748, 1904), CURIE and DANNE gave an account of some important experiments on the effect of temperature on the curves of decay of activity, and showed that the product radium B could be separated from radium C by volatilization at a suitable temperature.

Since $dN/dt = -\lambda N$, the rate of change at any time is always proportional to the amount of matter unchanged. It has previously been pointed out that this law of decay of the activity of the radio-active products is an expression of the fact that the change is of the same type as a monomolecular chemical change.

Suppose that P, Q, R represent the number of particles of the matter A, B, and C respectively at any time t. Let $\lambda_1, \lambda_2, \lambda_3$ be the constants of change of the matter A, B, and C respectively.

Each atom of the matter A is supposed to give rise to one atom of the matter B, one atom of B to one of C, and so on.

The expelled 'rays' or particles are non-radioactive and so do not enter into the theory.

The general theory will first be considered corresponding to the practical cases of a very short and of a very long exposure in the presence of the emanation, then finally for any time of exposure to a constant supply of the emanation.

10. *Short Exposure.* Suppose that a body has been exposed for a short interval in the presence of the radium or thorium emanation and then removed. The time is supposed to be so short that no appreciable portion of the deposited matter has undergone change during the time of exposure. It is required to find the number of particles P, Q, R of the matter A, B, C respectively present after any time t.

Then $P = ne^{-\lambda_1 t}$, if n is the number of particles that has been deposited during the short time of exposure. Now the increase of the number of particles dQ of the matter B per unit time is the number supplied by the change in the matter A, less the number due to the change of B into C, thus

$$dQ/dt = \lambda_1 P - \lambda_2 Q \quad . \quad . \quad . \quad . \quad (1).$$

Similarly

$$dR/dt = \lambda_2 Q - \lambda_3 R \quad . \quad . \quad . \quad . \quad (2).$$

Substituting in (1) the value of P in terms of n,

$$dQ/dt = \lambda_1 ne^{-\lambda_1 t} - \lambda_2 Q.$$

The solution of this equation is of the form

$$Q = n(ae^{-\lambda_1 t} + be^{-\lambda_2 t}) \quad . \quad . \quad . \quad . \quad (3).$$

By substitution it is found that $a = \lambda_1/(\lambda_2 - \lambda_1)$.

Since $Q = 0$ when $t = 0$, $b = -\lambda_1(\lambda_2 - \lambda_1)$.

Thus

$$Q = \frac{n\lambda_1}{\lambda_1 - \lambda_2}(e^{-\lambda_2 t} - e^{-\lambda_1 t}) \quad . \quad . \quad . \quad (4).$$

Substituting this value of Q in (2), it can readily be shown that

$$R = n(ae^{-\lambda_1 t} + be^{-\lambda_2 t} + ce^{-\lambda_3 t}) \quad . \quad . \quad . \quad (5).$$

where
$$a = \frac{\lambda_1 \lambda_2}{(\lambda_1 - \lambda_2)(\lambda_1 - \lambda_3)},$$

$$b = \frac{-\lambda_1 \lambda_2}{(\lambda_1 - \lambda_2)(\lambda_2 - \lambda_3)},$$

$$c = \frac{\lambda_1 \lambda_2}{(\lambda_1 - \lambda_3)(\lambda_2 - \lambda_3)}.$$

The variation of the values of P, Q, R with the time t after removal is shown graphically in fig. 8, curves A, B, and C respectively.   In

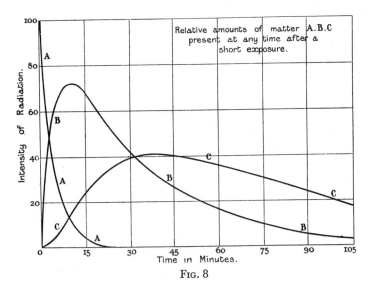

Fig. 8

order to draw the curves for the practical case corresponding to the first three changes in radium A, the values of λ_1, λ_2, λ_3 were taken as 3.85×10^{-3}, 5.38×10^{-4}, 4.13×10^{-4} respectively, *i.e.*, the times required for each type of matter to be half transformed are about 3, 21, and 28 minutes respectively.

The ordinates of the curves represent the relative number of atoms of the matter A, B, and C existing at any time, the value of n, the original number of atoms of the matter A deposited, being taken as 100.   The amount of matter B is initially zero, passes through a maximum about 10 minutes later, and then diminishes with the time.   In a similar way, the amount of C passes through a maximum about 37 minutes after removal.   After an interval of several hours the amount of both B and C diminishes very approximately according to an exponential law with the time, falling to half value after intervals of 21 and 28 minutes respectively.

11. *Long Exposure.*   The exposure is supposed to be so long that a state of equilibrium is reached between the emanation and the successive products resulting from it.   In this case the number n_0 of particles of A, deposited per second from the emanation, is equal to the number of particles of A which change into B per second, and of B into C, and so on.   This requires the relation

$$n_0 = \lambda_1 P_0 = \lambda_2 Q_0 = \lambda_3 R_0 \quad . \quad . \quad . \quad . \quad (6),$$

where P_0, Q_0, R_0 are the maximum numbers of particles of the matter A, B, and C when a steady state is reached.

The values of P, Q, R at any time t after removal from a long exposure are given by equations of the same form as (3) and (5) for a short exposure.   Remembering the condition that initially

$$P = P_0 = n_0/\lambda_1,$$

$$Q = Q_0 = n_0/\lambda_2,$$

$$R = R_0 = n_0/\lambda_3,$$

it can readily be shown that

$$P = \frac{n_0}{\lambda_1} e^{-\lambda_1 t} \quad . \quad . \quad . \quad . \quad . \quad . \quad (7),$$

$$Q = \frac{n_0}{\lambda_1 - \lambda_2} \left(\frac{\lambda_1}{\lambda_2} e^{-\lambda_2 t} - e^{-\lambda_1 t} \right) \quad . \quad . \quad . \quad (8),$$

$$R = n_0 (a e^{-\lambda_1 t} + b e^{-\lambda_2 t} + c e^{-\lambda_3 t}) \quad . \quad . \quad . \quad (9),$$

where

$$a = \frac{\lambda_2}{(\lambda_1 - \lambda_2)(\lambda_1 - \lambda_3)},$$

$$b = \frac{-\lambda_1}{(\lambda_1 - \lambda_2)(\lambda_2 - \lambda_3)},$$

$$c = \frac{\lambda_1 \lambda_2}{\lambda_3 (\lambda_1 - \lambda_3)(\lambda_2 - \lambda_3)}.$$

The relative numbers of atom of P, Q ,R existing at any time are shown graphically in fig. 9, curves A, B, and C respectively.   The number of atoms R_0 is taken as 100 for comparison, and values of $\lambda_1, \lambda_2, \lambda_3$ are taken corresponding to the 3, 21, and 28-minute changes in the active deposit of radium. A comparison with fig. 8 for a short exposure brings out very clearly the variation in the relative amounts of P, Q, R in the two cases. The amount of R initially decreases very slowly. This is due to the fact that the supply of C due to breaking up of B at first, nearly compensates for the breaking up of C. The values of Q and R after several hours decrease exponentially, reaching half value every 28 minutes.

12. *Any Time of Exposure.* Suppose that a body is exposed in the presence of a constant supply of emanation, and that n_0 particles of

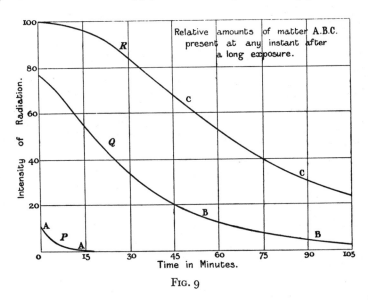

Fig. 9

the matter A are deposited each second. After a time of exposure T, the number of particles P_T of the matter A present is given by

$$P_T = n_0 \int_0^T e^{-\lambda_1 t}\, dt = \frac{n_0}{\lambda_1} \left(1 - e^{-\lambda_1 T}\right).$$

At any time t, after removal of the body from the emanation, the number of particles P of the matter A is given by

$$P = P_T e^{-\lambda_1 t} = \frac{n_0}{\lambda_1} \left(1 - e^{-\lambda_1 T}\right) e^{-\lambda_1 t}.$$

Consider the number of particles $n_0\, dt$ of the matter A deposited during the interval dt. At any time t later, the number of particles

$d\mathrm{Q}$ of the matter B, which results from the change in A, is given (see equation 4) by

$$d\mathrm{Q} = \frac{n_0\lambda_1}{\lambda_1-\lambda_2}\,(e^{-\lambda_2 t}-e^{-\lambda_1 t})\,.\,dt.\ =\ n_0\,f(t)\,dt\ .\ \ .\ \ (10).$$

After a time of exposure T, the number of particles $\mathrm{Q_T}$ of the matter B present is readily seen to be given by

$$\mathrm{Q_T} = n_0[f(\mathrm{T})\,dt + f(\mathrm{T}-dt)\,dt + \ldots \quad \ldots + f(\mathrm{o})\,dt]$$

$$= n_0 \int_0^{\mathrm{T}} f(t)\,dt.$$

If the body is removed from the emanation after an exposure T at any time t later the number of particles of B is in the same way given by

$$\mathrm{Q} = n_0 \int_t^{\mathrm{T}+t} f(t)\,dt.$$

It will be noted that the method of deduction of $\mathrm{Q_T}$ and Q is independent of the particular form of the function $f(t)$.

Substituting the particular value of $f(t)$ given in equation (10) and integrating, it can readily be deduced that

$$\frac{\mathrm{Q}}{\mathrm{Q_T}} = \frac{ae^{-\lambda_2 t}-be^{-\lambda_1 t}}{a-b}\ \cdot\quad\cdot\quad\cdot\quad\cdot\quad (11),$$

where

$$a = \frac{\mathrm{I}-e^{-\lambda_2 \mathrm{T}}}{\lambda_2},\quad b = \frac{\mathrm{I}-e^{-\lambda_1 \mathrm{T}}}{\lambda_1}.$$

In a similar way, the number of particles R of the matter C present at any time can be deduced by substitution of the value of $f(t)$ in equation (5). These equations are, however, too complicated in form for simple application to experiment, and will be omitted.

13. *Changes in the Active Deposit from Thorium.* If the variation of the activity, imparted to a body exposed for a short interval in the presence of the thorium emanation, is due to the fact that there are two successive changes in the deposited matter A, the first of which is a 'rayless' change, the activity I_t at any time t after removal should be proportional to the number Q_t of particles of the matter B present at that time. Now, from equation (4), it has been shown that

$$\mathrm{Q}_t = \frac{\lambda_1 n}{\lambda_1-\lambda_2}\,(e^{-\lambda_2 t}-e^{-\lambda_1 t}).$$

The value of Q_t passes through a maximum $\mathrm{Q_T}$ at the time T when

$$\lambda_2/\lambda_1 = e^{-(\lambda_1-\lambda_2)\mathrm{T}}.$$

The maximum activity I_T is proportional to Q_T and

$$\frac{I_t}{I_T} = \frac{Q_t}{Q_T} = \frac{e^{-\lambda_2 t} - e^{-\lambda_1 t}}{e^{-\lambda_2 T} - e^{-\lambda_1 T}} \quad . \quad . \quad . \quad (12).$$

It will be shown later that the variation with time of the activity, imparted to a body by a short exposure, is expressed by an equation of the above form.   It thus remains to fix the values of λ_1, λ_2.   Since the above equation is symmetrical with regard to λ_1, λ_2, it is not possible to settle from the agreement of the theoretical and experimental curve which value of λ refers to the first change.   The curve of variation of activity with time is unaltered if the values of λ_1 and λ_2 are interchanged.

It is found experimentally that the activity 5 or 6 hours after removal decays very approximately according to an exponential law with the time, falling to half value in 11 hours.   This is the normal rate of decay of thorium for all time of exposure, provided measurements are not begun until several hours after the removal of the active body from the emanation.

This fixes the value of the constants of one of the changes.   Let us assume for the moment that this gives the value of λ_1.

Then

$$\lambda_1 = 1.75 \times 10^{-5} \; (\text{sec})^{-1}.$$

Since the maximum activity is reached after an interval $T = 220$ minutes (see fig. 1, curve C), substituting the values of λ_1 and T in equation (12), the value of λ_2 comes out to be

$$\lambda_2 = 2.08 \times 10^{-4} \; (\text{sec})^{-1}.$$

This value of λ_2 corresponds to a change in which half the matter is transformed in 55 minutes.

Substituting now the values of λ_1, λ_2, T, the equation (12) reduces to

$$I_t/I_T = 1.37(e^{-\lambda_2 t} - e^{-\lambda_1 t}).$$

The agreement between the results of the theoretical equation and the observed values is shown in the following table:—

Time in minutes	Theoretical value of I_t/I_T	Observed value of I_t/I_T
15	.22	.23
30	.38	.37
60	.64	.63
120	.90	.91
220	1.00	1.00
305	.97	.96

It is thus seen that the curve of rise of activity for a short exposure is explained very satisfactorily on the supposition that two changes occur in the deposited matter, of which the first is a rayless change.

Further data are required in order to fix which of the time constants of the changes refers to the first change. In order to settle this point, it is necessary to isolate one of the products of the changes and to examine the variation of its activity with time. If, for example, a product can be separated whose activity decays to half value in 55 minutes, it would show that the second change is the more rapid of the two. Now PEGRAM[15] has examined the radio-active products obtained by electrolysis of thorium solutions. The rates of decay of the active products depended upon conditions, but he found that, in several cases, rapidly decaying products were obtained whose activity fell to half value in about 1 hour. Allowing for the probability that the product examined was not completely isolated by the electrolysis, but contained also a trace of the other product, this result would indicate that the last change which gives rise to rays is the more rapid of the two.

The results obtained by VON LERCH[16] in the electrolysis of solution of the active deposit also admit of a similar interpretation. Products were obtained on the electrodes of different rates of decay, but which lost half their activity in times varying from about 1 hour to 5 hours. This variation is possibly due to the admixture of the two products, but further experiment is necessary to settle this point with certainty. The evidence, as a whole, thus supports the conclusion that the active deposit from thorium undergoes two successive transformations as follows:—

(1) A 'rayless' change for which $\lambda_1 = 1.75 \times 10^{-5}$, *i.e.*, in which half the matter is transformed in 11 hours;

(2) A second change giving rise to α, β and γ rays, for which $\lambda_2 = 2.08 \times 10^{-4}$, *i.e.*, in which half the matter is transformed in 55 minutes.[17]

It is, at first sight, a somewhat unexpected result that the final rate of decay of the active deposit from thorium does not in reality give the rate of change of the last product itself, but of the preceding product, which does not give rise to rays at all.

A similar peculiarity is observed in the decay of the excited activity of actinium, which is discussed in section 15.

14. For a long exposure in the presence of a constant supply of

---

[15] *Phys. Rev.*, p. 424, December, 1903.

[16] *Ann. d. Physik*, November, 1903.

[17] The 'rayless change' certainly does not give out α rays, and special experiments showed that no appreciable amount of β rays were present. On the other hand, the second change gives out all three types of rays.

thorium emanation, the equation expressing the variation of activity with time is found from equation (8), section 11.

$$\frac{I_t}{I_0} = \frac{Q}{Q_0} = \frac{\lambda_2}{\lambda_2 - \lambda_1} e^{-\lambda_1 t} - \frac{\lambda_1}{\lambda_1 - \lambda_2} e^{-\lambda_2 t}$$

$$= \frac{\lambda_2 e^{-\lambda_1 t}}{\lambda_2 - \lambda_1} (1 - .083 \, e^{-1.90 \times 10^{-4} t}).$$

About 4 hours after removal, the second term in the brackets becomes very small, and the activity after that time will decay very nearly according to an exponential law with the time, falling to half value in 11 hours.   For any time of exposure T, the activity at time t after the removal (see equation 11) is given by

$$\frac{I_t}{I_0} = \frac{Q}{Q_T} = \frac{ae^{-\lambda_2 t} - be^{-\lambda_1 t}}{a - b},$$

where I_0 is the initial value of the activity, immediately after removal, and

$$a = \frac{1 - e^{-\lambda_2 T}}{\lambda_2}, \quad b = \frac{1 - e^{-\lambda_1 T}}{\lambda_1}.$$

By variation of T the curves of variation of activity for any time of exposure can be accurately deduced from the equation, when the values of the two constants λ_1, λ_2 are substituted.   Miss BROOKS has examined the decay curves of excited activity for thorium for different times of exposure and has observed a substantial agreement between experiment and theory.[18]

15. *Changes in Actinium.*   Dr. GIESEL kindly forwarded me a radioactive preparation from pitchblende and called by him the 'emanating substance,' on account of the large amount of emanation it gives out.   This had an activity, measured in the usual way, of about 250 times that of uranium.   The emanation and excited activity produced by it were kindly examined for me in detail by Miss BROOKS.   The emanation was found to have a very rapid rate of decay, its activity falling to half value in a few seconds.   The excited activity for a long exposure fell to half value in 41 minutes. DEBIERNE[19] has shown that actinium gives off an emanation which loses half its activity in 3.7 seconds and produces excited activity which falls to half value in 41 minutes.   There can be no doubt that the 'emanating substance' of GIESEL and the actinium of DEBIERNE contain the same radioactive constituent.   The name actinium will

---

[18] [*Phil. Mag.*, September, 1904.]
[19] *Comptes Rendus*, 138, p. 411, 1904.

thus be used in this paper to denote the 'emanating substance' of
Giesel. Miss Brooks investigated the rate of decay of the excited
activity of actinium for different times of exposure; but, for the
purpose of elucidation of the changes occurring, we need only
consider the curves of decay of excited activity for a short and for a
long exposure. For a long exposure the activity decays very nearly
according to an exponential law, falling to half value in 41 minutes.
The value of the change-constant λ is 2.80×10^{-4} (sec)$^{-1}$.

The activity for a short exposure at first increases, rapidly passes
through a maximum, and after some time decays according to an
exponential law, falling to half value in 41 minutes. The curve of
decay (measured by the α rays) for an exposure of 1.5 minutes in the
presence of the actinium emanation is shown in fig. 10.

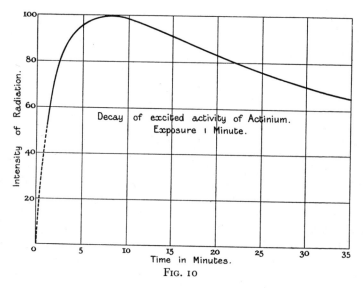

FIG. 10

The maximum is reached about 7.5 minutes, reckoning from the
moment the body is exposed to the emanation.

The curve is very similar in general shape to the corresponding
curve of thorium, and can be analysed in a similar way; the activity
at any time t is proportional to $e^{-\lambda_2 t} - e^{-\lambda_1 t}$.

These results show that the first change occurring in the active
deposit from actinium is a rayless change. Since the activity finally
decays according to an exponential law (half value in 41 minutes),
one of the constants of the change has a value 2.80×10^{-4}. By
substitution in the curve, the value of the other constant is found to
be 7.7×10^{-3} (half transformed in 1.5 minutes).

As in the case of thorium, a difficulty arises as to which value of λ applies to the rayless change, but the question in the case of actinium can at once be settled by means of electrolysis.

Miss Brooks performed the following experiment:—A platinum plate was made active in the presence of actinium and the active matter was dissolved off by hydrochloric acid and then electrolysed. The activity of the anode, after removal, fell very rapidly according to an exponential law, reaching half value in 1.5 minutes. The corresponding value of λ is 7.7×10^{-3}. There is thus no doubt that the second change is the most rapid of the two. We may thus conclude that the active deposit from actinium undergoes two distinct successive transformations:

(1) A rayless change, in which half the matter is transformed in 41 minutes;

(2) A change giving rise to α rays, in which half the matter is transformed in 1.5 minutes.[20]

It can readily be shown that, for a very short exposure of a body in the presence of the actinium emanation, the activity I_t at any time t is given by

$$I_t/I_T = 1.14\,(e^{-\lambda_1 t} - e^{-\lambda_2 t}),$$

where I_T is the maximum value of I which occurs at time $T = 7.5$ minutes.

For a very long exposure

$$I_t/I_0 = 1.038\,e^{-\lambda_1 t} - .038\,e^{-\lambda_2 t},$$

where I_0 is the initial value after removal, and

$$\lambda_1 = 2.80 \times 10^{-4}, \quad \lambda_2 = 7.7 \times 10^{-3}.$$

For the first 10 minutes after removal, the activity in consequence decays more slowly than is to be expected on a simple exponential law. This result has been observed experimentally. The variation of the activity for any time of exposure to the emanation is expressed by an equation of the same form as for thorium, equation (12), with values λ_1, λ_2 found above.

There is some evidence that there is a product actinium X in actinium, corresponding to thorium X in thorium. This point is at present under investigation, and the results will be given in a later paper. If this is the case, actinium and thorium are very closely allied in the number and nature of their products. Both give rise to an emanation, and this is transformed into an active deposit which

---

[20] The radiations from the products have not yet been examined to see whether β and γ rays are present.

undergoes two further transformations, the first change being a 'rayless' one.

16. *Changes in the Active Deposit from Radium.* In the case of the active deposit from radium, we are dealing with matter that undergoes at least four successive changes. For convenience, the matter initially produced from the emanation will be called the matter A and the succeeding products B, C, D, E respectively. The equations expressing the quantities of A, B, C, D present at any time are complicated, but the comparison of theory with experiment may be simplified by temporarily disregarding some unimportant terms. For example, the activity of the matter D is generally negligible compared with that of A or C, being as a rule less than 1/100,000 of the initial activity observed for the matter A or C. A still further simplification can be made by disregarding the first 3-minute change. In the course of 6 minutes after removal, three-quarters of the matter A has been transformed into B, and 20 minutes after removal all but about 1 per cent. has been transformed. The variation of the amount of matter B or C present at any time agrees more closely with the theory, if the first change is disregarded altogether. A discussion of this important point is given later in section 21.

17. *β-Ray Curves.* The explanation of the β-ray curves (see figs. 5 and 6), obtained for different times of exposure, will be first considered. For a very short exposure, the activity measured by the β rays is small at first, passes through a maximum about 36 minutes later, and then decays steadily with the time.

The curve shown in fig. 6 is very similar in general shape to the corresponding thorium and actinium curves. It is thus necessary to suppose that the change of the matter B into C does not give rise to β rays, while the change of C into D does. In such a case the activity (measured by the β rays) is proportional to the amount of C present. Disregarding the first rapid change, the activity I_t at any time t should be given by an equation of the same form (see equation 12, section 13) as for thorium and actinium, viz.,

$$\frac{I_t}{I_T} = \frac{e^{-\lambda_3 t} - e^{-\lambda_2 t}}{e^{-\lambda_3 T} - e^{-\lambda_2 T}},$$

where I_T is the maximum activity observed, which is reached after an interval T. Since the activity finally decays according to an exponential law (half value in 28 minutes), one of the values of λ is equal to 4.13×10^{-4}. As in the case of thorium and actinium, the experimental curves do not allow us to settle whether this value of λ is to be given to λ_2 or λ_3. From other data (see section 20) it will be shown later that it must refer to λ_3. Thus $\lambda_3 = 4.13 \times 10^{-4}$ (sec)$^{-1}$.

The experimental curve agrees very closely with theory if $\lambda_2 = 3.10 \times 10^{-4}$ (sec)$^{-1}$.

The agreement between theory and experiment is shown by the table given below. The maximum value I_T (which is taken as 100) is reached at a time $T = 36$ minutes.

In order to obtain the β-ray curve, the following procedure was adopted. A layer of thin aluminium was placed inside a glass tube, which was then exhausted. A large quantity of radium emanation was then suddenly introduced by opening a stopcock communicating with the emanation vessel, which was at atmospheric pressure. The emanation was left in the tube for 1.5 minutes and then was rapidly swept out by a current of air. The aluminium was then removed and was placed under an electroscope, such as is shown in fig. 3. The α rays from the aluminium were cut off by an interposed screen of aluminium .1 millim. thick. The time was reckoned from a period of 45 seconds after the introduction of the emanation.

Time in minutes	Theoretical value of activity	Observed value of activity
0	0	0
10	58.1	55
20	88.6	86
30	97.3	97
36	100	100
40	99.8	99.5
50	93.4	92
60	83.4	82
80	63.7	61.5
100	44.8	42.5
120	30.8	29

There is thus a fairly good agreement between the calculated and observed values of the activity measured by the β rays.

The results are thus satisfactorily explained if it is supposed:—

(1) That the change B into C (half transformed in 21 minutes) does not give rise to β rays;

(2) That the change C into D (half transformed in 28 minutes) gives rise to β rays.

These conclusions are very strongly supported by observations of the decay measured by the β rays for a long exposure. The curve of decay is shown in fig. 6 and fig. 11, curve I.

P. CURIE and DANNE made the important observation that the curve of decay C, shown in fig. 7, for a long exposure, could be accurately expressed by an empirical equation of the form

$$I_t/I_0 = ae^{-\lambda_3 t} - (a-1)e^{-\lambda_2 t},$$

where $\lambda_2 = 3.10 \times 10^{-4}$ (sec)$^{-1}$ and $\lambda_3 = 4.13 \times 10^{-4}$ (sec)$^{-1}$, and $a = 4.20$ is a numerical constant.

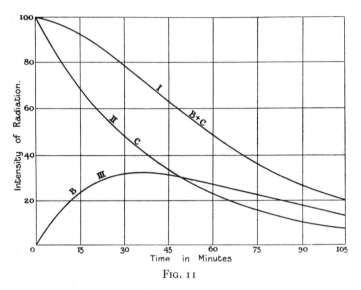

FIG. 11

I have found that within the limit of experimental error this equation represents the decay of excited activity of radium for a long exposure, measured by the β rays. The equation expressing the decay of activity, measured by the α rays, differs considerably from this, especially in the early part of the curve. Several hours after removal the activity decays according to an exponential law with the time, decreasing to half value in 28 minutes. This fixes the value of λ_3. The constant a and the value of λ_2 are deduced from the experimental curve by trial. Now we have already shown (section 14) that in the case of the active deposit from thorium, where there are two changes of constants λ_2 and λ_3, in which only the second change gives rise to a radiation, the value of

$$\frac{I_t}{I_0} = \frac{\lambda_2}{\lambda_2 - \lambda_3}e^{-\lambda_3 t} - \frac{\lambda_3}{\lambda_2 - \lambda_3}e^{-\lambda_2 t}$$

for a long time of exposure (see equation 8). This is an equation of the same form as that found experimentally by CURIE and DANNE. On substituting the values λ_2, λ_3 found by them,

$$\frac{\lambda_2}{\lambda_2-\lambda_3} = 4.3, \quad \text{and} \quad \frac{\lambda_1}{\lambda_1-\lambda_3} = 3.3.$$

Thus not only does the theoretical equation agree in form, but also closely in the values of the numerical constants. If the first as well as the second change gave rise to a radiation, the equation would be of the same general form, but the value of the numerical constants would be different, the values depending upon the ratio of the ionization in the first and second changes. If, for example, it is supposed that both changes give out β rays in equal amounts, it can readily be calculated that the equation of decay would be

$$\frac{I_t}{I_0} = \frac{.5\lambda_2}{\lambda_2-\lambda_3}e^{-\lambda_3 t} - .5\left(\frac{\lambda_3}{\lambda_2-\lambda_3}-1\right)e^{-\lambda_3 t}.$$

Taking the values of λ_2 and λ_3 found by CURIE, the numerical factor $e^{-\lambda_3 t}$ becomes 2.15 instead of 4.3 and 1.15 instead of 3.3. The theoretical curve of decay in this case would be readily distinguishable from the observed curve of decay. The fact that the equation of decay found by CURIE and DANNE involves the necessity of an initial rayless change can be simply shown as follows:—

Curve I. (fig. 11) shows the experimental curve. At the moment of removal of the body from the emanation (disregarding the initial rapid change), the matter must consist of both B and C. Consider the matter which existed in the form C at the moment of removal. It will be transformed according to an exponential law, the activity falling to half in 28 minutes. This is shown in curve II. Curve III. represents the difference between the ordinates of curves I. and II. It will be seen that it is identical in shape with the curve (fig. 5) showing the variation of the activity for a short exposure, measured by the β rays. It passes through a maximum at the same time (about 36 minutes). The explanation of such a curve is only possible on the assumption that the first change is a rayless one. The ordinates of curve III. express the activity added in consequence of the change of the matter B, present after removal, into the matter C. The matter B present gradually changes into C, and this, in its change to D, gives rise to the radiation observed. Since the matter B alone is considered, the variation of activity with time due to its further changes, shown by curve III., should agree with the curve obtained for a short exposure (see fig. 5), and this, as we have seen, is the case.

The agreement between theory and experiment is shown in the following tables. The first column gives the theoretical curve of decay for a long exposure deduced from the equation

$$\frac{I_t}{I_0} = \frac{\lambda_2}{\lambda_2 - \lambda_3} e^{-\lambda_3 t} - \frac{\lambda_3}{\lambda_2 - \lambda_3} e^{-\lambda_2 t},$$

taking the value of $\lambda_2 = 3.10 \times 10^{-4}$ and $\lambda_3 = 4.13 \times 10^{-4}$.

The second column gives the observed activity (measured by means of an electroscope) for a long exposure of 24 hours in the presence of the emanation.

Time in minutes	Calculated values	Observed values
0	100	100
10	96.8	97.0
20	89.4	88.5
30	78.6	77.5
40	69.2	67.5
50	59.9	57.0
60	49.2	48.2
80	34.2	33.5
100	22.7	22.5
120	14.9	14.5

In cases where a steady current of air is drawn over the active body, the observed values are slightly lower than the theoretical. This is probably due to a slight volatility of the product radium B at ordinary temperatures.

18. *α-Ray Curves.* The analysis of the decay curves of the excited activity of radium, measured by the α rays, will now be discussed. The following table shows the variation of the intensity of the radiation after a long exposure in the presence of the radium emanation. A platinum plate was made active by exposure of several days in a glass tube containing a large quantity of emanation. The active platinum after removal was placed on the lower of two parallel insulated lead plates, and a saturating electromotive force of 600 volts was applied. The ionization current was sufficiently large to be measured by means of a sensitive high-resistance galvanometer, and readings were taken as quickly as possible after removal of the platinum from the emanation vessel. The initial value of the current (taken as 100) was deduced by continuing the curves backwards to meet the vertical axis (see fig. 12), and was found to be 3×10^{-8} ampère.

Time in minutes	Current	Time in minutes	Current
0	100	30	40.4
2	80	40	35.6
4	69.5	50	30.4
6	62.4	60	25.4
8	57.6	80	17.4
10	52.0	100	11.6
15	48.4	120	7.6
20	45.4		

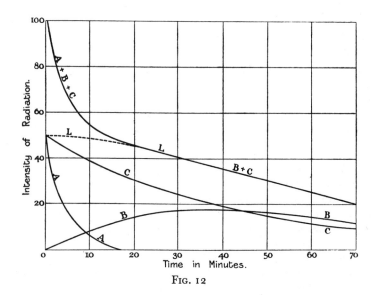

FIG. 12

These results are shown graphically in the upper curve of fig. 12. The initial rapid decrease is due to the decay of the activity of the matter A.   If the slope of the curve is produced backwards from a time 20 minutes after removal, it cuts the vertical axis at about 50. The difference between the ordinates of the curves A + B + C and LL at any time is shown in the curve AA.   The curve AA represents the activity at any time supplied by the change in radium A.   The curve LL starting from the vertical axis is identical with the curve already considered, representing the decay of activity measured by the β rays for a long exposure (see fig. 6).   This is shown by the agreement of the numbers in the following tables.   The first column in the table

below gives the theoretical values of the activity deduced from the
equation

$$\frac{I_t}{I_0} = \frac{\lambda_2}{\lambda_2 - \lambda_3} e^{-\lambda_3 t} - \frac{\lambda_3}{\lambda_2 - \lambda_3} e^{-\lambda_2 t}$$

for the values of λ_2, λ_3 previously employed. The second column
gives the observed values of the activity deduced from the decay
curve LL.

Time in minutes	Calculated value of activity	Observed value of activity
0	100	100
10	96.8	97.0
20	89.4	89.2
30	78.6	80.8
40	69.2	71.2
50	59.9	60.8
60	49.2	50.1
80	34.2	34.8
100	22.7	23.2
120	14.9	15.2

The close agreement of the curve LL with the theoretical curve
deduced on the assumption that there are two changes, the first of
which does not emit rays, shows that the change of radium B into C
does not emit α rays.   In a similar way, as in the curve I, fig. 11, the
curve LL may be analysed into its two components represented by
the two curves CC and BB.   The curve CC represents the activity
supplied by the matter C present at the moment of removal.   The
curve BB represents the activity resulting from the change B into C
and is identical with the corresponding curve in fig. 11.   Using the
same line of reasoning as before, we may thus conclude that the
change of B into C is not accompanied by α rays.   It has already been
shown that it does not give rise to β rays, and the identity of the β and
γ-ray curves show that it does not give rise to γ rays.   The change
B into C is thus a 'rayless' change, while the change C into D gives
rise to all three kinds of rays.

An analysis of the decay of the excited activity of radium thus
shows that three distinct rapid changes occur in the deposited
matter, viz.:—

(1) The matter A, derived from the change in the emanation, is
half transformed in 3 minutes and is accompanied by α rays
alone;

(2) The matter B is half transformed in 21 minutes and gives rise to no ionizing rays;

(3) The matter C is half transformed in 28 minutes and is accompanied by α, β and γ rays;

(4) A fourth very slow change, which will be discussed later (section 23).

19. *Equations Representing the Activity Curves.* The equations representing the variation of activity with time are for convenience collected below, where $\lambda_1 = 3.8 \times 10^{-3}$, $\lambda_2 = 3.10 \times 10^{-4}$, $\lambda_3 = 4.13 \times 10^{-4}$:—

(1) Short exposure: activity measured by β rays,

$$I_t/I_T = 10.3\,(e^{-\lambda_3 t} - e^{-\lambda_2 t}),$$

where I_T is the maximum value of the activity;

(2) Long exposure: activity measured by β rays,

$$I_t/I_0 = 4.3\,e^{-\lambda_3 t} - 3.3\,e^{-\lambda_2 t},$$

where I_0 is the initial value;

(3) Any time of exposure T: activity measured by the β rays,

$$\frac{I_t}{I_0} = \frac{a e^{-\lambda_3 t} - b e^{-\lambda_2 t}}{a - b},$$

where

$$a = \frac{1 - e^{-\lambda_3 T}}{\lambda_3}, \quad b = \frac{1 - e^{-\lambda_2 T}}{\lambda_2};$$

(4) Activity measured by α rays: long time of exposure,

$$\frac{I_t}{I_0} = \tfrac{1}{2} e^{-\lambda_1 t} + \tfrac{1}{2}(4.3\,e^{-\lambda_3 t} - 3.3\,e^{-\lambda_2 t}).$$

The equations for the α rays for any time of exposure can be readily deduced; but the expressions are somewhat complicated.

20. *Equations of Rise of Excited Activity.* The curves expressing the gradual increase to a maximum of the excited activity produced on a body exposed in the presence of a constant amount of emanation are complementary to the curves of decay for a long exposure. The sum of the ordinates of the rise and decay curves is at any time a constant. This necessarily follows from the theory and can also be simply deduced from *a priori* considerations. ('Radioactivity,' p. 267.)

The curves of rise and decay of the excited activity are shown graphically in fig. 13 for both the α and β rays. The thick line curves are for the α rays. The difference between the shapes of the decay curves when measured by the α or β rays is clearly brought out in the figure. The equations representing the rise of activity to a maximum are given below.

For the β and γ rays,

$$I_t/I_{max} = 1 - (4.3\, e^{-\lambda_3 t} - 3.3\, e^{-\lambda_2 t}).$$

For the α rays,

$$I_t/I_{max} = 1 - \tfrac{1}{2} e^{-\lambda_1 t} - \tfrac{1}{2}(4.3\, e^{-\lambda_3 t} - 3.3\, e^{-\lambda_2 t}).$$

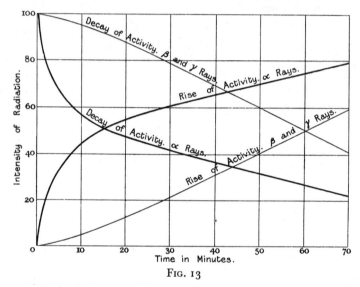

FIG. 13

21. *Effect of Temperature.* We have so far not considered the evidence on which the 28-minute rather than 21-minute change is supposed to take place in the matter C. This evidence has been supplied by some recent important experiments of P. Curie and Danne[21] on the volatilization of the active matter deposited by the emanation. Miss Gates[22] showed that this active matter was volatilized from a platinum wire above a red heat and deposited on the surface of a cold cylinder surrounding the wire. Curie and Danne extended these results by subjecting an active platinum wire *for a short time* to the action of temperatures varying between 15° C. and 1350° C., and then examining at room temperatures the decay curves not only for the active matter remaining on the wire, but also for the volatilized part. They found that the activity of the distilled

[21] *Comptes Rendus*, 138, p. 748, 1904.
[22] *Phys. Rev.*, p. 300, 1903.

part always increased after removal, passed through a maximum, and finally decayed according to an exponential law (half value in 28 minutes). At a temperature of about 630° C. the active matter left behind on the wire decayed at once according to an exponential law, falling to half value in 28 minutes. P. CURIE and DANNE showed that the matter B is much more volatile than C. The former is completely volatilized at about 600° C., while the latter is not completely volatilized even at a temperature of 1300° C. The fact that the matter C, left behind when B is completely volatilized, decays at once to half value in 28 minutes shows that the matter C itself and not B is half transformed in 28 minutes.

CURIE and DANNE also found that the rate of decay of the active matter varied with the temperature to which the platinum wire had been subjected. At 630° C. the rate of decay was normal, at 1100° C. the activity fell to half value in about 20 minutes, while at 1300° C. it fell to about half value in about 25 minutes.

I have repeated the experiments of CURIE and DANNE and obtained very similar results. It was thought possible that the measured rate of decay observed after heating might be due to a permanent increase in the rate of volatilization of C at ordinary temperatures. This explanation, however, is not tenable, for it was found that the activity decreased at the same rate whether the activity of the wire was tested in a closed tube or in the open with a current of air passed over it.

These results are of great importance, for they indicate that the rate of change of the product C is not a constant, but is affected by differences of temperature. This is the first case where temperature has been shown to exert an appreciable influence on the rate of change of any radioactive product.

22. *Effect of the First Rapid Change.* We have seen that the law of decay of activity, measured by the β or γ rays, can be very satisfactorily explained if the first 3-minute change is disregarded. The full theoretical examination of the question given in sections 10 and 11 and the curves of figs. 8 and 9 shows, however, that the presence of the first change should exercise an effect of sufficient magnitude to be detected in measurements of the activity due to the succeeding changes. The question is of great interest, for it involves the important theoretical point whether the substances A and B are produced independently of one another, or whether A is the parent of B. In the latter case, the matter A which is present changes into B, and, in consequence, the amount of B present after A is transformed should be somewhat greater than if B were produced independently. Since the change of A is fairly rapid, the effect should be most marked in the early part of the curve.

In order to examine this point experimentally, the curve of rise of activity, measured by the β rays, was determined immediately after the introduction of a large quantity of the radium emanation into a closed vessel. The curve of decay of activity on a body after removal of the emanation, and the rise of activity after the introduction of the emanation, are in all cases complementary to one another. While, however, it is difficult to measure with certainty whether the activity has fallen in a given time, for example, from 100 to 99 or 98.5, it is easy to be sure whether the corresponding rise of activity in the converse experiment is 1 or 1.5 per cent. of the final amount. Fig. 14, curve I., shows the rise of activity (measured by the β rays)

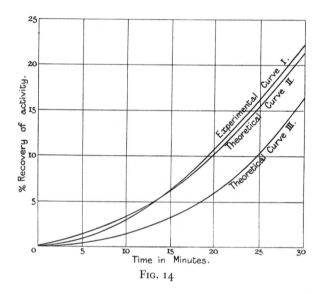

FIG. 14

obtained for an interval of 20 minutes after the introduction of the emanation. The ordinates represent the percentage amount of the final activity regained at any time.

Curve III. shows the theoretical curve obtained on the assumption that A is a parent of B. This curve is calculated from equation (9) discussed in section 11, and λ_1, λ_2, λ_3 are the values previously found.

Curve II. gives the theoretical activity at any time on the assumption that the substances A and B arise independently. This is calculated from an equation of the same form as (8).

It is seen that the experimental results agree best with the view that A and B arise independently. Such a conclusion, however, is of too great importance to be accepted before examining closely whether the theoretical conditions are fulfilled in the experiments. In the first place, it is assumed that the carriers which give rise to excited activity are deposited on the surface of the body, to be made active immediately after their formation.   There is some evidence, however, that some of these carriers exist for a considerable interval in the gas before their deposit on the body.   For example, it is found that if a body is introduced for a short interval, about 1 minute, into a vessel containing the radium emanation, which has remained undisturbed for several hours, the activity after the first rapid decay (see fig. 4, curve B) is in much greater proportion than if an electric field had been acting for some time previously.   This result indicates that the carriers of B and C both collect in the gas and are swept to the electrode when an electric field is applied.   This effect may in part be due to a slight volatility of the matter B at ordinary temperatures.[23]   If the matter B exists to some extent in the gas, the difference between the theoretical curves for three successive changes would be explained; for, in transferring the emanation to another vessel, the matter B mixed with it would commence at once to change into C and give rise to a part of the radiation observed.

The equal division of the activity between the products A and C (see fig. 12) supports the view that C is a product of A, for when radioactive equilibrium is reached, the number of particles of A changing per second is equal to the number of B or C changing per second.   If each atom of A and C expels an α particle of the same mass and with the same average velocity, the activity due to the matter A should be equal to that due to the matter C; and this, as we have seen, is the case.   Further investigations are in progress, which it is hoped will throw more light on this difficult question.

23. *Very Slow Change in the Active Deposit from Radium.*   M. and Mme. Curie[24] have observed that bodies which have been exposed for a long interval in the presence of the radium emanation do not lose all of their activity.   The excited activity at first decays according to the equations already considered, but a residual activity always remains, of the order of 1/20,000 of the initial activity.   This residual

---

[23] This result is supported by some recent experiments of Miss Brooks (*Nature*, July 21, 1904).   It was shown that the matter B is volatile at ordinary temperatures, and a small part escapes from the active body and is deposited in the neighbourhood. It was also observed that the volatility of the matter B was far more marked during the first 10 minutes after removal, *i.e.*, during the time the first change is in progress. If A is the parent of B, the expulsion of a charged α particle must set B in motion, and in consequence some of the atoms of B may acquire sufficient velocity to escape from the active body.

[24] 'Thèse présentée à la Faculté des Sciences,' Paris, 1903, p. 116.

activity seemed fairly permanent, for it did not decay during an interval of six months. GIESEL observed that a platinum wire which has been exposed to the radium emanation shows residual activity, and he states that the radiation consists entirely of α rays.

I have examined this residual activity in the following way. The emanation from 30 milligs. of pure radium bromide was condensed in a small glass tube and the ends of the tube sealed. After standing for a month the tube was opened, and left to stand for several days, in order to allow all the remaining emanation to escape. The inside of the glass tube was found to show considerable activity. The tube was then filled with dilute sulphuric acid, and, after standing several hours, the acid was removed and evaporated down to dryness in a flat glass dish. Most of the active matter in the glass tube was dissolved out by the acid, and, after evaporation, a strongly active residue was obtained in the glass dish. The active matter was found to give out both α and β rays, and the β rays were present in a very unusual proportion; thus, compared with the intensity of the α rays, the β rays were present in at least 10 times greater proportion than for a thin layer of uranium, thorium, or radium, in a state of radio-active equilibrium.

The intensity of the α radiation was first tested when the active deposit was about 2 months old. The activity, at that time, did not vary apparently over a week's interval. Owing to a numerical error it was at first thought that the activity did not change during a further interval of 3 months; but the corrected result showed that the activity had more than doubled itself during that interval. Still later observations show that the α-ray activity is steadily increasing.

The increase of the α-ray activity with time has been confirmed by observations of the residual activity left behind on a platinum plate exposed to the emanation. The results then showed that the α-ray activity during the first month, after removal, increases considerably. The relative proportion of β to α rays steadily diminishes with the time. This is not due to a diminution of the β-ray activity, but to an increase of the α-ray activity. Further observations are in progress to examine the variations of the activity over long periods of time.

The results, so far as they have gone, show that the residual activity produced on bodies by exposure to the radium emanation is very complicated. The results discussed in the next section show that the large β-ray activity is due to matter of different chemical properties from that which gives rise to the α rays.

The increase of the α-ray activity with time indicates that the deposited matter undergoes a slow 'rayless' change. The evidence at present obtained points to the conclusion that the deposited matter is initially complex. A small portion of the total amount undergoes a change, accompanied by the emission of β rays alone. The main portion of the deposited matter undergoes a very slow 'rayless' transformation, and the resulting product or products give rise to α rays.

Observations extending over a long period of time will be required to determine the period of these changes. It seems probable that radium C breaks up into two distinct products. The major part of the product then undergoes a further change or succession of changes.[25]

24. *Connection of Slowly Decaying Product with Radio-Tellurium.* Some evidence will now be considered which points to the strong probability that one of these slowly changing products of radium is the same as the active constituent present in radio-tellurium, separated from pitchblende by MARCKWALD.

It will be recalled that the polonium of Mme. CURIE is always obtained with bismuth, but can be partially separated from it by several distinct methods. GIESEL early observed that a bismuth plate dipped into a radium solution became permanently active and gave out only α rays, and in this respect resembled the polonium of Mme. CURIE.

GIESEL has throughout insisted that polonium was nothing more than 'induced bismuth'—apparently considering that the bismuth acquired the radioactive property by mixture with a radium solution. Taking the point of view that radioactivity is always the result of changes occurring in special kinds of matter, the experiments of GIESEL indicate that a radioactive product is deposited from the radium solution on to the bismuth plate, and that the activity of the plate is not due to the bismuth at all, but to radioactive matter deposited on its surface.

MARCKWALD found that a bismuth plate dipped into a solution of pitchblende was coated with a radioactive deposit. He at first thought this activity was due to the tellurium which was deposited on the plate, and consequently gave it the name radio-tellurium. Later results have, however, shown that the activity has nothing whatever to do with the tellurium, and by suitable chemical methods he has separated an extremely active substance. MARCKWALD

---

[25] [*October* 10, 1904.—Further experimental work on this subject has led to a modification of the above conclusions. It has been found that the results are best explained on the supposition that radium C gives rise to radium D, which in breaking up emits only β (and probably γ) rays. Radium D produces radium E, which breaks up with the emission of only α rays. It has been deduced that D is probably half transformed in 40 years and E in about 1 year. This modification has been introduced into the subsequent schedules in the text. A full account of these experiments was communicated to the Electrical Congress at St. Louis (September 16, 1904) in a paper entitled "Further Transformation Products of Radium."]

states that the radio-tellurium gives out only α rays, and has not appreciably changed during six months after separation. Mme. CURIE found that the active constituent present in bismuth, which had been made active by placing it in a radium solution, could be fractionated in the same way as polonium, and in that way was able to obtain bismuth 2000 times as active as uranium, but this activity decreased with the time.

An account will now be given of some experiments to ascertain if there is any connection between this slowly decaying product of radium and radio-tellurium or polonium.

The active matter deposited on the glass tube, in which a large amount of radium emanation had been stored for a month, was dissolved in sulphuric acid. A bismuth plate was introduced into the solution and left for several hours. The bismuth plate was found to be strongly active and to give out only α rays. On adding a second bismuth plate, very little active matter was deposited upon it. The remaining solution was then evaporated, and the residue was found to be about as active as the bismuth plate, and to give out both α and β rays. There is thus no doubt that the matter dissolved off the glass is complex, and one part is deposited on bismuth and the other not. The activity of the bismuth plate did not appreciably change during a month's interval.[26] Part of the active matter obtained from the sulphuric acid solution then behaves in a similar way to the radio-tellurium of MARCKWALD, inasmuch as it gives out only α rays, and is readily deposited on bismuth. In order to test the apparent similarity still further, an accurate comparison was made between the penetrating power of the rays from the active bismuth and a bismuth plate of radio-tellurium obtained from Dr. STHAMER, of Hamburg. The rays were found initially to be about half absorbed in a thickness of .00034 centim. of aluminium, and exhibited the characteristic property of the rays of rapidly increasing absorption with the thickness of matter traversed. No appreciable difference in the penetrating power of the α rays from the two substances was observed, although the intensity of the radiations was reduced to less than 1 per cent. of the initial value. It has been found experimentally that the rays from the different radioactive products differ in penetrating power, and the curve of absorption for different thicknesses of absorbing material is, in general, a characteristic of each product.

The identity of the curves of absorption of the α rays from the active bismuth and the radio-tellurium, coupled with the similarity

---

[26] This bismuth plate was unfortunately mislaid during my visit to England in May. I am, in consequence, unable to give a more definite statement in regard to the change of the activity with time.

of the radiations and chemical properties, is very strong evidence that the active product is in each case the same. I think there can be little doubt that the active constituent of radio-tellurium of MARCKWALD is a disintegration product of radium.

The polonium (radioactive bismuth) obtained by me from Paris loses its activity fairly rapidly, and the α rays from it are more readily absorbed than the α rays of radio-tellurium. This greater absorption may, however, be due in part to the fact that the radiations from the polonium come from the mass of the bismuth, and in consequence are made up of rays of widely different penetrating power, while the rays from the radio-tellurium arise from a thin film of matter deposited on the bismuth plate, in which the absorption of the issuing rays would be small. The identity or otherwise of the constituent present in the polonium of Mme. CURIE and the radio-tellurium of MARCKWALD has been a much vexed question. A definite answer cannot be given until accurate observations have been made of the change of activity with time of these products.

25. *Radioactivity observed in Ordinary Matter.* A large number of experimenters have observed that ordinary matter possesses the property of radioactivity to a feeble degree. R. J. STRUTT found that different samples of the same metal showed wide differences in radio-active power. It is a matter of great importance to settle whether the weak radioactivity observed is a property of the substance under examination or is due to a minute radioactive impurity. I think there is little doubt that the radioactivity observed in some substances is due in part to a deposit of radioactive matter on its surface from the atmosphere. It has now been conclusively shown that the radium emanation is present in the atmosphere. This, in the course of its disintegration, gives rise to the slowly decaying product, which will be deposited from the air on the surface of all bodies exposed in the open. Such bodies will thus be covered with an invisible film of radioactive matter of very slow rate of change. The results of COOKE[27] are a strong confirmation of this point of view. By carefully polishing the surface of a brass electroscope, he was able to reduce its rate of discharge to almost one-third of the normal amount. In such a case the radioactive matter was removed from the surface by the process of polishing. The strong radioactivity observed in a room in which radium preparations have once been used, is probably due to the deposit on the walls of the room of this slowly decaying matter from the emanation.

26. *Comparison of the Changes in the Radio-Elements.* The changes occurring in the three radio-elements and the radiations which

---

[27] *Phil. Mag.*, August, 1903.

accompany them are shown graphically in fig. 15. The radiations
from actinium have not yet been sufficiently examined to be certain
where the β or γ rays appear in the last change as in the case of
thorium. It will be seen that there are, at least, six successive
changes in radium, five in thorium, and two in uranium. The first
five changes in radium are analogous, in many respects, to the corresponding changes in thorium and actinium. Each of these elements
gives rise to a gaseous product, the emanation, and this in turn is
transformed into a type of matter which is deposited on the surface

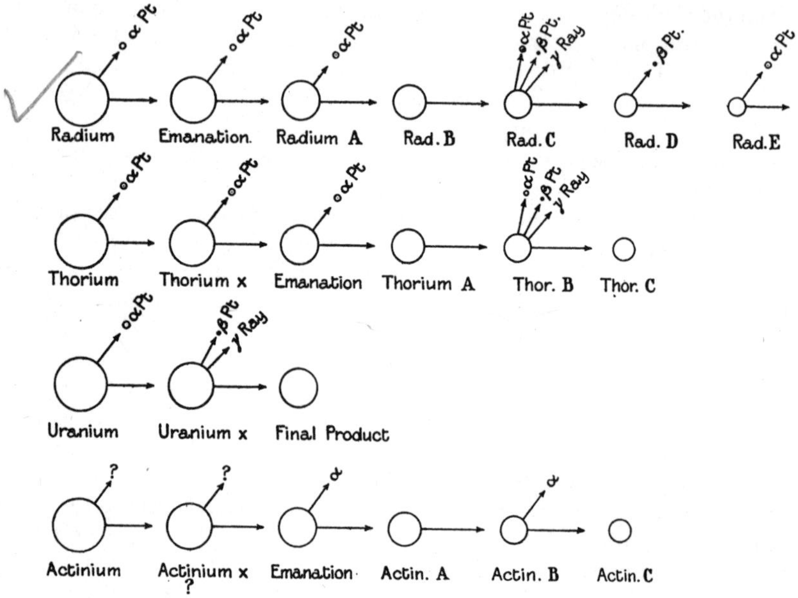

Fig. 15

of bodies. In both thorium and radium, the fourth change is
followed by a change in which all three types of rays appear together,
while the third product in all three elements does not emit rays at all.
The remarkable similarity in the nature of the changes occurring in
radium, thorium, and actinium, indicates that the constitution of the
atoms of these bodies is very similar.

The time T taken for each product to be half transformed, and
the value of the related constant λ, the fractional amount of the
product changed per second, are shown in the following table,
together with some of the physical and chemical properties of the
products:—

Product	T	λ (sec)$^{-1}$	Some physical and chemical properties
URANIUM $\rightarrow$	10^9 years	2.2×10^{-17}	Soluble in excess of ammonium carbonate.
Uranium X $\rightarrow$	22 days	3.6×10^{-7}	Insoluble in excess of ammonium carbonate.
Final product	—	—	
THORIUM $\rightarrow$	3×10^9	7×10^{-18}	Insoluble in ammonia.
Thorium X $\rightarrow$	4 days	2.00×10^{-6}	Soluble in ammonia.
Thorium emanation $\rightarrow$	1 minute	1.15×10^{-2}	Chemically inert gas; condenses about $-120°$ C.
Thorium A $\rightarrow$	11 hours	1.75×10^{-5}	Behaves as solid; insoluble in ammonia; volatilized at a white heat; soluble in strong acids; Thorium A can be separated from B by electrolysis.
Thorium B $\rightarrow$	55 minutes	2.1×10^{-4}	
Thorium C (final product)	—	—	

Product	T	λ (sec)$^{-1}$	Some physical and chemical properties
ACTINIUM $\rightarrow$	—	—	
Actinium X? $\rightarrow$	—	—	
Actinium emanation $\rightarrow$	3.7 seconds	1.87×10^{-1}	Behaves as a gas.
Actinium A $\rightarrow$	41 minutes	2.80×10^{-4}	Behaves as solid; soluble in strong acids; A can be partially separated from B by electrolysis.
Actinium B $\rightarrow$	1.5 minutes	7.7×10^{-3}	
Actinium C (final product)	—	—	
RADIUM $\rightarrow$	800 years	2.8×10^{-11}	
Radium emanation $\rightarrow$	4 days	2.00×10^{-6}	Chemically inert gas; condenses about $-150°$ C. Definite spectrum; volume diminishes with time.
Radium A $\rightarrow$	3 minutes	3.8×10^{-3}	Behaves as solid; soluble in strong acids; volatilized at a white heat; B is more volatile than A or C and can thus be temporarily separated from them.
Radium B $\rightarrow$	21 minutes	5.38×10^{-4}	
Radium C $\rightarrow$	28 minutes	4.13×10^{-4}	
Radium D $\rightarrow$	About 40 years	—	Gives out only β rays. Soluble in strong acids.
Radium E	About 1 year	—	Probably active constituent of radio-tellurium; soluble in strong acids; volatilized at a red heat: deposited on bismuth in solution.

The value of T may be taken as a comparative measure of the stability of the atoms of each product. The atoms of the radium emanation and thorium X have about the same stability. The apparent agreement of the rate of change in the two cases must be considered as a coincidence, and does not, in any way, indicate that the atoms of the two products are the same, for ThX and the radium emanation differ both in physical and chemical properties. If the atoms of the two products were identical, it would be expected that the subsequent changes would take place in the same way and at the same rate; but such is not the case. The stability of the atoms of the products varies over a very wide range. The stability of the atom of ThX, for example, is about 100,000 times greater than that of the actinium emanation. There is every reason to believe that the radio-elements themselves must be regarded as radioactive products of very slow rate of change. In a case like uranium, which is probably half transformed in about 1,000,000,000 years, the atoms must be considered as very stable compared with products like the emanations of thorium or radium.

27. *Rayless Changes.* The existence of a well-marked change in radium, thorium, and actinium, which is not accompanied by the expulsion of α or β particles, is of great interest and importance.

Since the rayless changes are not accompanied by any appreciable ionization of the gas, their presence cannot be detected by direct means. The rate of change of the substance can, however, be indirectly determined, as we have seen, by determination of the variation with time of the activity of the succeeding product. The law of change has been found to be the same as for the changes which give rise to α rays. The rayless changes are thus analogous, in some respects, to the monomolecular changes observed in chemistry, with the difference that the changes are in the atoms themselves, and are not due to a molecular combination of the atoms with another substance.

It must be supposed that a rayless change is not of so violent a character as one which gives rise to the expulsion of α or β particles. The change may be accounted for either by supposing that there is a re-arrangement of the components of the atom, or that the atom breaks up without the expulsion of its parts with sufficient velocity to produce ionization by collision with the gas. The latter point of view, if correct, at once indicates the possibility that changes of a similar character may be taking place slowly in the non-radioactive elements; or, in other words, that all matter may be undergoing a slow process of change. The changes taking place in the radio-elements have been detected only in consequence of the expulsion with great velocity of the parts of the disintegrated atom. If the α

particles had been expelled with a velocity less than 10^8 centims. per second, it is improbable that any ionization would have been produced, and the changes, in consequence, could not have been followed by the electric method.

28. *Radiations from the Products.* The radiations from the successive products of the disintegration of radium have been very closely investigated, and it has been found that, with the exception of the rayless change, all the changes are accompanied by the emission of α particles with great velocity. The β and γ rays appear only in the fifth change. In the case of thorium, it has not been found possible to completely free the product ThX from β rays, on account of the difficulty of entirely removing from it the products of the subsequent change. The proportion of β rays is, however, greatly reduced if the emanation produced by the ThX is removed by passing a rapid current of air through a solution of ThX. The emanation itself gives out only α rays, but the second product, thorium B, arising from it gives out all three types of rays. A removal of part of the emanation thus decreases the amount of β rays from the ThX. I think there is little doubt that, if the emanation could be removed from the ThX as fast as it was formed, it would be found that the ThX itself gives out only α rays, and that the β and γ rays, as in the case of radium, appear only in the fifth change.

It is remarkable that the β and γ rays of uranium, thorium, and radium appear only in the last of the rapid succession of changes occurring in those bodies. It has already been pointed out that the β and γ rays always appear together and in the same proportion. There is now little doubt that the γ rays are electromagnetic pulses, similar to X rays, generated at the moment of the sudden expulsion of the β particle from the radio-atom.

In the three radio-elements, the expulsion of the β particle results in the appearance of a product either permanently stable, or, in the case of radium, of a product far more stable than the preceding one. It would appear that the initial changes are accompanied only by the expulsion of an α particle, and that once the β particle is expelled, the components of the residual atom fall into an arrangement of fairly stable equilibrium, when the rate of disintegration is very slow. I think that it is more than a coincidence that the β and γ rays appear only in the last of the rapid changes in the three radio-elements.

It appears probable that the β particle, which is finally expelled, may be regarded as the active agent in promoting the disintegration of the radio-atom in successive stages. According to the modern point of view of regarding atomic structure, the atoms of the radio-element may be supposed to be made up of electrons (β particles) and groups of electrons (α particles) in rapid motion, and held in equilibrium by their mutual forces. If the atom is to remain permanently stable, it is necessary that there should be no loss of energy as a whole from the moving charged parts of which the atom is built up. LARMOR has shown that this condition is fulfilled if the vector sum of the accelerations of the moving particles is permanently null. If this is not the case, there must be a continuous drain of energy from the atom in the form of electromagnetic radiation. This, in the course of time, must disturb the equilibrium of the atom, and result either in a re-arrangement of its component parts or to its final disintegration. It may, perhaps, be supposed that occasionally one of the outlying revolving electrons, comprising the radio-atom, lapses into a position which results in a slow loss of energy from the atom in the form of radiation. In consequence of this loss of energy, the atom becomes unstable, and ultimately an α particle flies off with its great orbital velocity, but the atom still retains the disturbing cause. The residue, in consequence, again becomes unstable and ejects another α particle, and the process goes on from stage to stage, until finally the β particle is violently ejected from the system.

Following the general point of view suggested by Sir OLIVER LODGE in a recent letter to *Nature*, it may be possible that, as a result of continuous radiation, the velocity of the β particle in its orbit has steadily increased, until finally in the last stage a sudden lapse into a new state of the atom occurs, in which not only does an α particle escape, but also the β particle. When the β particle is removed from it, the residual atom adjusts itself again into a position of more permanent equilibrium.

The experimental evidence as a whole points strongly to the conclusion that the change in which the β rays appear is far more disruptive in character than any of the preceding ones; for not only is the β particle thrown off with nearly the velocity of light, but the α particle, ejected at the same time, has greater penetrating power and probably greater kinetic energy than in any of the other changes.

In addition, there is at present some evidence that this final change is of such a violent character that the atom is in some cases disrupted into several fragments, and that, in addition to the α and β particles, two or more atoms are produced, each of which has some distinctive physical and chemical properties, and also a distinctive rate of decay. If the greater proportion of the matter resulting from the disintegration is of one kind, it would be difficult to detect the presence of a small quantity of rapidly changing matter from observations of the curves of decay; but if the products have distinctive electrochemical behaviour, a partial separation, in some cases, should be effected by electrolysis. The electrolytic method is a very powerful means of separating active products which may be present in small quanti-

compared with the other radioactive products. It has already been mentioned (section 13) that the results of PEGRAM and VON LERCH, obtained by electrolysis of thorium solutions, may be in part explained on the supposition that thorium A and thorium B have distinctive electrochemical behaviour. PEGRAM, however, in addition, observed the presence of a product which lost half of its activity in about 6 minutes. This active product was obtained by electrolysing a solution of pure thorium salt, to which a small quantity of copper nitrate was added. The copper deposit was found to be radioactive to a slight extent, and the activity decayed to half value in about 6 minutes.

The presence of such radioactive products, which do not come under the main scheme of changes, indicates that at some stage of the disintegration more than one radioactive substance results. In the violent disintegration which occurs in radium C and thorium B, such a result is to be expected; for it is not improbable that there are several arrangements of the constituents of the atoms to form a system of some slight stability. The two radioactive products resulting from the disintegration of a single atom would probably be present in unequal proportions. A closer investigation of the radioactive bodies will very probably lead to the separation of a number of radioactive products, present in a small proportion among the main products.

29. *Difference between Radioactive and Chemical Change.* The successive changes occurring in the radio-elements are distinguished in certain important particulars from ordinary chemical change. We have seen that each active product, left to itself, is transformed according to a definite law and at a definite rate. The law of change is the same as for a monomolecular reaction in chemistry, and shows that only one changing system is involved. The constant of change λ is independent of the degree of concentration of the product, and of the nature and presence of the surrounding gas, and, in most cases, is not much affected by wide differences of temperature. The work of CURIE and DANNE, however, shows that the constant λ of the product radium C (see section 21) is certainly altered by temperature. After this substance has been subjected for a few minutes to a temperature of about 1100° C., its value of λ (when cooled to atmospheric temperature) *is permanently altered.* The value of λ at 1100° C. is about 1.4 times the normal value. Above 1100° C. the value of λ decreases again, and at 1300° C. it is about 1.1 times the normal. These results show that increase of temperature to a certain point increases the rate of disintegration of radium C, but that on exposure to a still higher temperature the rate of disintegration decreases again and becomes nearly equal to the normal value.

The two features which differentiate the radioactive changes from ordinary chemical change are:—

(1) The expulsion of charged particles with great velocity;
(2) The emission of an enormous amount of energy compared with the amount of matter involved.

Except in the case of the radio-elements, no chemical change is known which is accompanied by an expulsion with great velocity of a product of the change. In each change that is accompanied by the expulsion of α rays, the amount of energy liberated, weight for weight, is over 100,000 times greater than has previously been observed in any chemical reaction. Dr. BARNES and the writer[28] showed that 75 per cent. of the heat-emission of radium was due to the emanation and its further products. The emanation from a gramme of radium gives out heat at the rate of 75 gramme-calories per hour. The total amount of heat liberated during its life is 10,000 gramme-calories approximately. Now from the work of RAMSAY and SODDY it is known that the volume of the emanation extracted from 1 gramme of radium is not greater than 1 cub. millim. The energy emitted from 1 cub. centim. of the radium emanation is therefore equal to 10^7 gramme-calories. Now the heat emitted during the combination of 1 cub. centim. of hydrogen and oxygen to form water is 2 gramme-calories. Thus the emanation gives out during its changes 5×10^6 times as much energy as the combination of an equal volume of hydrogen and oxygen to form water. The energy emitted from a vessel containing the radium emanation is almost equally divided between the emanation and the products radium A and radium C. Each of these products gives out α rays. It is probable that the 'rayless' product radium B gives out far less heat than the other products.

There seems to be little doubt that the energy emitted from radium is about equally divided between the products which break up with the expulsion of α particles, *i.e.*, 25 per cent. of the total heat emission is supplied in each case by the breaking up of radium, the emanation, radium A and radium C. The energy radiated is, in all probability, mainly derived from the kinetic energy of the expelled α particles. Since the α particles expelled from the products of uranium, thorium, and actinium are projected with about the same velocity as from radium, it necessarily follows that each atom of the radioactive products which breaks up with the expulsion of an α particle gives out about an equal quantity of energy. This amount of energy is about 6×10^{-6} erg for each atom at each stage of its disintegration.

---

[28] *Phil. Mag.*, February, 1904.

Since there is the same number of changes in thorium as in radium, the heating effect of thorium will be proportional to its activity, *i.e.*, will be only about 5×10^{-7} of that from an equal quantity of radium.

Since the discovery of the actual production of helium from the radium emanation by RAMSAY and SODDY, there has been a tendency to assume that helium is the final transformation product of radium. There is no evidence in support of such a conclusion, for, as we have already seen, the radium atom goes on through a further series of slow changes after the first rapid changes have taken place during which the helium makes its appearance. In addition, the evidence supports the view that one α particle is expelled from each atom at each stage of its disintegration, excepting possibly the rayless change. The expulsion of four α particles, of mass about that of the helium atom, still leaves a heavy atom behind. I have previously pointed out that the α particles, in all probability, consist of helium atoms expelled at the successive stages of the disintegration. This conclusion is supported by measurements of the mass of the α particle, and by the observations of the rate of production of helium by the radium emanation made by RAMSAY and SODDY.

The similarity of the α particles from the different radio-elements indicates that they consist of expelled particles of the same kind. On this view, helium should be produced by each of the radio-elements. The presence of helium in minerals such as thorium, for example, in monazite sand, and the Ceylon mineral described by RAMSAY, suggests that helium is a product of thorium as well as of radium.

Taking the view that the α particles are projected helium atoms, we must regard the atoms of the radio-elements as compounds of some known or unknown substance with helium. These compounds break up spontaneously and at a very slow rate even in the case of radium. The disintegration takes place in successive stages, and at most of the stages a helium atom is projected with great velocity. This disintegration is accompanied by an enormous emission of energy. The liberation of such a large amount of energy in the radioactive changes at once explains the independence of the rate of change on the physical and chemical agencies at our command. On this view, uranium, thorium, and radium are in reality compounds of helium. The helium, however, is held in such strong combination that the compound cannot be broken up by chemical or physical forces and, in consequence, these bodies behave as chemical elements in the ordinary accepted chemical sense.

It appears not unlikely that many of the so-called chemical elements may prove to be compounds of helium, or, in other words, that the helium atom is probably one of the secondary units with which the heavier atoms are built up.

30. *The Charge Carried by the α Rays.* It is of great importance to determine as directly as possible the total number of α particles expelled from a known weight of radium in order to deduce the number of atoms which break up per second. The most direct method of determining this number is to measure the positive charge carried off by the α rays. Assuming that the charge of the α particle is equal in magnitude to that carried by the ions in gases, the number of α particles expelled per second can at once be determined.

A thin film of radium was obtained on a plate by evaporation of a radium bromide solution of known strength. Some hours after evaporation, the activity of radium measured by the α rays is about 25 per cent. of its maximum value, and the β rays are almost com-

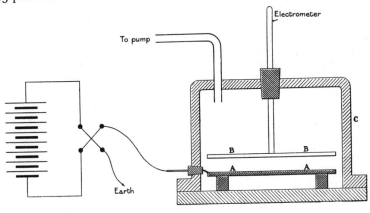

FIG. 16

pletely absent. The arrangement of the experiment is shown in fig. 16.

The active plate A was insulated in a metal vessel, C, and was connected to one pole of the battery, the other pole being earthed. The upper plate B was insulated and connected to a Dolezalek electrometer. The outside vessel C could be connected to either A or B, or to earth. By means of a mercury pump, the vessel C was exhausted to a very low pressure. If the α rays carried a positive charge, the current between the two plates measured by the electrometer should be greater when A is charged positive than when A is negative. No appreciable difference, however, between the currents in the two directions was observed even when a very good vacuum was obtained. In addition, it was found that the current between the plates at first diminished rapidly with the pressure, but reached a limiting value which was not altered by further lowering the pressure. These results are very difficult of interpretation. There is no doubt that the α particle behaves as a positively charged body, inasmuch as it is deviated in a magnetic and electric field in the opposite direction to the β particle. The failure to detect the charge carried by the α rays is probably due in part to a strong secondary ionization set up by the α rays at the surface of the plates A and B. The current due to this effect does not diminish with pressure below a certain limit, and does not seem to be much altered if the air is replaced by hydrogen. At the same time, taking the estimate of the number of particles from 1 gramme of radium, discussed in section 31, it was deduced that the charge carried by them should certainly have been detected by reversal of the electric field, notwithstanding the presence of surface ionization.

A large number of experiments have been made under different conditions, but the results have so far all been negative. It is very difficult to avoid the conclusion that the α particles do carry with them a positive charge, but it must be supposed that the effect of this charge is in some way exactly neutralized. In this connection, it is significant that the charge carried by the 'canal rays,' which are analogous to the α rays of the radio-elements, has not so far been detected, although careful experiments upon that point have been made by WIEN. The apparent absence of charge on the α particles would be explained if an equal number of negatively charged particles, or electrons, were expelled at the same time with a slow velocity. If the electrons had about the same penetrating power as the α particles, it would be difficult to detect their presence by the electric method, as the ionization produced by the α particles would probably mask that produced by the electrons. The electron should be readily deflected in a magnetic field and experiments are, at present, in progress to examine whether the α rays show any trace of positive charge when the rays are exposed to a strong magnetic field.

31. *Magnitude of the Changes Occurring in the Radio-elements.* I have shown ('Radioactivity,' pp. 154–158) that probably about 10^{11} of the α particles are expelled per second from 1 gramme of radium in radio-active equilibrium. This estimate has been deduced as an average of three distinct methods of calculation based on—

(1) The charge carried off by the β rays;
(2) The energy required to produce an ion;
(3) The number of ions produced per centimetre of path by an α particle.

A check on this estimate can be made from calculations of the heating effect observed in radium. There is little doubt that the heating effect of radium is due mainly to the bombardment of the radium by the α particles expelled from its substance. Now, since

$e/m = 6.3 \times 10^3$ for the α particle, and the velocity v is 2.5×10^9, the kinetic energy of the α particle is

$$\tfrac{1}{2}mv^2 = \tfrac{1}{2}\frac{m}{e}.v^2.e = 6 \times 10^{-6} \text{ erg,}$$

if the charge $e = 3.4 \times 10^{-10}$ electrostatic unit.

The rate of heat emission from 1 gramme of radium is equal to 100 gramme-calories per hour, *i.e.*, is mechanically equivalent to 1.2×10^6 ergs per second. If the heating effect is supposed to be due to the kinetic energy of the expelled α particles, 2×10^{11} α particles must be expelled per second to account for the heat emission. This number is in good accordance with the calculated estimate already given. Knowing the number of α particles expelled per second, the volume of the emanation stored up in 1 gramme of radium can at once be deduced. For the purpose of calculation, it is assumed that each atom in breaking up gives rise to one α particle and to one atom of the succeeding product. This is supported by the observed result that each active product of radium supplies almost an equal proportion of the total activity measured by the α rays, *i.e.*, each active product expels about the same number of rays. Now, α rays are expelled by the radium itself, by the emanation, and the products radium A and C. The amount of the slowly changing products radium D and E present is too small to take into account. There are thus four α particles expelled for each radium atom which breaks up. There are thus 2.5×10^{10} atoms of radium breaking up per second. In a state of radioactive equilibrium the number n of atoms of emanation present per gramme of radium is given by $n/q = 1/\lambda$, where q is the number supplied per second, or the number of radium atoms breaking up per second, λ is the radioactive constant. Since $1/\lambda = 500,000$ for the emanation, and $q = 2.5 \times 10^{10}$, we have $n = 1.25 \times 10^{16}$. Townsend showed that $Ne = 1.21 \times 10^{10}$, where N is the number of molecules of hydrogen per unit volume at atmospheric pressure and temperature.

Taking J. J. Thomson's value of e, 3.4×10^{-10} electrostatic unit, we find $N = 3.6 \times 10^{19}$. The volume of the emanation from 1 gramme of radium is n/N cub. centims., which is

$$\frac{1.25 \times 10^{16}}{3.6 \times 10^9},$$

or 3.5×10^{-4} cub. centim., at standard pressure and temperature.

Now, Ramsay and Soddy have recently isolated the emanation, and deduced that the volume from 1 gramme was equal to about 1 cub. millim. The calculated volume is thus of the right order of magnitude. The agreement would be still closer if the number of α particles were taken as 2×10^{11}, the number deduced from the heating effect of radium, rather than 10^{11}. It is probable that the volume obtained by RAMSAY and SODDY is a maximum estimate, on account of the difficulty of removing traces of other gases.

We may thus conclude with some confidence that about 2×10^{11} α particles are expelled per second per gramme, and that the number of atoms per gramme breaking up per second is 5×10^{10}.

Since 1 cub. centim. of hydrogen contains 3.6×10^{19} molecules, it can readily be deduced that 1 gramme of radium contains 1.8×10^{21} atoms, taking the atomic weight of radium as 225.

The fraction of radium breaking up is thus

$$\frac{5 \times 10^{10}}{1.8 \times 10^{21}},$$

or 2.8×10^{-11} per second, that is, 8.8×10^{-4} per year. Thus in a gramme of radium almost one milligramme breaks up per year.

Now there is every reason to suppose that the amount of radium breaking up per second is always proportional to the amount present, as in the case of all the active products. If N_0 is the number of atoms initially present, the number N_t at any time t is given by $N_t/N_0 = e^{-\lambda t}$, where λ is equal to the fraction of the radium disintegrating per second, *i.e.*, for radium $\lambda = 2.8 \times 10^{-11}$ $(\text{sec})^{-1} = 8.8 \times 10^{-4}$ $(\text{year})^{-1}$.

The time taken for the radium to be half transformed will be about 800 years; while the *average life* of the radium is λ^{-1}, or 1100 years approximately.

Now, pure radium bromide has an activity nearly 2,000,000 times that of uranium, measured by the α rays, and the activity of thorium, weight for weight, is about the same as uranium. Taking, as a first approximation, that the activity is proportional to the number of α particles expelled, it can readily be deduced that in thorium, where there are four products which expel α rays, as in the case of radium, the *average life* λ^{-1} is $1100 \times 2 \times 10^6$, or 2×10^9 years.

In uranium, where there is only evidence of one change emitting α rays, the average life is only one quarter as long, *i.e.*, 5×10^8 years.

Since each radio-atom expels one α particle of atomic weight about that of hydrogen or helium, the atoms of the intermediate products will not differ much in weight from the parent atom.

The approximate weight of each product present in a gramme of radium can be readily deduced. Let N_A, N_B, N_C be the number of atoms of the products A, B, C present per gramme in radioactive equilibrium. Let λ_A, λ_B, λ_C be the corresponding constants of change. Then if q is the number of the parent atoms breaking up per second,

$$q = \lambda_A N_A = \lambda_B N_B = \lambda_C N_C.$$

Consider the case of the radium products where the value of q is 5×10^{10} per gramme. The value of N for each of the products is shown in the following table, along with the corresponding weights:—

Product	Value of λ (sec)$^{-1}$	Number of atoms present per gramme	Weight of product in milligrammes
Radium emanation	2.0×10^{-6}	2.5×10^{16}	1.4×10^{-2}
↓ Radium A	3.8×10^{-3}	1.3×10^{13}	7×10^{-6}
↓ Radium B	5.4×10^{-4}	9×10^{13}	5×10^{-5}
↓ Radium C	4.1×10^{-4}	1.2×10^{14}	7×10^{-5}

With the small quantities of radium available, the amounts of the products radium A, B, and C are too small to weigh. It may be possible, however, to detect their presence by means of the spectroscope.

In the case of thorium, the weight of product ThX, which is present in greatest quantity, is far too small to detect. Since the value of λ for ThX is about the same as for the radium emanation, the maximum weight present per gramme is about $1/2 \times 10^{-6}$ of the weight of the emanation, *i.e.*, about 10^{-11} gramme. Even from a kilogramme of thorium, the amount of ThX is too small to detect by its weight.

The evidence at present obtained points strongly to the conclusion that the expelled α particle becomes helium after its charge is neutralized. If this is the case, the volume of helium produced from radium per year can at once be estimated. Since the emanation, radium A, and radium C, expel α particles, the volume of helium produced during the life of the emanation should be three times the initial volume of the emanation. It is difficult to estimate experimentally the volume of helium produced, on account of its absorption by the walls of the tube, but the experiments of RAMSAY and SODDY show it is about this order of magnitude. Since 2×10^{11} atoms of helium are expelled per second, the number expelled per year is 6.3×10^{18}. The volume of helium produced per gramme of radium per year is

$$\frac{6.3 \times 10^{18}}{3.6 \times 10^{19}},$$

or .18 cub. centim.

32. *Origin of the Radio-elements.*   We have seen that 1/1000 of a
given quantity of radium is transformed per year and half after a
period of 800 years.   At the end of 8000 years only about 1/1000, and
at the end of 16,000 years only $1/10^6$ of a given quantity of radium
would remain unchanged.   Thus if the whole earth had been
initially composed of pure radium, its activity 16,000 years later
would not be greater than a good specimen of pitchblende to-day.
Since there is little doubt that the radioactive minerals are very much
older than this, we are forced to the conclusion that radium must be
produced from some source, and that the present supply is maintained
by the continuous production of fresh radium to balance its rate of
disappearance.

The question of possible parentage has been discussed by the
writer ('Radioactivity,' p. 334) and it has been shown that uranium
best fulfils the conditions of being the parent of radium.   In the first
place, uranium has an average life 5×10^8 years, which is very long
compared with the life of radium.   In addition, the activity observed
in pitchblende is about what would be expected if uranium were the
parent of radium.   If each atom of uranium in breaking up gives rise
to one atom of radium, the activity of the uranium and its products
(measured by the α rays) would be about six times that of the uranium
itself.   This follows since each atom of uranium in breaking up gives
out only one α particle, while the radium arising from it would give
out during its succession of changes five α particles (including the α
particle from radium E).

Taking into account that actinium and thorium, as well as
uranium and radium, are found in pitchblende, the observed activity
of about six or seven times that of uranium is almost what is to be
expected if radium is a product of uranium.

Now, from the data given in section 31, the amount of radium
produced per year on the above hypothesis can readily be calculated.
The fraction of uranium changing per year is about 2×10^{-9}.
Assuming that the uranium passes directly through rapid stages into
radium, the weight of radium produced per year, per gramme of
uranium, would be nearly equal to the weight of uranium changed,
i.e., 2×10^{-9} gramme.   The emanation from this quantity of radium
would discharge an ordinary electroscope in about 10 minutes and,
thus a very small fraction of the above amount should be detectable.
If a kilogramme of uranium is used instead of a gramme, the amount
of radium produced per year is 2×10^{-6} gramme.   The emanation
from this amount would discharge an electroscope almost instantly.
The amount of radium produced in a single day should be readily
recognizable.

The suggestion that uranium was a possible parent of radium was given in the paper on 'Radioactive Change,' and it was arranged between Mr. SODDY and the writer that the former should try experiments to ascertain whether radium were produced from uranium. Mr. SODDY has published a preliminary account of his experiments.[29] He found no evidence of the production of radium from uranium and calculated that if radium were produced at all, it was certainly at less than 1/100,000 of the theoretical rate.

On my part, I have examined both thorium and actinium to find whether radium is produced from them. It was thought possible that actinium might be an intermediate product between uranium and radium. The theoretical outlook for thorium did not seem very promising, but the observation that some pure thorium nitrate, obtained from Dr. KNÖFFLER, of Berlin, gave off a considerable quantity of radium emanation, led me to examine thorium as well as actinium.

About 500 grammes of thorium nitrate was taken and dissolved in water. A small quantity of barium nitrate was mixed with it and sufficient sulphuric acid added to precipitate the barium as sulphate. After two successive precipitations all but a small percentage of the radium was removed with the barium. The treated thorium solution was then placed in a closed glass vessel and the emanation allowed to collect in the air-space above the solution. The air was drawn off at intervals and passed into a suitable electroscope. The rate of discharge observed was proportional to the amount of emanation present and thus served as a convenient means of determining the variation from time to time of the amount of radium in the solution.

In a similar way, some of GIESEL'S emanating substance was dissolved in acid and the radium removed by precipitation with barium. The solution has been set aside in a stoppered bottle and the amount of emanation present determined from time to time.

The observations on actinium have been in progress for three months and for thorium about four months. The earlier observations seemed to indicate a change of the amount of radium present in both the actinium and thorium solutions, but later observations show that if radium is produced at all, it is produced at a very small fraction of the theoretical rate. The experiments on thorium and actinium are being continued, and in the course of a few years it is hoped that a definite answer to the question will be given.

In experiments of this character certain precautions are essential in order to avoid large possible sources of error in deducing the amount of emanation present by means of the rate of discharge of an electroscope. These sources of error are especially marked in

---

[29] *Nature*, May, 1904.

experiments with solutions of thorium or actinium. The emanations from these substances escape into the air-space above the solution. If any dust or water globules are present, excited activity is produced on them. On removal of the air these active carriers are removed with it and unless they are allowed time to settle, or removed by passage through a filter of cotton wool, they are carried into the electroscope and produce an increased rate of discharge. I have found that if the air after removal is stored over water in a gas-holder for an hour the carriers of excited activity are removed from the gas. The effect in the electroscope is then due to the emanation alone.

No definite experimental evidence is yet forthcoming that radium can be produced by uranium, thorium or actinium. It is not unlikely, however, that the negative results so far obtained may be due to the presence of one or more rayless changes between the parent substance and the radium. We have seen that such rayless changes exist in radium, thorium and actinium, and the failure to detect the production of radium would be explained if the intervening 'rayless' products were removed by the same chemical operation which freed the substance of radium.

There is one direct method of attack of the question. If uranium is the parent of radium, the amount of radium for different pitch-blendes should always be proportional to the amount of uranium present.[30] The origin of the other radio-elements could be attacked in a similar way.

The whole subject of the relative connection and origin of the radio-elements is of the greatest interest and importance. The close similarity of the changes in radium, thorium and actinium is very remarkable and indicates some peculiarity of atomic constitution which still remains to be elucidated.

---

[30] BOLTWOOD has recently published some numbers (*Nature*, May 25, 1904, p. 80) which seem to show that in the pitchblendes examined the amount of radium is strictly proportional to the amount of uranium in the mineral. Further results of this character are very much required.

Indexes

Numbers in **boldface** give the pages on which the reprinted papers are located. Numbers in ordinary type refer to names or topics contained within the reprinted papers. Numbers inside square brackets refer to names or topics contained in the introduction and editorial comments. *Italic* numbers indicate that a name occurs within bibliographical references cited by the editor.

A. Index of Names

Aitken, J., 36
d'Arsonval, A., 120
Barnes, H., *173*, 187, 221
Barthélemy, [7]
Baskerville, C., 91
Becquerel, H., [1–3], [7–8], *8*, **8–9**, **10–12**, [12–13], **13–18**, [18], **19–21**, [22], 68, 70, [116–17], **117–20**, [120], 122, [123], 125, 135, *151*, 158
Bémont, G., 71, 80
Benoist, L., *22*
Bodländer, G., 172
Boltwood, B., 230
Brauner, B., 91
Brooks, H. T., 89, 179, 181, 186, 195–97, 209
Cooke, H. L., 213
Crookes, W., [2–3], [70], **70–84**, 90–91, [116–17], 117–18, 122, [123–24], 130, 135, 146
Curie, M., [1], [3], *23*, 38, 68, 70–71, 80, 89, [120], **121–23**, [123], 135, 146, 153, 158–59, 161, *171*, [173], 209, 211–13
Curie, P., [1], [3–4], 38, 68, 70–71, 80, 89, *117*, 118–19, [120], **121–23**, [123], 135, 146, 158, [166], **167–69**, [173], 181, 184, 187, 200–01, 206–07, 209, 220
Danne, J., 181, 184–85, 187, 200–01, 206–07, 220
Darboux, G., 7
Debierne, A., 82, 91, *117*, 117–18, 195
Demarçay, E., 81, 169
Dennis, 104
Dorn, E., 89, 105

Eimer & Amend, 36, 40, 103
Elster, J., 89–90
Eve, A. S., *86*
Feather, N., *124*
Fournier d'Albe, E. E., *70*
Gates, F., 206
Geitel, H., 89–90
Giesel, F., 117, 153, 160, *170*, [170–71], 172, [173], 195–96, 210, 211
Glasser, O., 7
Grier, A. G., 143, *148*
Haen, P. de, 89
Henry, C., 8
Hoffmann, K. A., 160
Hurmuzescu, D., 14, 20, *22*
Knöffler, 83, 124, 229
Laborde, A., [4], [166], **167–69**, [173]
Larmor, J., 219
Lerch, F. von, 194, 220
Lockyer, N., 166
Lodge, O., 219
Marckwald, W., 161, 211–13
Moissan, H., *18*, 20, 74
Niewenglowski, G., 9
Oudin, [7]
Owens, R. B., [2], [23–24], *24*, 25, 50–51
Pegram, G., 194, 220
Perrier, E., 7
Perrin, J., 122
Poincaré, H., [7–8]
Ramsay, W., [4], [*151*], *170*, [170–71], **171–72**, 178, 221–22, 225–27
Rayleigh, Lord, [4], [*170*]
Righi, A., *22*

B. Index of Topics

Catalogue of Dover
SCIENCE BOOKS

BOOKS THAT EXPLAIN SCIENCE

THE NATURE OF LIGHT AND COLOUR IN THE OPEN AIR, M. Minnaert. Why is falling snow sometimes black? What causes mirages, the fata morgana, multiple suns and moons in the sky; how are shadows formed? Prof. Minnaert of U. of Utrecht answers these and similar questions in optics, light, colour, for non-specialists. Particularly valuable to nature, science students, painters, photographers. "Can best be described in one word—fascinating!" Physics Today. Translated by H. M. Kremer-Priest, K. Jay. 202 illustrations, including 42 photos. xvi + 362pp. 5⅜ x 8.　　　　　　　　　　　　　　　　T196 Paperbound **$1.95**

THE RESTLESS UNIVERSE, Max Born. New enlarged version of this remarkably readable account by a Nobel laureate. Moving from sub-atomic particles to universe, the author explains in very simple terms the latest theories of wave mechanics. Partial contents: air and its relatives, electrons and ions, waves and particles, electronic structure of the atom, nuclear physics. Nearly 1000 illustrations, including 7 animated sequences. 325pp. 6 x 9.　　　　　　　　　　　　　　　　　　　　　　T412 Paperbound **$2.00**

MATTER AND LIGHT, THE NEW PHYSICS, L. de Broglie. Non-technical papers by a Nobel laureate explain electromagnetic theory, relativity, matter, light, radiation, wave mechanics, quantum physics, philosophy of science. Einstein, Planck, Bohr, others explained so easily that no mathematical training is needed for all but 2 of the 21 chapters. "Easy simplicity and lucidity . . . should make this source-book of modern physcis available to a wide public," Saturday Review. Unabridged. 300pp. 5⅜ x 8.　　　　　T35 Paperbound **$1.60**

THE COMMON SENSE OF THE EXACT SCIENCES, W. K. Clifford. Introduction by James Newman, edited by Karl Pearson. For 70 years this has been a guide to classical scientific, mathematical thought. Explains with unusual clarity basic concepts such as extension of meaning of symbols, characteristics of surface boundaries, properties of plane figures, vectors, Cartesian method of determining position, etc. Long preface by Bertrand Russell. Bibliography of Clifford. Corrected. 130 diagrams redrawn. 249pp. 5⅜ x 8.
　　　　　　　　　　　　　　　　　　　　　　　　　　T61 Paperbound **$1.60**

THE EVOLUTION OF SCIENTIFIC THOUGHT FROM NEWTON TO EINSTEIN, A. d'Abro. Einstein's special, general theories of relativity, with historical implications, analyzed in non-technical terms. Excellent accounts of contributions of Newton, Riemann, Weyl, Planck, Eddington, Maxwell, Lorentz, etc., are treated in terms of space, time, equations of electromagnetics, finiteness of universe, methodology of science. "Has become a standard work," Nature. 21 diagrams. 482pp. 5⅜ x 8.　　　　　　　　　　　　　　　T2 Paperbound **$2.00**

BRIDGES AND THEIR BUILDERS, D. Steinman, S. R. Watson. Engineers, historians, everyone ever fascinated by great spans will find this an endless source of information and interest. Dr. Steinman, recent recipient of Louis Levy Medal, is one of the great bridge architects, engineers of all time. His analysis of great bridges of history is both authoritative and easily followed. Greek, Roman, medieval, oriental bridges; modern works such as Brooklyn Bridge, Golden Gate Bridge, etc. described in terms of history, constructional principles, artistry, function. Most comprehensive, accurate semi-popular history of bridges in print in English. New, greatly revised, enlarged edition. 23 photographs, 26 line drawings. xvii + 401pp. 5⅜ x 8.　　　　　　　　　　　　　　　　　　T431 Paperbound **$1.95**

CONCERNING THE NATURE OF THINGS, Sir William Bragg. Christmas lectures at Royal Society by Nobel laureate, dealing with atoms, gases, liquids, and various types of crystals. No scientific background is needed to understand this remarkably clear introduction to basic processes and aspects of modern science. "More interesting than any bestseller," London Morning Post. 32pp. of photos. 57 figures. xii + 232pp. 5⅜ x 8. T31 Paperbound **$1.35**

THE RISE OF THE NEW PHYSICS, A. d'Abro. Half million word exposition, formerly titled "The Decline of Mechanism," for readers not versed in higher mathematics. Only thorough explanation in everyday language of core of modern mathematical physical theory, treating both classical, modern views. Scientifically impeccable coverage of thought from Newtonian system through theories of Dirac, Heisenberg, Fermi's statistics. Combines history, exposition; broad but unified, detailed view, with constant comparison of classical, modern views. "A must for anyone doing serious study in the physical sciences," J. of the Franklin Inst. "Extraordinary faculty . . . to explain ideas and theories . . . in language of everyday life," Isis. Part I of set: philosophy of science, from practice of Newton, Maxwell, Poincaré, Einstein, etc. Modes of thought, experiment, causality, etc. Part II: 100 pp. on grammar, vocabulary of mathematics, discussions of functions, groups, series, Fourier series, etc. Remainder treats concrete, detailed coverage of both classical, quantum physics: analytic mechanics, Hamilton's principle, electromagnetic waves, thermodynamics, Brownian movement, special relativity, Bohr's atom, de Broglie's wave mechanics, Heisenberg's uncertainty, scores of other important topics. Covers discoveries, theories of d'Alembert, Born, Cantor, Debye, Euler, Foucault, Galois, Gauss, Hadamard, Kelvin, Kepler Laplace, Maxwell, Pauli, Rayleigh Volterra, Weyl, more than 180 others. 97 illustrations. ix + 982pp. 5⅜ x 8.
T3 Vol. 1 Paperbound **$2.00**
T4 Vol. II Paperbound **$2.00**

SPINNING TOPS AND GYROSCOPIC MOTION, John Perry. Well-known classic of science still unsurpassed for lucid, accurate, delightful exposition. How quasi-rigidity is induced in flexible, fluid bodies by rapid motions; why gyrostat falls, top rises; nature, effect of internal fluidity on rotating bodies; etc. Appendixes describe practical use of gyroscopes in ships, compasses, monorail transportation. 62 figures. 128pp. 5⅜ x 8.
T416 Paperbound **$1.00**

FOUNDATIONS OF PHYSICS, R. B. Lindsay, H. Margenau. Excellent bridge between semi-popular and technical writings. Discussion of methods of physical description, construction of theory; valuable to physicist with elementary calculus. Gives meaning to data, tools of modern physics. Contents: symbolism, mathematical equations; space and time; foundations of mechanics; probability; physics, continua; electron theory; relativity; quantum mechanics; causality; etc. "Thorough and yet not overdetailed. Unreservedly recommended," Nature. Unabridged corrected edition. 35 illustrations. xi + 537pp. 5⅜ x 8. S377 Paperbound **$2.45**

FADS AND FALLACIES IN THE NAME OF SCIENCE, Martin Gardner. Formerly entitled "In the Name of Science," the standard account of various cults, quack systems, delusions which have masqueraded as science: hollow earth fanatics, orgone sex energy, dianetics, Atlantis, Forteanism, flying saucers, medical fallacies like zone therapy, etc. New chapter on Bridey Murphy, psionics, other recent manifestations. A fair reasoned appraisal of eccentric theory which provides excellent innoculation. "Should be read by everyone, scientist or non-scientist alike," R. T. Birge, Prof. Emeritus of Physics, Univ. of Calif; Former Pres., Amer. Physical Soc. x + 365pp. 5⅜ x 8. T394 Paperbound **$1.50**

ON MATHEMATICS AND MATHEMATICIANS, R. E. Moritz. A 10 year labor of love by discerning, discriminating Prof. Moritz, this collection conveys the full sense of mathematics and personalities of great mathematicians. Anecdotes, aphorisms, reminiscences, philosophies, definitions, speculations, biographical insights, etc. by great mathematicians, writers: Descartes, Mill, Locke, Kant, Coleridge, Whitehead, etc. Glimpses into lives of great mathematicians, from Archimedes to Euler, Gauss, Weierstrass. To mathematicians, a superb browsing-book. To laymen, exciting revelation of fullness of mathematics. Extensive cross index. 410pp. 5⅜ x 8. T489 Paperbound **$1.95**

GUIDE TO THE LITERATURE OF MATHEMATICS AND PHYSICS, N. G. Parke III. Over 5000 entries under approximately 120 major subject headings, of selected most important books, monographs, periodicals, articles in English, plus important works in German, French, Italian, Spanish, Russian (many recently available works). Covers every branch of physics, math, related engineering. Includes author, title, edition, publisher, place, date, number of volumes, number of pages. 40 page introduction on basic problems of research, study provides useful information on organization, use of libraries, psychology of learning, etc. Will save you hours of time. 2nd revised edition. Indices of authors, subjects. 464pp. 5⅜ x 8. S447 Paperbound **$2.49**

THE STRANGE STORY OF THE QUANTUM, An Account for the General Reader of the Growth of Ideas Underlying Our Present Atomic Knowledge, B. Hoffmann. Presents lucidly, expertly, with barest amount of mathematics, problems and theories which led to modern quantum physics. Begins with late 1800's when discrepancies were noticed; with illuminating analogies, examples, goes through concepts of Planck, Einstein, Pauli, Schroedinger, Dirac, Sommerfield, Feynman, etc. New postscript through 1958. "Of the books attempting an account of the history and contents of modern atomic physics which have come to my attention, this is the best," H. Margenau, Yale U., in Amer. J. of Physics. 2nd edition. 32 tables, illustrations. 275pp. 5⅜ x 8. T518 Paperbound **$1.45**

2

HISTORY OF SCIENCE
AND PHILOSOPHY OF SCIENCE

THE VALUE OF SCIENCE, Henri Poincaré. Many of most mature ideas of "last scientific universalist" for both beginning, advanced workers. Nature of scientific truth, whether order is innate in universe or imposed by man, logical thought vs. intuition (relating to Weierstrass, Lie, Riemann, etc), time and space (relativity, psychological time, simultaneity), Herz's concept of force, values within disciplines of Maxwell, Carnot, Mayer, Newton, Lorentz, etc. iii + 147pp. 5⅜ x 8.   S469 Paperbound **$1.35**

PHILOSOPHY AND THE PHYSICISTS, L. S. Stebbing. Philosophical aspects of modern science examined in terms of lively critical attack on ideas of Jeans, Eddington. Tasks of science, causality, determinism, probability, relation of world physics to that of everyday experience, philosophical significance of Planck-Bohr concept of discontinuous energy levels, inferences to be drawn from Uncertainty Principle, implications of "becoming" involved in 2nd law of thermodynamics, other problems posed by discarding of Laplacean determinism. 285pp. 5⅜ x 8.   T480 Paperbound **$1.65**

THE PRINCIPLES OF SCIENCE, A TREATISE ON LOGIC AND THE SCIENTIFIC METHOD, W. S. Jevons. Milestone in development of symbolic logic remains stimulating contribution to investigation of inferential validity in sciences. Treats inductive, deductive logic, theory of number, probability, limits of scientific method; significantly advances Boole's logic, contains detailed introduction to nature and methods of probability in physics, astronomy, everyday affairs, etc. In introduction, Ernest Nagel of Columbia U. says,"[Jevons] continues to be of interest as an attempt to articulate the logic of scientific inquiry." liii + 786pp. 5⅜ x 8.   S446 Paperbound **$2.98**

A HISTORY OF ASTRONOMY FROM THALES TO KEPLER, J. L. E. Dreyer. Only work in English to give complete history of cosmological views from prehistoric times to Kepler. Partial contents: Near Eastern astronomical systems, Early Greeks, Homocentric spheres of Euxodus, Epicycles, Ptolemaic system, Medieval cosmology, Copernicus, Kepler, much more. "Especially useful to teachers and students of the history of science . . . unsurpassed in its field," Isis. Formerly "A History of Planetary Systems from Thales to Kepler." Revised foreword by W. H. Stahl. xvii + 430pp. 5⅜ x 8.   S79 Paperbound **$1.98**

A CONCISE HISTORY OF MATHEMATICS, D. Struik. Lucid study of development of ideas, techniques, from Ancient Near East, Greece, Islamic science, Middle Ages, Renaissance, modern times. Important mathematicians described in detail. Treatment not anecdotal, but analytical development of ideas. Non-technical—no math training needed. "Rich in content, thoughtful in interpretations," U.S. Quarterly Booklist. 60 illustrations including Greek, Egyptian manuscripts, portraits of 31 mathematicians. 2nd edition. xix + 299pp. 5⅜ x 8.   S255 Paperbound **$1.75**

THE PHILOSOPHICAL WRITINGS OF PEIRCE, edited by Justus Buchler. A carefully balanced expositon of Peirce's complete system, written by Peirce himself. It covers such matters as scientific method, pure chance vs. law, symbolic logic, theory of signs, pragmatism, experiment, and other topics. "Excellent selection . . . gives more than adequate evidence of the range and greatness," Personalist. Formerly entitled "The Philosophy of Peirce." xvi + 368pp.   T217 Paperbound **$1.95**

SCIENCE AND METHOD, Henri Poincaré. Procedure of scientific discovery, methodology, experiment, idea-germination—processes by which discoveries come into being. Most significant and interesting aspects of development, application of ideas. Chapters cover selection of facts, chance, mathematical reasoning, mathematics and logic; Whitehead, Russell, Cantor, the new mechanics, etc. 288pp. 5⅜ x 8.   S222 Paperbound **$1.35**

SCIENCE AND HYPOTHESIS, Henri Poincaré. Creative psychology in science. How such concepts as number, magnitude, space, force, classical mechanics developed, how modern scientist uses them in his thought. Hypothesis in physics, theories of modern physics. Introduction by Sir James Larmor. "Few mathematicians have had the breadth of vision of Poincaré, and none is his superior in the gift of clear exposition," E. T. Bell. 272pp. 5⅜ x 8.   S221 Paperbound **$1.35**

ESSAYS IN EXPERIMENTAL LOGIC, John Dewey. Stimulating series of essays by one of most influential minds in American philosophy presents some of his most mature thoughts on wide range of subjects. Partial contents: Relationship between inquiry and experience; dependence of knowledge upon thought; character logic; judgments of practice, data, and meanings; stimuli of thought, etc. viii + 444pp. 5⅜ x 8.   T73 Paperbound **$1.95**

WHAT IS SCIENCE, Norman Campbell. Excellent introduction explains scientific method, role of mathematics, types of scientific laws. Contents: 2 aspects of science, science and nature, laws of chance, discovery of laws, explanation of laws, measurement and numerical laws, applications of science. 192pp. 5⅜ x 8.   S43 Paperbound **$1.25**

FROM EUCLID TO EDDINGTON: A STUDY OF THE CONCEPTIONS OF THE EXTERNAL WORLD, Sir Edmund Whittaker. Foremost British scientist traces development of theories of natural philosophy from western rediscovery of Euclid to Eddington, Einstein, Dirac, etc. 5 major divisions: Space, Time and Movement; Concepts of Classical Physics; Concepts of Quantum Mechanics; Eddington Universe. Contrasts inadequacy of classical physics to understand physical world with present day attempts of relativity, non-Euclidean geometry, space curvature, etc. 212pp. 5⅜ x 8. T491 Paperbound **$1.35**

THE ANALYSIS OF MATTER, Bertrand Russell. How do our senses accord with the new physics? This volume covers such topics as logical analysis of physics, prerelativity physics, causality, scientific inference, physics and perception, special and general relativity, Weyl's theory, tensors, invariants and their physical interpretation, periodicity and qualitative series. "The most thorough treatment of the subject that has yet been published," The Nation. Introduction by L. E. Denonn. 422pp. 5⅜ x 8. T231 Paperbound **$1.95**

LANGUAGE, TRUTH, AND LOGIC, A. Ayer. A clear introduction to the Vienna and Cambridge schools of Logical Positivism. Specific tests to evaluate validity of ideas, etc. Contents: function of philosophy, elimination of metaphysics, nature of analysis, a priori, truth and probability, etc. 10th printing. "I should like to have written it myself," Bertrand Russell. 160pp. 5⅜ x 8. T10 Paperbound **$1.25**

THE PSYCHOLOGY OF INVENTION IN THE MATHEMATICAL FIELD, J. Hadamard. Where do ideas come from? What role does the unconscious play? Are ideas best developed by mathematical reasoning, word reasoning, visualization? What are the methods used by Einstein, Poincaré, Galton, Riemann? How can these techniques be applied by others? One of the world's leading mathematicians discusses these and other questions. xiii + 145pp. 5⅜ x 8. T107 Paperbound **$1.25**

GUIDE TO PHILOSOPHY, C. E. M. Joad. By one of the ablest expositors of all time, this is not simply a history or a typological survey, but an examination of central problems in terms of answers afforded by the greatest thinkers: Plato, Aristotle, Scholastics, Leibniz, Kant, Whitehead, Russell, and many others. Especially valuable to persons in the physical sciences; over 100 pages devoted to Jeans, Eddington, and others, the philosophy of modern physics, scientific materialism, pragmatism, etc. Classified bibliography. 592pp. 5⅜ x 8. T50 Paperbound **$2.00**

SUBSTANCE AND FUNCTION, and EINSTEIN'S THEORY OF RELATIVITY, Ernst Cassirer. Two books bound as one. Cassirer establishes a philosophy of the exact sciences that takes into consideration new developments in mathematics, shows historical connections. Partial contents: Aristotelian logic, Mill's analysis, Helmholtz and Kronecker, Russell and cardinal numbers, Euclidean vs. non-Euclidean geometry, Einstein's relativity. Bibliography. Index. xxi + 464pp. 5⅜ x 8. T50 Paperbound **$2.00**

FOUNDATIONS OF GEOMETRY, Bertrand Russell. Nobel laureate analyzes basic problems in the overlap area between mathematics and philosophy: the nature of geometrical knowledge, the nature of geometry, and the applications of geometry to space. Covers history of non-Euclidean geometry, philosophic interpretations of geometry, especially Kant, projective and metrical geometry. Most interesting as the solution offered in 1897 by a great mind to a problem still current. New introduction by Prof. Morris Kline, N.Y. University. "Admirably clear, precise, and elegantly reasoned analysis," International Math. News. xii + 201pp. 5⅜ x 8. S233 Paperbound **$1.60**

THE NATURE OF PHYSICAL THEORY, P. W. Bridgman. How modern physics looks to a highly unorthodox physicist—a Nobel laureate. Pointing out many absurdities of science, demonstrating inadequacies of various physical theories, weighs and analyzes contributions of Einstein, Bohr, Heisenberg, many others. A non-technical consideration of correlation of science and reality. xi + 138pp. 5⅜ x 8. S33 Paperbound **$1.25**

EXPERIMENT AND THEORY IN PHYSICS, Max Born. A Nobel laureate examines the nature and value of the counterclaims of experiment and theory in physics. Synthetic versus analytical scientific advances are analyzed in works of Einstein, Bohr, Heisenberg, Planck, Eddington, Milne, others, by a fellow scientist. 44pp. 5⅜ x 8. S308 Paperbound **60¢**

A SHORT HISTORY OF ANATOMY AND PHYSIOLOGY FROM THE GREEKS TO HARVEY, Charles Singer. Corrected edition of "The Evolution of Anatomy." Classic traces anatomy, physiology from prescientific times through Greek, Roman periods, dark ages, Renaissance, to beginning of modern concepts. Centers on individuals, movements, that definitely advanced anatomical knowledge. Plato, Diocles, Erasistratus, Galen, da Vinci, etc. Special section on Vesalius. 20 plates. 270 extremely interesting illustrations of ancient, Medieval, Renaissance, Oriental origin. xii + 209pp. 5⅜ x 8. T389 Paperbound **$1.75**

SPACE-TIME-MATTER, Hermann Weyl. "The standard treatise on the general theory of relativity," (Nature), by world renowned scientist. Deep, clear discussion of logical coherence of general theory, introducing all needed tools: Maxwell, analytical geometry, non-Euclidean geometry, tensor calculus, etc. Basis is classical space-time, before absorption of relativity. Contents: Euclidean space, mathematical form, metrical continuum, general theory, etc. 15 diagrams. xviii + 330pp. 5⅜ x 8. S267 Paperbound **$1.75**

MATTER AND MOTION, James Clerk Maxwell. Excellent exposition begins with simple particles, proceeds gradually to physical systems beyond complete analysis; motion, force, properties of centre of mass of material system; work, energy, gravitation, etc. Written with all Maxwell's original insights and clarity. Notes by E. Larmor. 17 diagrams. 178pp. 5⅜ x 8.   S188 Paperbound **$1.25**

PRINCIPLES OF MECHANICS, Heinrich Hertz. Last work by the great 19th century physicist is not only a classic, but of great interest in the logic of science. Creating a new system of mechanics based upon space, time, and mass, it returns to axiomatic analysis, understanding of the formal or structural aspects of science, taking into account logic, observation, a priori elements. Of great historical importance to Poincaré, Carnap, Einstein, Milne. A 20 page introduction by R. S. Cohen, Wesleyan University, analyzes the implications of Hertz's thought and the logic of science. 13 page introduction by Helmholtz. xlii + 274pp. 5⅜ x 8.   S316 Clothbound **$3.50**
                                                          S317 Paperbound **$1.75**

FROM MAGIC TO SCIENCE, Charles Singer. A great historian examines aspects of science from Roman Empire through Renaissance. Includes perhaps best discussion of early herbals, penetrating physiological interpretation of "The Visions of Hildegarde of Bingen." Also examines Arabian, Galenic influences; Pythagoras' sphere, Paracelsus; reawakening of science under Leonardo da Vinci, Vesalius; Lorica of Gildas the Briton; etc. Frequent quotations with translations from contemporary manuscripts. Unabridged, corrected edition. 158 unusual illustrations from Classical, Medieval sources. xxvii + 365pp. 5⅜ x 8.
                                                          T390 Paperbound **$2.00**

A HISTORY OF THE CALCULUS, AND ITS CONCEPTUAL DEVELOPMENT, Carl B. Boyer. Provides laymen, mathematicians a detailed history of the development of the calculus, from beginnings in antiquity to final elaboration as mathematical abstraction. Gives a sense of mathematics not as technique, but as habit of mind, in progression of ideas of Zeno, Plato, Pythagoras, Eudoxus, Arabic and Scholastic mathematicians, Newton, Leibniz, Taylor, Descartes, Euler, Lagrange, Cantor, Weierstrass, and others. This first comprehensive, critical history of the calculus was originally entitled "The Concepts of the Calculus." Foreword by R. Courant. 22 figures. 25 page bibliography. v + 364pp. 5⅜ x 8.
                                                          S509 Paperbound **$2.00**

A DIDEROT PICTORIAL ENCYCLOPEDIA OF TRADES AND INDUSTRY, Manufacturing and the Technical Arts in Plates Selected from "L'Encyclopédie ou Dictionnaire Raisonné des Sciences, des Arts, et des Métiers" of Denis Diderot. Edited with text by C. Gillispie. First modern selection of plates from high-point of 18th century French engraving. Storehouse of technological information to historian of arts and science. Over 2,000 illustrations on 485 full page plates, most of them original size, show trades, industries of fascinating era in such great detail that modern reconstructions might be made of them. Plates teem with men, women, children performing thousands of operations; show sequence, general operations, closeups, details of machinery. Illustrates such important, interesting trades, industries as sowing, harvesting, beekeeping, tobacco processing, fishing, arts of war, mining, smelting, casting iron, extracting mercury, making gunpowder, cannons, bells, shoeing horses, tanning, papermaking, printing, dying, over 45 more categories. Professor Gillispie of Princeton supplies full commentary on all plates, identifies operations, tools, processes, etc. Material is presented in lively, lucid fashion. Of great interest to all studying history of science, technology. Heavy library cloth. 920pp. 9 x 12.
                                                          T421 2 volume set **$18.50**

DE MAGNETE, William Gilbert. Classic work on magnetism, founded new science. Gilbert was first to use word "electricity," to recognize mass as distinct from weight, to discover effect of heat on magnetic bodies; invented an electroscope, differentiated between static electricity and magnetism, conceived of earth as magnet. This lively work, by first great experimental scientist, is not only a valuable historical landmark, but a delightfully easy to follow record of a searching, ingenious mind. Translated by P. F. Mottelay. 25 page biographical memoir. 90 figures. lix + 368pp. 5⅜ x 8.   S470 Paperbound **$2.00**

HISTORY OF MATHEMATICS, D. E. Smith. Most comprehensive, non-technical history of math in English. Discusses lives and works of over a thousand major, minor figures, with footnotes giving technical information outside book's scheme, and indicating disputed matters. Vol. I: A chronological examination, from primitive concepts through Egypt, Babylonia, Greece, the Orient, Rome, the Middle Ages, The Renaissance, and to 1900. Vol. II: The development of ideas in specific fields and problems, up through elementary calculus. "Marks an epoch . . . will modify the entire teaching of the history of science," George Sarton. 2 volumes, total of 510 illustrations, 1355pp. 5⅜ x 8. Set boxed in attractive container.   T429, 430 Paperbound, the set **$5.00**

THE PHILOSOPHY OF SPACE AND TIME, H. Reichenbach. An important landmark in development of empiricist conception of geometry, covering foundations of geometry, time theory, consequences of Einstein's relativity, including: relations between theory and observations; coordinate definitions; relations between topological and metrical properties of space; psychological problem of visual intuition of non-Euclidean structures; many more topics important to modern science and philosophy. Majority of ideas require only knowledge of intermediate math. "Still the best book in the field," Rudolf Carnap. Introduction by R. Carnap. 49 figures. xviii + 296pp. 5⅜ x 8.   S443 Paperbound **$2.00**

FOUNDATIONS OF SCIENCE: THE PHILOSOPHY OF THEORY AND EXPERIMENT, N. Campbell. A critique of the most fundamental concepts of science, particularly physics. Examines why certain propositions are accepted without question, demarcates science from philosophy, etc. Part I analyzes presuppositions of scientific thought: existence of material world, nature of laws, probability, etc; part 2 covers nature of experiment and applications of mathematics: conditions for measurement, relations between numerical laws and theories, error, etc. An appendix covers problems arising from relativity, force, motion, space, time. A classic in its field. "A real grasp of what science is," Higher Educational Journal. xiii + 565pp. 5⅝ x 8⅜. S372 Paperbound **$2.95**

THE STUDY OF THE HISTORY OF MATHEMATICS and **THE STUDY OF THE HISTORY OF SCIENCE, G. Sarton.** Excellent introductions, orientation, for beginning or mature worker. Describes duty of mathematical historian, incessant efforts and genius of previous generations. Explains how today's discipline differs from previous methods. 200 item bibliography with critical evaluations, best available biographies of modern mathematicians, best treatises on historical methods is especially valuable. 10 illustrations. 2 volumes bound as one. 113pp. + 75pp. 5⅜ x 8. T240 Paperbound **$1.25**

MATHEMATICAL PUZZLES

MATHEMATICAL PUZZLES OF SAM LOYD, selected and edited by **Martin Gardner.** 117 choice puzzles by greatest American puzzle creator and innovator, from his famous "Cyclopedia of Puzzles." All unique style, historical flavor of originals. Based on arithmetic, algebra, probability, game theory, route tracing, topology, sliding block, operations research, geometrical dissection. Includes famous "14-15" puzzle which was national craze, "Horse of a Different Color" which sold millions of copies. 120 line drawings, diagrams. Solutions. xx + 167pp. 5⅜ x 8. T498 Paperbound **$1.00**

SYMBOLIC LOGIC and THE GAME OF LOGIC, Lewis Carroll. "Symbolic Logic" is not concerned with modern symbolic logic, but is instead a collection of over 380 problems posed with charm and imagination, using the syllogism, and a fascinating diagrammatic method of drawing conclusions. In "The Game of Logic" Carroll's whimsical imagination devises a logical game played with 2 diagrams and counters (included) to manipulate hundreds of tricky syllogisms. The final section, "Hit or Miss" is a lagniappe of 101 additional puzzles in the delightful Carroll manner. Until this reprint edition, both of these books were rarities costing up to $15 each. Symbolic Logic: Index. xxxi + 199pp. The Game of Logic: 96pp. 2 vols. bound as one. 5⅜ x 8. T492 Paperbound **$1.50**

PILLOW PROBLEMS and A TANGLED TALE, Lewis Carroll. One of the rarest of all Carroll's works, "Pillow Problems" contains 72 original math puzzles, all typically ingenious. Particularly fascinating are Carroll's answers which remain exactly as he thought them out, reflecting his actual mental process. The problems in "A Tangled Tale" are in story form, originally appearing as a monthly magazine serial. Carroll not only gives the solutions, but uses answers sent in by readers to discuss wrong approaches and misleading paths, and grades them for insight. Both of these books were rarities until this edition, "Pillow Problems" costing up to $25, and "A Tangled Tale" $15. Pillow Problems: Preface and Introduction by Lewis Carroll. xx + 109pp. A Tangled Tale: 6 illustrations. 152pp. Two vols. bound as one. 5⅜ x 8. T493 Paperbound **$1.50**

NEW WORD PUZZLES, G. L. Kaufman. 100 brand new challenging puzzles on words, combinations, never before published. Most are new types invented by author, for beginners and experts both. Squares of letters follow chess moves to build words; symmetrical designs made of synonyms; rhymed crostics; double word squares; syllable puzzles where you fill in missing syllables instead of missing letter; many other types, all new. Solutions. "Excellent," Recreation. 100 puzzles. 196 figures. vi + 122pp. 5⅜ x 8. T344 Paperbound **$1.00**

MATHEMATICAL EXCURSIONS, H. A. Merrill. Fun, recreation, insights into elementary problem solving. Math expert guides you on by-paths not generally travelled in elementary math courses—divide by inspection, Russian peasant multiplication; memory systems for pi; odd, even magic squares; dyadic systems; square roots by geometry; Tchebichev's machine; dozens more. Solutions to more difficult ones. "Brain stirring stuff . . . a classic," Genie. 50 illustrations. 145pp. 5⅜ x 8. T350 Paperbound **$1.00**

THE BOOK OF MODERN PUZZLES, G. L. Kaufman. Over 150 puzzles, absolutely all new material based on same appeal as crosswords, deduction puzzles, but with different principles, techniques. 2-minute teasers, word labyrinths, design, pattern, logic, observation puzzles, puzzles testing ability to apply general knowledge to peculiar situations, many others. Solutions. 116 illustrations. 192pp. 5⅜ x 8. T143 Paperbound **$1.00**

MATHEMAGIC, MAGIC PUZZLES, AND GAMES WITH NUMBERS, R. V. Heath. Over 60 puzzles, stunts, on properties of numbers. Easy techniques for multiplying large numbers mentally, identifying unknown numbers, finding date of any day in any year. Includes The Lost Digit, 3 Acrobats, Psychic Bridge, magic squares, triangles, cubes, others not easily found elsewhere. Edited by J. S. Meyer. 76 illustrations. 128pp. 5⅜ x 8. T110 Paperbound **$1.00**

PUZZLE QUIZ AND STUNT FUN, J. Meyer. 238 high-priority puzzles, stunts, tricks—math puzzles like The Clever Carpenter, Atom Bomb, Please Help Alice; mysteries, deductions like The Bridge of Sighs, Secret Code; observation puzzlers like The American Flag, Playing Cards, Telephone Dial; over 200 others with magic squares, tongue twisters, puns, anagrams. Solutions. Revised, enlarged edition of "Fun-To-Do." Over 100 illustrations. 238 puzzles, stunts, tricks. 256pp. 5⅜ x 8. **T337 Paperbound $1.00**

101 PUZZLES IN THOUGHT AND LOGIC, C. R. Wylie, Jr. For readers who enjoy challenge, stimulation of logical puzzles without specialized math or scientific knowledge. Problems entirely new, range from relatively easy to brainteasers for hours of subtle entertainment. Detective puzzles, find the lying fisherman, how a blind man identifies color by logic, many more. Easy-to-understand introduction to logic of puzzle solving and general scientific method. 128pp. 5⅜ x 8. **T367 Paperbound $1.00**

CRYPTANALYSIS, H. F. Gaines. Standard elementary, intermediate text for serious students. Not just old material, but much not generally known, except to experts. Concealment, Transposition, Substitution ciphers; Vigenere, Kasiski, Playfair, multafid, dozens of other techniques. Formerly "Elementary Cryptanalysis." Appendix with sequence charts, letter frequencies in English, 5 other languages, English word frequencies. Bibliography. 167 codes. New to this edition: solutions to codes. vi + 230pp. 5⅜ x 8⅜. **T97 Paperbound $1.95**

CRYPTOGRAPY, L. D. Smith. Excellent elementary introduction to enciphering, deciphering secret writing. Explains transposition, substitution ciphers; codes; solutions; geometrical patterns, route transcription, columnar transposition, other methods. Mixed cipher systems; single, polyalphabetical substitutions; mechanical devices; Vigenere; etc. Enciphering Japanese; explanation of Baconian biliteral cipher; frequency tables. Over 150 problems. Bibliography. Index. 164pp. 5⅜ x 8. **T247 Paperbound $1.00**

MATHEMATICS, MAGIC AND MYSTERY, M. Gardner. Card tricks, metal mathematics, stage mind-reading, other "magic" explained as applications of probability, sets, number theory, etc. Creative examination of laws, applications. Scores of new tricks, insights. 115 sections on cards, dice, coins; vanishing tricks, many others. No sleight of hand—math guarantees success. "Could hardly get more entertainment . . . easy to follow," Mathematics Teacher. 115 illustrations. xii + 174pp. 5⅜ x 8. **T335 Paperbound $1.00**

AMUSEMENTS IN MATHEMATICS, H. E. Dudeney. Foremost British originator of math puzzles, always witty, intriguing, paradoxical in this classic. One of largest collections. More than 430 puzzles, problems, paradoxes. Mazes, games, problems on number manipulations, unicursal, other route problems, puzzles on measuring, weighing, packing, age, kinship, chessboards, joiners', crossing river, plane figure dissection, many others. Solutions. More than 450 illustrations. viii + 258pp. 5⅜ x 8. **T473 Paperbound $1.25**

THE CANTERBURY PUZZLES H. E. Dudeney. Chaucer's pilgrims set one another problems in story form. Also Adventures of the Puzzle Club, the Strange Escape of the King's Jester, the Monks of Riddlewell, the Squire's Christmas Puzzle Party, others. All puzzles are original, based on dissecting plane figures, arithmetic, algebra, elementary calculus, other branches of mathematics, and purely logical ingenuity. "The limit of ingenuity and intricacy," The Observer. Over 110 puzzles, full solutions. 150 illustrations. viii + 225 pp. 5⅜ x 8. **T474 Paperbound $1.25**

MATHEMATICAL PUZZLES FOR BEGINNERS AND ENTHUSIASTS, G. Mott-Smith. 188 puzzles to test mental agility. Inference, interpretation, algebra, dissection of plane figures, geometry, properties of numbers, decimation, permutations, probability, all are in these delightful problems. Includes the Odic Force, How to Draw an Ellipse, Spider's Cousin, more than 180 others. Detailed solutions. Appendix with square roots, triangular numbers, primes, etc. 135 illustrations. 2nd revised edition. 248pp. 5⅜ x 8. **T198 Paperbound $1.00**

MATHEMATICAL RECREATIONS, M. Kraitchik. Some 250 puzzles, problems, demonstrations of recreation mathematics on relatively advanced level. Unusual historical problems from Greek, Medieval, Arabic, Hindu sources; modern problems on "mathematics without numbers," geometry, topology, arithmetic, etc. Pastimes derived from figurative, Mersenne, Fermat numbers: fairy chess; latruncles: reversi; etc. Full solutions. Excellent insights into special fields of math. "Strongly recommended to all who are interested in the lighter side of mathematics," Mathematical Gaz. 181 illustrations. 330pp. 5⅜ x 8. **T163 Paperbound $1.75**

FICTION

FLATLAND, E. A. Abbott. A perennially popular science-fiction classic about life in a 2-dimensional world, and the impingement of higher dimensions. Political, satiric, humorous, moral overtones. This land where women are straight lines and the lowest and most dangerous classes are isosceles triangles with 3° vertices conveys brilliantly a feeling for many concepts of modern science. 7th edition. New introduction by Banesh Hoffmann. 128pp. 5⅜ x 8. **T1 Paperbound $1.00**

SEVEN SCIENCE FICTION NOVELS OF H. G. WELLS. Complete texts, unabridged, of seven of Wells' greatest novels: The War of the Worlds, The Invisible Man, The Island of Dr. Moreau, The Food of the Gods, First Men in the Moon, In the Days of the Comet, The Time Machine. Still considered by many experts to be the best science-fiction ever written, they will offer amusements and instruction to the scientific minded reader. "The great master," Sky and Telescope. 1051pp. 5⅜ x 8. **T264 Clothbound $3.95**

28 SCIENCE FICTION STORIES OF H. G. WELLS. Unabridged! This enormous omnibus contains 2 full length novels—Men Like Gods, Star Begotten—plus 26 short stories of space, time, invention, biology, etc. The Crystal Egg, The Country of the Blind, Empire of the Ants, The Man Who Could Work Miracles, Aepyornis Island, A Story of the Days to Come, and 20 others "A master . . . not surpassed by . . . writers of today," The English Journal. 915pp. 5⅜ x 8. **T265 Clothbound $3.95**

FIVE ADVENTURE NOVELS OF H. RIDER HAGGARD. All the mystery and adventure of darkest Africa captured accurately by a man who lived among Zulus for years, who knew African ethnology, folkways as did few of his contemporaries. They have been regarded as examples of the very best high adventure by such critics as Orwell, Andrew Lang, Kipling. Contents: She, King Solomon's Mines, Allan Quatermain, Allan's Wife, Maiwa's Revenge. "Could spin a yarn so full of suspense and color that you couldn't put the story down," Sat. Review. 821pp. 5⅜ x 8. **T108 Clothbound $3.95**

CHESS AND CHECKERS

LEARN CHESS FROM THE MASTERS, Fred Reinfeld. Easiest, most instructive way to improve your game—play 10 games against such masters as Marshall, Znosko-Borovsky, Bronstein, Najdorf, etc., with each move graded by easy system. Includes ratings for alternate moves possible. Games selected for interest, clarity, easily isolated principles. Covers Ruy Lopez, Dutch Defense, Vienna Game openings; subtle, intricate middle game variations; all-important end game. Full annotations. Formerly "Chess by Yourself." 91 diagrams. viii + 144pp. 5⅜ x 8. **T362 Paperbound $1.00**

REINFELD ON THE END GAME IN CHESS, Fred Reinfeld. Analyzes 62 end games by Alekhine, Flohr, Tarrasch, Morphy, Capablanca, Rubinstein, Lasker, Reshevsky, other masters. Only 1st rate book with extensive coverage of error—tell exactly what is wrong with each move you might have made. Centers around transitions from middle play to end play. King and pawn, minor pieces, queen endings; blockage, weak, passed pawns, etc. "Excellent . . . a boon," Chess Life. Formerly "Practical End Play." 62 figures. vi + 177pp. 5⅜ x 8. **T417 Paperbound $1.25**

HYPERMODERN CHESS as developed in the games of its greatest exponent, ARON NIMZOVICH, edited by Fred Reinfeld. An intensely original player, analyst, Nimzovich's approaches startled, often angered the chess world. This volume, designed for the average player, shows how his iconoclastic methods won him victories over Alekhine, Lasker, Marshall, Rubinstein, Spielmann, others, and infused new life into the game. Use his methods to startle opponents, invigorate play. "Annotations and introductions to each game . . . are excellent," Times (London). 180 diagrams. viii + 220pp. 5⅜ x 8. **T448 Paperbound $1.35**

THE ADVENTURE OF CHESS, Edward Lasker. Lively reader, by one of America's finest chess masters, including: history of chess, from ancient Indian 4-handed game of Chaturanga to great players of today; such delights and oddities as Maelzel's chess-playing automaton that beat Napoleon 3 times; etc. One of most valuable features is author's personal recollections of men he has played against—Nimzovich, Emanuel Lasker, Capablanca, Alekhine, etc. Discussion of chess-playing machines (newly revised). 5 page chess primer. 11 illustrations. 53 diagrams. 296pp. 5⅜ x 8. **S510 Paperbound $1.45**

THE ART OF CHESS, James Mason. Unabridged reprinting of latest revised edition of most famous general study ever written. Mason, early 20th century master, teaches beginning, intermediate player over 90 openings; middle game, end game, to see more moves ahead, to plan purposefully, attack, sacrifice, defend, exchange, govern general strategy. "Classic . . . one of the clearest and best developed studies," Publishers Weekly. Also included, a complete supplement by F. Reinfeld, "How Do You Play Chess?", invaluable to beginners for its lively question-and-answer method. 448 diagrams. 1947 Reinfeld-Bernstein text. Bibliography. xvi + 340pp. 5⅜ x 8. **T463 Paperbound $1.85**

MORPHY'S GAMES OF CHESS, edited by P. W. Sergeant. Put boldness into your game by flowing brilliant, forceful moves of the greatest chess player of all time. 300 of Morphy's best games, carefully annotated to reveal principles. 54 classics against masters like Anderssen, Harrwitz, Bird, Paulsen, and others. 52 games at odds; 54 blindfold games; plus over 100 others. Follow his interpretation of Dutch Defense, Evans Gambit, Giuoco Piano, Ruy Lopez, many more. Unabridged reissue of latest revised edition. New introduction by F. Reinfeld. Annotations, introduction by Sergeant. 235 diagrams. x + 352pp. 5⅜ x 8. **T386 Paperbound $1.75**

WIN AT CHECKERS, M. Hopper. (Formerly "Checkers.") Former World's Unrestricted Checker Champion discusses principles of game, expert's shots, traps, problems for beginner, standard openings, locating best move, end game, opening "blitzkrieg" moves to draw when behind, etc. Over 100 detailed questions, answers anticipate problems. Appendix. 75 problems with solutions, diagrams. 79 figures. xi + 107pp. 5⅜ x 8.　　T363 Paperbound **$1.00**

HOW TO FORCE CHECKMATE, Fred Reinfeld. If you have trouble finishing off your opponent, here is a collection of lightning strokes and combinations from actual tournament play. Starts with 1-move checkmates, works up to 3-move mates. Develops ability to look ahead, gain new insights into combinations, complex or deceptive positions; ways to estimate weaknesses, strengths of you and your opponent. "A good deal of amusement and instruction," Times, (London). 300 diagrams. Solutions to all positions. Formerly "Challenge to Chess Players." 111pp. 5⅜ x 8.　　T417 Paperbound **$1.25**

A TREASURY OF CHESS LORE, edited by Fred Reinfeld. Delightful collection of anecdotes, short stories, aphorisms by, about masters; poems, accounts of games, tournaments, photographs; hundreds of humorous, pithy, satirical, wise, historical episodes, comments, word portraits. Fascinating "must" for chess players; revealing and perhaps seductive to those who wonder what their friends see in game. 49 photographs (14 full page plates). 12 diagrams. xi + 306pp. 5⅜ x 8.　　T458 Paperbound **$1.75**

WIN AT CHESS, Fred Reinfeld. 300 practical chess situations, to sharpen your eye, test skill against masters. Start with simple examples, progress at own pace to complexities. This selected series of crucial moments in chess will stimulate imagination, develop stronger, more versatile game. Simple grading system enables you to judge progress. "Extensive use of diagrams is a great attraction," Chess. 300 diagrams. Notes, solutions to every situation. Formerly "Chess Quiz." vi + 120pp. 5⅜ x 8.　　T433 Paperbound **$1.00**

MATHEMATICS:
ELEMENTARY TO INTERMEDIATE

HOW TO CALCULATE QUICKLY, H. Sticker. Tried and true method to help mathematics of everyday life. Awakens "number sense"—ability to see relationships between numbers as whole quantities. A serious course of over 9000 problems and their solutions through techniques not taught in schools: left-to-right multiplications, new fast division, etc. 10 minutes a day will double or triple calculation speed. Excellent for scientist at home in higher math, but dissatisfied with speed and accuracy in lower math. 256pp. 5 x 7¼.
　　Paperbound **$1.00**

FAMOUS PROBLEMS OF ELEMENTARY GEOMETRY, Felix Klein. Expanded version of 1894 Easter lectures at Göttingen. 3 problems of classical geometry: squaring the circle, trisecting angle, doubling cube, considered with full modern implications: transcendental numbers, pi, etc. "A modern classic . . . no knowledge of higher mathematics is required," Scientia. Notes by R. Archibald. 16 figures. xi + 92pp. 5⅜ x 8.　　T298 Paperbound **$1.00**

HIGHER MATHEMATICS FOR STUDENTS OF CHEMISTRY AND PHYSICS, J. W. Mellor. Practical, not abstract, building problems out of familiar laboratory material. Covers differential calculus, coordinate, analytical geometry, functions, integral calculus, infinite series, numerical equations, differential equations, Fourier's theorem probability, theory of errors, calculus of variations, determinants. "If the reader is not familiar with this book, it will repay him to examine it," Chem. and Engineering News. 800 problems. 189 figures. xxi + 641pp. 5⅜ x 8.　　S193 Paperbound **$2.25**

TRIGONOMETRY REFRESHER FOR TECHNICAL MEN, A. A. Klaf. 913 detailed questions, answers cover most important aspects of plane, spherical trigonometry—particularly useful in clearing up difficulties in special areas. Part I: plane trig, angles, quadrants, functions, graphical representation, interpolation, equations, logs, solution of triangle, use of slide rule, etc. Next 188 pages discuss applications to navigation, surveying, elasticity, architecture, other special fields. Part 3: spherical trig, applications to terrestrial, astronomical problems. Methods of time-saving, simplification of principal angles, make book most useful. 913 questions answered. 1738 problems, answers to odd numbers. 494 figures. 24 pages of formulas, functions. x + 629pp. 5⅜ x 8.　　T371 Paperbound **$2.00**

CALCULUS REFRESHER FOR TECHNICAL MEN, A. A. Klaf. 756 questions examine most important aspects of integral, differential calculus. Part I: simple differential calculus, constants, variables, functions, increments, logs, curves, etc. Part 2: fundamental ideas of integrations, inspection, substitution, areas, volumes, mean value, double, triple integration, etc. Practical aspects stressed. 50 pages illustrate applications to specific problems of civil, nautical engineering, electricity, stress, strain, elasticity, similar fields. 756 questions answered. 566 problems, mostly answered. 36pp. of useful constants, formulas. v + 431pp. 5⅜ x 8.　　T370 Paperbound **$2.00**

MONOGRAPHS ON TOPICS OF MODERN MATHEMATICS, edited by J. W. A. Young. Advanced mathematics for persons who have forgotten, or not gone beyond, high school algebra. 9 monographs on foundation of geometry, modern pure geometry, non-Euclidean geometry, fundamental propositions of algebra, algebraic equations, functions, calculus, theory of numbers, etc. Each monograph gives proofs of important results, and descriptions of leading methods, to provide wide coverage. "Of high merit," Scientific American. New introduction by Prof. M. Kline, N.Y. Univ. 100 diagrams. xvi + 416pp. 6⅛ x 9¼.
S289 Paperbound **$2.00**

MATHEMATICS IN ACTION, O. G. Sutton. Excellent middle level application of mathematics to study of universe, demonstrates how math is applied to ballistics, theory of computing machines, waves, wave-like phenomena, theory of fluid flow, meteorological problems, statistics, flight, similar phenomena. No knowledge of advanced math required. Differential equations, Fourier series, group concepts, Eigenfunctions, Planck's constant, airfoil theory, and similar topics explained so clearly in everyday language that almost anyone can derive benefit from reading this even if much of high-school math is forgotten. 2nd edition. 88 figures. viii + 236pp. 5⅜ x 8.
T450 Clothbound **$3.50**

ELEMENTARY MATHEMATICS FROM AN ADVANCED STANDPOINT, Felix Klein. Classic text, an outgrowth of Klein's famous integration and survey course at Göttingen. Using one field to interpret, adjust another, it covers basic topics in each area, with extensive analysis. Especially valuable in areas of modern mathematics. "A great mathematician, inspiring teacher, . . . deep insight," Bul., Amer. Math Soc.

Vol. I. ARITHMETIC, ALGEBRA, ANALYSIS. Introduces concept of function immediately, enlivens discussion with graphical, geometric methods. Partial contents: natural numbers, special properties, complex numbers. Real equations with real unknowns, complex quantities. Logarithmic, exponential functions, infinitesimal calculus. Transcendence of e and pi, theory of assemblages. Index. 125 figures. ix + 274pp. 5⅜ x 8.   S151 Paperbound **$1.75**

Vol. II. GEOMETRY. Comprehensive view, accompanies space perception inherent in geometry with analytic formulas which facilitate precise formulation. Partial contents: Simplest geometric manifold; line segments, Grassman determinant principles, classification of configurations of space. Geometric transformations: affine, projective, higher point transformations, theory of the imaginary. Systematic discussion of geometry and its foundations. 141 illustrations. ix + 214pp. 5⅜ x 8.   S151 Paperbound **$1.75**

A TREATISE ON PLANE AND ADVANCED TRIGONOMETRY, E. W. Hobson. Extraordinarily wide coverage, going beyond usual college level, one of few works covering advanced trig in full detail. By a great expositor with unerring anticipation of potentially difficult points. Includes circular functions; expansion of functions of multiple angle; trig tables; relations between sides, angles of triangles; complex numbers; etc. Many problems fully solved. "The best work on the subject," Nature. Formerly entitled "A Treatise on Plane Trigonometry." 689 examples. 66 figures. xvi + 383pp. 5⅜ x 8.   S353 Paperbound **$1.95**

NON-EUCLIDEAN GEOMETRY, Roberto Bonola. The standard coverage of non-Euclidean geometry. Examines from both a historical and mathematical point of view geometries which have arisen from a study of Euclid's 5th postulate on parallel lines. Also included are complete texts, translated, of Bolyai's "Theory of Absolute Space," Lobachevsky's "Theory of Parallels." 180 diagrams. 431pp. 5⅜ x 8.   S27 Paperbound **$1.95**

GEOMETRY OF FOUR DIMENSIONS, H. P. Manning. Unique in English as a clear, concise introduction. Treatment is synthetic, mostly Euclidean, though in hyperplanes and hyperspheres at infinity, non-Euclidean geometry is used. Historical introduction. Foundations of 4-dimensional geometry. Perpendicularity, simple angles. Angles of planes, higher order. Symmetry, order, motion; hyperpyramids, hypercones, hyperspheres; figures with parallel elements; volume, hypervolume in space; regular polyhedroids. Glossary. 78 figures. ix + 348pp. 5⅜ x 8.   S182 Paperbound **$1.95**

MATHEMATICS: INTERMEDIATE TO ADVANCED

GEOMETRY (EUCLIDEAN AND NON-EUCLIDEAN)

THE GEOMETRY OF RENÉ DESCARTES. With this book, Descartes founded analytical geometry. Original French text, with Descartes's own diagrams, and excellent Smith-Latham translation. Contains: Problems the Construction of Which Requires only Straight Lines and Circles; On the Nature of Curved Lines; On the Construction of Solid or Supersolid Problems. Diagrams. 258pp. 5⅜ x 8.   S68 Paperbound **$1.50**

THE WORKS OF ARCHIMEDES, edited by T. L. Heath. All the known works of the great Greek mathematician, including the recently discovered Method of Archimedes. Contains: On Sphere and Cylinder, Measurement of a Circle, Spirals, Conoids, Spheroids, etc. Definitive edition of greatest mathematical intellect of ancient world. 186 page study by Heath discusses Archimedes and history of Greek mathematics. 563pp. 5⅜ x 8.   S9 Paperbound **$2.00**

COLLECTED WORKS OF BERNARD RIEMANN. Important sourcebook, first to contain complete text of 1892 "Werke" and the 1902 supplement, unabridged. 31 monographs, 3 complete lecture courses, 15 miscellaneous papers which have been of enormous importance in relativity, topology, theory of complex variables, other areas of mathematics. Edited by R. Dedekind, H. Weber, M. Noether, W. Wirtinger. German text; English introduction by Hans Lewy. 690pp. 5⅜ x 8.   S226 Paperbound **$2.85**

THE THIRTEEN BOOKS OF EUCLID'S ELEMENTS, edited by Sir Thomas Heath. Definitive edition of one of very greatest classics of Western world. Complete translation of Heiberg text, plus spurious Book XIV. 150 page introduction on Greek, Medieval mathematics, Euclid, texts, commentators, etc. Elaborate critical apparatus parallels text, analyzing each definition, postulate, proposition, covering textual matters, refutations, supports, extrapolations, etc. This is the full Euclid. Unabridged reproduction of Cambridge U. 2nd edition. 3 volumes. 995 figures. 1426pp. 5⅜ x 8.   S88, 89, 90, 3 volume set, paperbound **$6.00**

AN INTRODUCTION TO GEOMETRY OF N DIMENSIONS, D. M. Y. Sommerville. Presupposes no previous knowledge of field. Only book in English devoted exclusively to higher dimensional geometry. Discusses fundamental ideas of incidence, parallelism, perpendicularity, angles between linear space, enumerative geometry, analytical geometry from projective and metric views, polytopes, elementary ideas in analysis situs, content of hyperspacial figures. 60 diagrams. 196pp. 5⅜ x 8.   S494 Paperbound **$1.50**

ELEMENTS OF NON-EUCLIDEAN GEOMETRY, D. M. Y. Sommerville. Unique in proceeding step-by-step. Requires only good knowledge of high-school geometry and algebra, to grasp elementary hyperbolic, elliptic, analytic non-Euclidean Geometries; space curvature and its implications; radical axes; homopethic centres and systems of circles; parataxy and parallelism; Gauss' proof of defect area theorem; much more, with exceptional clarity. 126 problems at chapter ends. 133 figures. xvi + 274pp. 5⅜ x 8.   S460 Paperbound **$1.50**

THE FOUNDATIONS OF EUCLIDEAN GEOMETRY, H. G. Forder. First connected, rigorous account in light of modern analysis, establishing propositions without recourse to empiricism, without multiplying hypotheses. Based on tools of 19th and 20th century mathematicians, who made it possible to remedy gaps and complexities, recognize problems not earlier discerned. Begins with important relationship of number systems in geometrical figures. Considers classes, relations, linear order, natural numbers, axioms for magnitudes, groups, quasi-fields, fields, non-Archimedian systems, the axiom system (at length), particular axioms (two chapters on the Parallel Axioms), constructions, congruence, similarity, etc. Lists: axioms employed, constructions, symbols in frequent use. 295pp. 5⅜ x 8.
S481 Paperbound **$2.00**

CALCULUS, FUNCTION THEORY (REAL AND COMPLEX), FOURIER THEORY

FIVE VOLUME "THEORY OF FUNCTIONS" SET BY KONRAD KNOPP. Provides complete, readily followed account of theory of functions. Proofs given concisely, yet without sacrifice of completeness or rigor. These volumes used as texts by such universities as M.I.T., Chicago, N.Y. City College, many others. "Excellent introduction . . . remarkably readable, concise, clear, rigorous," J. of the American Statistical Association.

ELEMENTS OF THE THEORY OF FUNCTIONS, Konrad Knopp. Provides background for further volumes in this set, or texts on similar level. Partial contents: Foundations, system of complex numbers and Gaussian plane of numbers, Riemann sphere of numbers, mapping by linear functions, normal forms, the logarithm, cyclometric functions, binomial series. "Not only for the young student, but also for the student who knows all about what is in it," Mathematical Journal. 140pp. 5⅜ x 8.   S154 Paperbound **$1.35**

THEORY OF FUNCTIONS, PART I, Konrad Knopp. With volume II, provides coverage of basic concepts and theorems. Partial contents: numbers and points, functions of a complex variable, integral of a continuous function, Cauchy's intergral theorem, Cauchy's integral formulae, series with variable terms, expansion and analytic function in a power series, analytic continuation and complete definition of analytic functions, Laurent expansion, types of singularities. vii + 146pp. 5⅜ x 8.   S156 Paperbound **$1.35**

THEORY OF FUNCTIONS, PART II, Konrad Knopp. Application and further development of general theory, special topics. Single valued functions, entire, Weierstrass. Meromorphic functions: Mittag-Leffler. Periodic functions. Multiple valued functions. Riemann surfaces. Algebraic functions. Analytical configurations, Riemann surface. x + 150pp. 5⅜ x 8.
S157 Paperbound **$1.35**

PROBLEM BOOK IN THE THEORY OF FUNCTIONS, VOLUME I, Konrad Knopp. Problems in elementary theory, for use with Knopp's "Theory of Functions," or any other text. Arranged according to increasing difficulty. Fundamental concepts, sequences of numbers and infinite series, complex variable, integral theorems, development in series, conformal mapping. Answers. viii + 126pp. 5⅜ x 8.   S 158 **Paperbound $1.35**

PROBLEM BOOK IN THE THEORY OF FUNCTIONS, VOLUME II, Konrad Knopp. Advanced theory of functions, to be used with Knopp's "Theory of Functions," or comparable text. Singularities, entire and meromorphic functions, periodic, analytic, continuation, multiple-valued functions, Riemann surfaces, conformal mapping. Includes section of elementary problems. "The difficult task of selecting . . . problems just within the reach of the beginner is here masterfully accomplished," AM. MATH. SOC. Answers. 138pp. 5⅜ x 8.
                                                    S159 **Paperbound $1.35**

ADVANCED CALCULUS, E. B. Wilson. Still recognized as one of most comprehensive, useful texts. Immense amount of well-represented, fundamental material, including chapters on vector functions, ordinary differential equations, special functions, calculus of variations, etc., which are excellent introductions to these areas. Requires only one year of calculus. Over 1300 exercises cover both pure math and applications to engineering and physical problems. Ideal reference, refresher. 54 page introductory review. ix + 566pp. 5⅜ x 8.
                                                    S504 **Paperbound $2.45**

LECTURES ON THE THEORY OF ELLIPTIC FUNCTIONS, H. Hancock. Reissue of only book in English with so extensive a coverage, especially of Abel, Jacobi, Legendre, Weierstrass, Hermite, Liouville, and Riemann. Unusual fullness of treatment, plus applications as well as theory in discussing universe of elliptic integrals, originating in works of Abel and Jacobi. Use is made of Riemann to provide most general theory. 40-page table of formulas. 76 figures. xxiii + 498pp. 5⅜ x 8.   S483 **Paperbound $2.55**

THEORY OF FUNCTIONALS AND OF INTEGRAL AND INTEGRO-DIFFERENTIAL EQUATIONS, Vito Volterra. Unabridged republication of only English translation. General theory of functions depending on continuous set of values of another function. Based on author's concept of transition from finite number of variables to a continually infinite number. Includes much material on calculus of variations. Begins with fundamentals, examines generalization of analytic functions, functional derivative equations, applications, other directions of theory, etc. New introduction by G. C. Evans. Biography, criticism of Volterra's work by E. Whittaker. xxxx + 226pp. 5⅜ x 8.   S502 **Paperbound $1.75**

AN INTRODUCTION TO FOURIER METHODS AND THE LAPLACE TRANSFORMATION, Philip Franklin. Concentrates on essentials, gives broad view, suitable for most applications. Requires only knowledge of calculus. Covers complex qualities with methods of computing elementary functions for complex values of argument and finding approximations by charts; Fourier series; harmonic anaylsis; much more. Methods are related to physical problems of heat flow, vibrations, electrical transmission, electromagnetic radiation, etc. 828 problems, answers. Formerly entitled "Fourier Methods." x + 289pp. 5⅜ x 8.
                                                    S452 **Paperbound $1.75**

THE ANALYTICAL THEORY OF HEAT, Joseph Fourier. This book, which revolutionized mathematical physics, has been used by generations of mathematicians and physicists interested in heat or application of Fourier integral. Covers cause and reflection of rays of heat, radiant heating, heating of closed spaces, use of trigonometric series in theory of heat, Fourier integral, etc. Translated by Alexander Freeman. 20 figures. xxii + 466pp. 5⅜ x 8.
                                                    S93 **Paperbound $2.00**

ELLIPTIC INTEGRALS, H. Hancock. Invaluable in work involving differential equations with cubics, quatrics under root sign, where elementary calculus methods are inadequate. Practical solutions to problems in mathematics, engineering, physics; differential equations requiring integration of Lamé's, Briot's, or Bouquet's equations; determination of arc of ellipse, hyperbola, lemiscate; solutions of problems in elastics; motion of a projectile under resistance varying as the cube of the velocity; pendulums; more. Exposition in accordance with Legendre-Jacobi theory. Rigorous discussion of Legendre transformations. 20 figures. 5 place table. 104pp. 5⅜ x 8.   S484 **Paperbound $1.25**

THE TAYLOR SERIES, AN INTRODUCTION TO THE THEORY OF FUNCTIONS OF A COMPLEX VARIABLE, P. Dienes. Uses Taylor series to approach theory of functions, using ordinary calculus only, except in last 2 chapters. Starts with introduction to real variable and complex algebra, derives properties of infinite series, complex differentiation, integration, etc. Covers biuniform mapping, overconvergence and gap theorems, Taylor series on its circle of convergence, etc. Unabridged corrected reissue of first edition. 186 examples, many fully worked out. 67 figures. xii + 555pp. 5⅜ x 8.   S391 **Paperbound $2.75**

LINEAR INTEGRAL EQUATIONS, W. V. Lovitt. Systematic survey of general theory, with some application to differential equations, calculus of variations, problems of math, physics. Includes: integral equation of 2nd kind by successive substitutions; Fredholm's equation as ratio of 2 integral series in lambda, applications of the Fredholm theory, Hilbert-Schmidt theory of symmetric kernels, application, etc. Neumann, Dirichlet, vibratory problems. ix + 253pp. 5⅜ x 8.   S175 **Clothbound $3.50**
                                                    S176 **Paperbound $1.60**

DICTIONARY OF CONFORMAL REPRESENTATIONS, H. Kober. Developed by British Admiralty to solve Laplace's equation in 2 dimensions. Scores of geometrical forms and transformations for electrical engineers, Joukowski aerofoil for aerodynamics, Schwartz-Christoffel transformations for hydro-dynamics, transcendental functions. Contents classified according to analytical functions describing transformations with corresponding regions. Glossary. Topological index. 447 diagrams. 6⅛ x 9¼. .S160 Paperbound **$2.00**

ELEMENTS OF THE THEORY OF REAL FUNCTIONS, J. E. Littlewood. Based on lectures at Trinity College, Cambridge, this book has proved extremely successful in introducing graduate students to modern theory of functions. Offers full and concise coverage of classes and cardinal numbers, well ordered series, other types of series, and elements of the theory of sets of points. 3rd revised edition. vii + 71pp. 5⅜ x 8. S171 Clothbound **$2.85**
S172 Paperbound **$1.25**

INFINITE SEQUENCES AND SERIES, Konrad Knopp. 1st publication in any language. Excellent introduction to 2 topics of modern mathematics, designed to give student background to penetrate further alone. Sequences and sets, real and complex numbers, etc. Functions of a real and complex variable. Sequences and series. Infinite series. Convergent power series. Expansion of elementary functions. Numerical evaluation of series. v + 186pp. 5⅜ x 8. S152 Clothbound **$3.50**
S153 Paperbound **$1.75**

THE THEORY AND FUNCTIONS OF A REAL VARIABLE AND THE THEORY OF FOURIER'S SERIES, E. W .Hobson. One of the best introductions to set theory and various aspects of functions and Fourier's series. Requires only a good background in calculus. Exhaustive .coverage of: metric and descriptive properties of sets of points; transfinite numbers and order types; functions of a real variable; the Riemann and Lebesgue integrals; sequences and series of numbers; power-series; functions representable by series sequences of continuous functions; trigonometrical series; representation of functions by Fourier's series; and much more. "The best possible guide," Nature. Vol. I: 88 detailed examples, 10 figures. Index. xv + 736pp. Vol. II: 117 detailed examples, 13 figures. x + 780pp. 6⅛ x 9¼.
Vol. I: S387 Paperbound **$3.00**
Vol. II: S388 Paperbound **$3.00**

ALMOST PERIODIC FUNCTIONS, A. S. Besicovitch. Unique and important summary by a well known mathematician covers in detail the two stages of development in Bohr's theory of almost periodic functions: (1) as a generalization of pure periodicity, with results and proofs; (2) the work done by Stepanof, Wiener, Weyl, and Bohr in generalizing the theory. xi + 180pp. 5⅜ x 8. S18 Paperbound **$1.75**

INTRODUCTION TO THE THEORY OF FOURIER'S SERIES AND INTEGRALS, H. S. Carslaw. 3rd revised edition, an outgrowth of author's courses at Cambridge. Historical introduction, rational, irrational numbers, infinite sequences and series, functions of a single variable, definite integral, Fourier series, and similar topics. Appendices discuss practical harmonic analysis, periodogram analysis, Lebesgue's theory. 84 examples. xiii + 368pp. 5⅜ x 8. S48 Paperbound **$2.00**

SYMBOLIC LOGIC

THE ELEMENTS OF MATHEMATICAL LOGIC, Paul Rosenbloom. First publication in any language. For mathematically mature readers with no training in symbolic. logic. Development of lectures given at Lund Univ., Sweden, 1948. Partial contents: Logic of classes, fundamental theorems, Boolean algebra, logic of propositions, of propositional functions, expressive languages, combinatory logics, development of math within an object language, paradoxes, theorems of Post, Goedel, Church, and similar topics. iv + 214pp. 5⅜ x 8. S227 Paperbound **$1.45**

INTRODUCTION TO SYMBOLIC LOGIC AND ITS APPLICATION, R. Carnap. Clear, comprehensive, rigorous, by perhaps greatest living master. Symbolic languages analyzed, one constructed. Applications to math (axiom systems for set theory, real, natural numbers), topology (Dedekind, Cantor continuity explanations), physics (general analysis of determination, causality, space-time topology), biology (axiom system for basic concepts). "A masterpiece," Zentralblatt für Mathematik und Ihre Grenzgebiete. Over 300 exercises. 5 figures. xvi + 241pp. 5⅜ x 8. S453 Paperbound **$1.85**

AN INTRODUCTION TO SYMBOLIC LOGIC, Susanne K. Langer. Probably clearest book for the philosopher, scientist, layman—no special knowledge of math required. Starts with simplest symbols, goes on to give remarkable grasp of Boole-Schroeder, Russell-Whitehead systems, clearly, quickly. Partial Contents: Forms, Generalization, Classes, Deductive System of Classes, Algebra of Logic, Assumptions of Principia Mathematica, Logistics, Proofs of Theorems, etc. "Clearest . . . simplest introduction . . . the intelligent non-mathematician should have no difficulty," MATHEMATICS GAZETTE. Revised, expanded 2nd edition. Truth-value tables. 368pp. 5⅜ 8. S164 Paperbound **$1.75**

TRIGONOMETRICAL SERIES, Antoni Zygmund. On modern advanced level. Contains carefully organized analyses of trigonometric, orthogonal, Fourier systems of functions, with clear adequate descriptions of summability of Fourier series, proximation theory, conjugate series, convergence, divergence of Fourier series. Especially valuable for Russian, Eastern European coverage. 329pp. 5⅜ x 8. S290 Paperbound **$1.50**

THE LAWS OF THOUGHT, George Boole. This book founded symbolic logic some 100 years ago. It is the 1st significant attempt to apply logic to all aspects of human endeavour. Partial contents: derivation of laws, signs and laws, interpretations, eliminations, conditions of a perfect method, analysis, Aristotelian logic, probability, and similar topics. xvii + 424pp. 5⅜ x 8. S28 Paperbound **$2.00**

SYMBOLIC LOGIC, C. I. Lewis, C. H. Langford. 2nd revised edition of probably most cited book in symbolic logic. Wide coverage of entire field; one of fullest treatments of paradoxes; plus much material not available elsewhere. Basic to volume is distinction between logic of extensions and intensions. Considerable emphasis on converse substitution, while matrix system presents supposition of variety of non-Aristotelian logics. Especially valuable sections on strict limitations, existence theorems. Partial contents: Boole-Schroeder algebra; truth value systems, the matrix method; implication and deductibility; general theory of propositions; etc. "Most valuable," Times, London. 506pp. 5⅜ x 8. S170 Paperbound **$2.00**

GROUP THEORY AND LINEAR ALGEBRA, SETS, ETC.

LECTURES ON THE ICOSAHEDRON AND THE SOLUTION OF EQUATIONS OF THE FIFTH DEGREE, Felix Klein. Solution of quintics in terms of rotations of regular icosahedron around its axes of symmetry. A classic, indispensable source for those interested in higher algebra, geometry, crystallography. Considerable explanatory material included. 230 footnotes, mostly bibliography. "Classical monograph . . . detailed, readable book," Math. Gazette. 2nd edition. xvi + 289pp. 5⅜ x 8. S314 Paperbound **$1.85**

INTRODUCTION TO THE THEORY OF GROUPS OF FINITE ORDER, R. Carmichael. Examines fundamental theorems and their applications. Beginning with sets, systems, permutations, etc., progresses in easy stages through important types of groups: Abelian, prime power, permutation, etc. Except 1 chapter where matrices are desirable, no higher math is needed. 783 exercises, problems. xvi + 447pp. 5⅜ x 8. S299 Clothbound **$3.95**
S300 Paperbound **$2.00**

THEORY OF GROUPS OF FINITE ORDER, W. Burnside. First published some 40 years ago, still one of clearest introductions. Partial contents: permutations, groups independent of representation, composition series of a group, isomorphism of a group with itself, Abelian groups, prime power groups, permutation groups, invariants of groups of linear substitution, graphical representation, etc. "Clear and detailed discussion . . . numerous problems which are instructive," Design News. xxiv + 512pp. 5⅜ x 8. S38 Paperbound **$2.45**

COMPUTATIONAL METHODS OF LINEAR ALGEBRA, V. N. Faddeeva, translated by C. D. Benster. 1st English translation of unique, valuable work, only one in English presenting systematic exposition of most important methods of linear algebra—classical, contemporary. Details of deriving numerical solutions of problems in mathematical physics. Theory and practice. Includes survey of necessary background, most important methods of solution, for exact, iterative groups. One of most valuable features is 23 tables, triple checked for accuracy, unavailable elsewhere. Translator's note. x + 252pp. 5⅜ x 8. S424 Paperbound **$1.95**

THE CONTINUUM AND OTHER TYPES OF SERIAL ORDER, E. V. Huntington. This famous book gives a systematic elementary account of the modern theory of the continuum as a type of serial order. Based on the Cantor-Dedekind ordinal theory, which requires no technical knowledge of higher mathematics, it offers an easily followed analysis of ordered classes, discrete and dense series, continuous series, Cantor's transfinite numbers. "Admirable introduction to the rigorous theory of the continuum . . . reading easy," Science Progress. 2nd edition. viii + 82pp. 5⅜ x 8. S129 Clothbound **$2.75**
S130 Paperbound **$1.00**

THEORY OF SETS, E. Kamke. Clearest, amplest introduction in English, well suited for independent study. Subdivisions of main theory, such as theory of sets of points, are discussed, but emphasis is on general theory. Partial contents: rudiments of set theory, arbitrary sets, their cardinal numbers, ordered sets, their order types, well-ordered sets, their cardinal numbers. vii + 144pp. 5⅜ x 8. S141 Paperbound **$1.35**

CONTRIBUTIONS TO THE FOUNDING OF THE THEORY OF TRANSFINITE NUMBERS, Georg Cantor. These papers founded a new branch of mathematics. The famous articles of 1895-7 are translated, with an 82-page introduction by P. E. B. Jourdain dealing with Cantor, the background of his discoveries, their results, future possibilities. ix + 211pp. 5⅜ x 8. S45 Paperbound **$1.25**

14

NUMERICAL AND GRAPHICAL METHODS, TABLES

JACOBIAN ELLIPTIC FUNCTION TABLES, L. M. Milne-Thomson. Easy-to-follow, practical, not only useful numerical tables, but complete elementary sketch of application of elliptic functions. Covers description of principle properties; complete elliptic integrals; Fourier series, expansions; periods, zeros, poles, residues, formulas for special values of argument; cubic, quartic polynomials; pendulum problem; etc. Tables, graphs form body of book: Graph, 5 figure table of elliptic function sn (u m); cn (u m); dn (u m). 8 figure table of complete elliptic integrals K, K′, E, E′, nome q. 7 figure table of Jacobian zeta-function Z(u). 3 figures. xi + 123pp. 5⅜ x 8. **S194 Paperbound $1.35**

TABLES OF FUNCTIONS WITH FORMULAE AND CURVES, E. Jahnke, F. Emde. Most comprehensive 1-volume English text collection of tables, formulae, curves of transcendent functions. 4th corrected edition, new 76-page section giving tables, formulae for elementary functions not in other English editions. Partial contents: sine, cosine, logarithmic integral; error integral; elliptic integrals; theta functions; Legendre, Bessel, Riemann, Mathieu, hypergeometric functions; etc. "Out-of-the-way functions for which we know no other source." Scientific Computing Service, Ltd. 212 figures. 400pp. 5⅝ x 8⅜. **S133 Paperbound $2.00**

MATHEMATICAL TABLES, H. B. Dwight. Covers in one volume almost every function of importance in applied mathematics, engineering, physical sciences. Three extremely fine tables of the three trig functions, inverses, to 1000th of radian; natural, common logs; squares, cubes; hyperbolic functions, inverses; ($a^2 + b^2$) exp. ½a; complete elliptical integrals of 1st, 2nd kind; sine, cosine integrals; exponential integrals; Ei(x) and Ei($-x$); binomial coefficients; factorials to 250; surface zonal harmonics, first derivatives; Bernoulli, Euler numbers, their logs to base of 10; Gamma function; normal probability integral; over 60pp. Bessel functions; Riemann zeta function. Each table with formulae generally used, sources of more extensive tables, interpolation data, etc. Over half have columns of differences, to facilitate interpolation. viii + 231pp. 5⅜ x 8. **S445 Paperbound $1.75**

PRACTICAL ANALYSIS, GRAPHICAL AND NUMERICAL METHODS, F. A. Willers. Immensely practical hand-book for engineers. How to interpolate, use various methods of numerical differentiation and integration, determine roots of a single algebraic equation, system of linear equations, use empirical formulas, integrate differential equations, etc. Hundreds of shortcuts for arriving at numerical solutions. Special section on American calculating machines, by T. W. Simpson. Translation by R. T. Beyer. 132 illustrations. 422pp. 5⅜ x 8. **S273 Paperbound $2.00**

NUMERICAL SOLUTIONS OF DIFFERENTIAL EQUATIONS, H. Levy, E. A. Baggott. Comprehensive collection of methods for solving ordinary differential equations of first and higher order. 2 requirements: practical, easy to grasp; more rapid than school methods. Partial contents: graphical integration of differential equations, graphical methods for detailed solution. Numerical solution. Simultaneous equations and equations of 2nd and higher orders. "Should be in the hands of all in research and applied mathematics, teaching," Nature. 21 figures. viii + 238pp. 5⅜ x 8. **S168 Paperbound $1.75**

NUMERICAL INTEGRATION OF DIFFERENTIAL EQUATIONS, Bennet, Milne, Bateman. Unabridged republication of original prepared for National Research Council. New methods of integration by 3 leading mathematicians: "The Interpolational Polynomial," "Successive Approximation," A. A. Bennett, "Step-by-step Methods of Integration," W. W. Milne. "Methods for Partial Differential Equations," H. Bateman. Methods for partial differential equations, solution of differential equations to non-integral values of a parameter will interest mathematicians, physicists. 288 footnotes, mostly bibliographical. 235 item classified bibliography. 108pp. 5⅜ x 8. **S305 Paperbound $1.35**